United States History and Geography
Modern Times

CHAPTER TESTS AND LESSON QUIZZES

Bothell, WA • Chicago, IL • Columbus, OH • New York, NY

Cover Image Credit: Intellectual Properties Management/Dan Dos Santos

www.mheonline.com/networks

Send all inquiries to:
McGraw-Hill Education
8787 Orion Place
Columbus, OH 43240

ISBN: 978-0-07-664133-8
MHID: 0-07-664133-3

Printed in the United States of America.

2 3 4 5 6 7 8 9 RHR 16 15 14 13

networks

Table of Contents

Chapter 7 World War I and Its Aftermath

Chapter 8 The Jazz Age

Chapter 9 The Great Depression Begins

Chapter 10 Roosevelt and the New Deal

Chapter 11 A World in Flames

Chapter 12 America and World War II

Table of Contents continued

Table of Contents continued

NAME ______________________ DATE ______________ CLASS ____________

Lesson Quiz 1-1

networks

Creating a Nation

DIRECTIONS: Completion Enter the appropriate word(s) to complete the statement.

1. The American continent is named after the Italian explorer Amerigo ______________.

2. ______________ became the first country to recognize the United States as an independent nation.

3. Both the Enlightenment and the ______________ served to emphasize an individualism that supported America's political independence.

4. In Europe, the ______________ brought a rebirth of interest in ancient Greece and Rome, a renewed commitment to reason, and a scientific revolution that would make sea travel easier.

5. In the seventeenth century, English business and government leaders saw ______________ as sources of raw materials and as markets for English goods.

DIRECTIONS: Multiple Choice Indicate the answer choice that best completes the statement or answers the question.

_______ **6.** Anthropologists think the first people to build a civilization in America were the

A. Anasazi.

B. Hohokam.

C. Maya.

D. Olmec.

_______ **7.** The men who led expeditions to conquer what today is Mexico and Central America became known as

A. *conquistadors.*

B. *encomenderos.*

C. *mestizos.*

D. *peninsulares.*

_______ **8.** Who argued that governments exist because people allow them to exist?

A. Sir Edmund Andros

B. King Charles II

C. King James II

D. John Locke

_______ **9.** What became known in the colonies as the Intolerable Acts?

A. the Coercive Acts and Tea Act

B. the Coercive Acts and Townshend Acts

C. the Quebec Act and Coercive Acts

D. the Tea Act and Townshend Acts

NAME ______________________ DATE ____________ CLASS ____________

Lesson Quiz 1-2

networks

Creating a Nation

DIRECTIONS: Matching Match each item with the correct statement below.

_____ **1.** not explicitly listed in the Constitution but necessary for government to do its job

_____ **2.** land the United States bought from France that doubled the size of the nation

_____ **3.** group of delegates from each state that made up the entire government under the Articles of Confederation

_____ **4.** signed by negotiators to end the War of 1812

_____ **5.** headed by a president who would implement and enforce federal laws

A. Congress

B. Treaty of Ghent

C. Louisiana Purchase

D. executive branch of government

E. implied powers

DIRECTIONS: Multiple Choice Indicate the answer choice that best completes the statement or answers the question.

_____ **6.** The system created to prevent any one of the three branches of government from becoming too powerful is called

A. popular sovereignty.
B. amendments.
C. checks and balances.
D. impeachment.

_____ **7.** The Great Compromise proposed that in one house of Congress—the House of Representatives—the states would be represented according to the size of their

A. acreage.
B. state banks.
C. trade income.
D. population.

_____ **8.** The nation's first two political parties were the Federalists and the

A. Democratic-Republicans.
B. Independents.
C. Anti-Federalists.
D. Speculators.

_____ **9.** The presidential election of 1800 resulted in a tie between which two candidates?

A. Adams and Pinckney
B. Jefferson and Burr
C. Jefferson and Adams
D. Burr and Pinckney

_____ **10.** The United States declared war on __________ in 1812.

A. Britain
B. France
C. Spain
D. Germany

NAME ______________________ DATE ____________ CLASS ____________

Lesson Quiz 1-3

networks

Creating a Nation

DIRECTIONS: Modified True/False In the blank, indicate whether the statement is true (T) or false (F). If false, edit the statement to make it a true statement.

_______ **1.** State slave codes forbade enslaved men and women from owning property or leaving a slaveholder's premises without permission.

____

_______ **2.** Even though industry expanded in the Northeast during the early 1800s, agriculture remained the country's leading economic activity.

____

_______ **3.** The rise of Southern industry kept pace with the spread of cotton plantations across the South.

____

_______ **4.** Missouri's application for statehood stirred up the issue of whether slavery was constitutional.

____

DIRECTIONS: Multiple Choice Indicate the answer choice that best completes the statement or answers the question.

_______ **5.** What made river travel more reliable and upstream travel easier?

A. canals
B. sails
C. steamboats
D. iron horses

_______ **6.** While the House of Representatives had a majority of Northerners in 1819, admitting any new state, either slave or free, would upset the balance in

A. the Senate.
B. the courts.
C. city governments.
D. state governments.

_______ **7.** By the mid-1800s, especially in the northeastern states, the development of factories and other work centers separated the workplace from the

A. church.
B. home.
C. reform centers.
D. public school system.

_______ **8.** A cotton gin

A. picks cotton.
B. spins cotton into cloth.
C. removes cotton seeds.
D. bales cotton.

_______ **9.** The solution that emerged in the Missouri Compromise was to admit Missouri

A. and Maine as slave states.
B. as a slave state and Maine as a free state.
C. as a slave state but prohibit slavery in the rest of the western territories.
D. as a slave state and ban free African Americans from entering the state.

NAME ______________________ DATE ______________ CLASS __________

networks

Lesson Quiz 1-4

Creating a Nation

DIRECTIONS: Matching Match each item with the correct statement below.

_____ **1.** taking states out of the Union

_____ **2.** the idea that God had given the continent to Americans and wanted them to settle western land

_____ **3.** the official takeover of territory

_____ **4.** antislavery novel that changed Northern perceptions of slavery

_____ **5.** organized the Nebraska Territory

A. *Uncle Tom's Cabin*

B. Kansas-Nebraska Act

C. Manifest Destiny

D. annexation

E. secession

DIRECTIONS: Multiple Choice Indicate the answer choice that best completes the statement or answers the question.

_____ **6.** Texas joined the Union in

A. 1848.
B. 1845.
C. 1836.
D. 1860.

_____ **7.** On February 2, 1848, Mexico's leaders signed the

A. Treaty of Guadalupe Hidalgo.
B. Release of the Bear Flag Republic.
C. Adams-Onís Treaty.
D. Rio Grande Treaty.

_____ **8.** The issue of slavery's expansion divided the country not along party lines, but along

A. religious lines.
B. international lines.
C. judicial lines.
D. sectional lines.

_____ **9.** A free African American could be falsely taken into custody under the terms of the

A. Fugitive Slave Act.
B. Missouri Compromise.
C. Wilmot Proviso.
D. Kansas-Nebraska Act.

_____ **10.** If California entered the Union as a free state, the slaveholding states would become a minority in the

A. House of Representatives.
B. Senate.
C. West.
D. courts.

NAME ______________________ DATE ______________ CLASS ____________

Lesson Quiz 1-5

networks

Creating a Nation

DIRECTIONS: Completion Enter the appropriate word(s) to complete the statement.

1. Having gained the right to ______________________, African Americans quickly began to organize politically and to take part in governing the South.

2. Lincoln's plan for Reconstruction offered a general ______________________, or pardon, to Southerners who abided by certain conditions.

3. The ______________________ Proclamation, by its very existence, transformed the conflict over preserving the Union into a war of liberation.

4. The ______________________ Amendment banned slavery in the United States.

DIRECTIONS: Multiple Choice Indicate the answer choice that best completes the statement or answers the question.

_______ **5.** In 1860 approximately what percentage of the nation's factories were located in Northern states?

A. 30
B. 50
C. 90
D. 100

_______ **6.** Lacking sufficient money from taxes or bonds, the Confederacy was forced to print paper money to pay its bills, causing rapid

A. trade alliances.
B. building of banks.
C. use of credit.
D. inflation in the South.

_______ **7.** It was clear that a large, well-trained army would be needed to defeat the South after the Union defeat at

A. the First Battle of Bull Run.
B. Fort Donelson.
C. the Battle of Antietam.
D. New Orleans.

_______ **8.** What Union victory cut the Confederacy in two?

A. Gettysburg
B. Fredericksburg
C. Vicksburg
D. Chancellorsville

_______ **9.** In addition to ending the enslavement of millions of African Americans, the North's victory in the Civil War also saved the Union and strengthened the power of the federal government over the

A. military.
B. church.
C. South.
D. states.

NAME ________________ DATE ________________ CLASS ________________

Chapter 1 Test, Form A

networks

Creating a Nation

DIRECTIONS: Matching Match each item with the correct statement below.

_______ **1.** ended the War of 1812

_______ **2.** declared that no state could deny any person "equal protection of the laws"

_______ **3.** with its defeat in this battle, the South lost its best chance at gaining international recognition and support

_______ **4.** stood for the rights of states over the power of the federal government

_______ **5.** declaring a federal law invalid

_______ **6.** rose from slavery to become a prominent leader of the antislavery movement

_______ **7.** first battleground between those favoring the extension of slavery and those opposing it

_______ **8.** organized the Seneca Falls Convention, which marked the beginning of an organized women's movement

_______ **9.** practice of appointing people to government jobs on the basis of party loyalty and support

_______ **10.** declared that the right to vote "shall not be denied . . . on account of race, color, or previous condition of servitude"

A. spoils system

B. nullification

C. Frederick Douglass

D. Fourteenth Amendment

E. Fifteenth Amendment

F. Treaty of Ghent

G. Bleeding Kansas

H. Lucretia Mott and Elizabeth Cady Stanton

I. Democratic-Republicans

J. Battle of Antietam

DIRECTIONS: Multiple Choice Indicate the answer choice that best completes the statement or answers the question.

_______ **11.** Current scientific evidence suggests that people arrived in America between _______ years ago.

A. 5,000 and 10,000

B. 15,000 and 30,000

C. 30,000 and 40,000

D. 80,000 and 100,000

_______ **12.** The United States gained the Louisiana Territory by

A. buying it from France.
B. buying it from Spain.
C. winning it in the War of 1812.
D. winning it in the Quasi-War.

_______ **13.** According to an accepted amendment to the Missouri Compromise, slavery

A. could expand into the Arkansas territory but not the rest of the Louisiana Purchase.
B. could not expand into any other western territories.
C. could expand into the Great Plains but not to the rest of the Louisiana Purchase.
D. would be allowed in a new state only if a free state entered the Union at the same time.

_______ **14.** The leading economic activity in the United States in the early 1800s was

A. farming.
B. road and canal building.
C. textile mills.
D. building railroads.

_______ **15.** Abolitionists argued that enslaved African Americans should be

A. freed immediately, without compensation to former slaveholders.
B. freed gradually with compensation to former slaveholders.
C. freed gradually to give the South's economy time to adjust.
D. sent to their ancestral homelands in Africa.

_______ **16.** Manifest Destiny was the idea that God had given the continent to

A. white men, and expected them to bring Christianity to the Native Americans.
B. Americans, and it was their destiny to become the greatest nation in the world.
C. Americans, and wanted them to settle western land.
D. Americans, and it was their duty to protect the environment.

_______ **17.** Anger over the Kansas-Nebraska Act resulted in a new coalition that became the _____________ Party.

A. Free-Soil
B. Know-Nothing
C. Republican
D. Liberty

______ **18.** The Emancipation Proclamation

A. ended the Civil War immediately.

B. decreed freedom for all enslaved people in areas still in rebellion against the Union.

C. decreed freedom for all enslaved people in the loyal border states.

D. amended the Constitution to free all enslaved people.

______ **19.** Capturing Vicksburg was an important objective for the North during the Civil War because

A. its location made it an invasion route to the North.

B. its capture would give the North control of the Mississippi River delta.

C. it was the last Confederate stronghold on the Mississippi River.

D. its capture would prevent the South from shipping its cotton to Europe.

______ **20.** The Thirteenth Amendment to the Constitution prohibited

A. war.

B. discrimination.

C. secession.

D. slavery.

DIRECTIONS: Short Answer Answer each of the following questions.

> "If the end be clearly comprehended within any of the specified powers, and if the measure have an obvious relation to that end, and is not forbidden by any particular provision of the constitution—it may safely be deemed to come within the compass of the national authority. There is also this further criterion which may materially assist the decision: Does the proposed measure abridge a pre-existing right of any State, or of any individual? If it does not, there is a strong presumption in favour of its constitutionality . . ."
>
> —Alexander Hamilton, "Opinion on the Constitutionality of Establishing a National Bank, 1791"

21. Explain Alexander Hamilton's constitutional argument in favor of establishing a national bank.

____

____

____

____

> "It is emphatically the province and duty of the judicial department to say what the law is. Those who apply the rule to particular cases, must of necessity expound and interpret that rule. If two laws conflict with each other, the courts must decide on the operation of each. So if a law be in opposition to the constitution; if both the law and the constitution apply to a particular case, so that the court must either decide that case conformably to the law, disregarding the constitution; or conformably to the constitution, disregarding the law; the court must determine which of these conflicting rules governs the case. This is of the very essence of judicial duty."
>
> —Chief Justice John Marshall in *Marbury* v. *Madison*

22. Describe the Supreme Court's decision in *Marbury* v. *Madison* and explain its importance.

____

____

23. Describe the status of enslaved people under state slave codes. What are some ways in which enslaved men and women opposed the dreadful lifestyle forced upon them?

____

____

> "It is the opinion of the court that the Act of Congress which prohibited a citizen from holding and owning [enslaved persons] in the territory of the United States north of the line therein mentioned is not warranted by the Constitution and is therefore void."
>
> —from *Dred Scott* v. *Sandford*

24. Describe the case of *Dred Scott* v. *Sandford*, the decision, and its significance.

____

____

25. What political, social, and economic changes did the nation experience as it emerged from the Civil War?

____

____

NAME ______________________ DATE ____________ CLASS ____________

Chapter 1 Test, Form B

networks

Creating a Nation

DIRECTIONS: Short Answer Answer each of the following questions on a separate piece of paper.

"They [Spanish soldiers] came in battle array, as conquerors. . . . Their spears glinted in the sun, and their pennons fluttered like bats. They made a loud clamor as they marched, for their coats of mail and their weapons clashed and rattled. . . . They terrified everyone who saw them. . . .

"The Spaniards grinned like little beasts and patted each other with delight. When they entered the hall of treasures, it was as if they had arrived in Paradise. They . . . coveted everything; they were slaves to their own greed. . . . They seized these treasures as if they were their own, as if this plunder were merely a stroke of good luck."

—anonymous Aztec

The Broken Spears: The Aztec Account of the Conquest of Mexico, by Miguel Leon-Portilla.
Copyright © 1962, 1990 by Miguel Leon-Portilla Copyright.
Reprinted by Permission of Beacon Press, Boston.

1. What effect did the Spanish soldiers have on the Aztec, judging by the quote above?

2. By this account, what was the main reason for the Spanish conquest of the Aztec?

A New Government Faces Issues

Problem	Solution
Opponents of the proposed new federal government feared that it would become too powerful.	The Constitution divided power between the federal government and the state governments and established three branches of power in the federal government.
Constitutional delegates feared that one branch of the federal government would become too powerful.	The Constitution gave each branch of the federal government the ability to limit the power of the other branches.

3. How does the Constitution prevent one branch of government from becoming too powerful?

4. How did the Constitution's supporters appease the opponents of the new government, who feared that this new government would become too powerful?

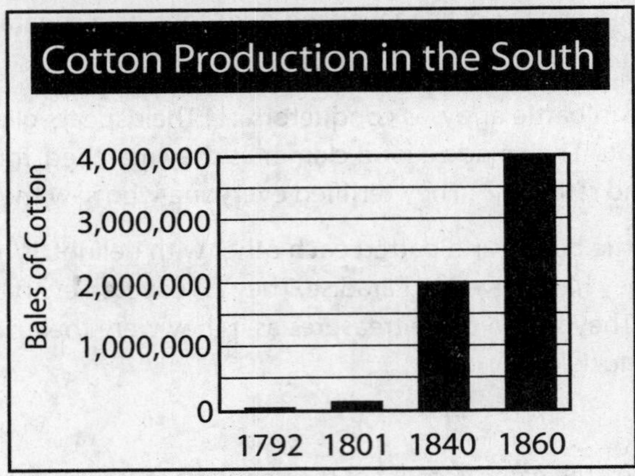

5. According to the chart, what changes occurred in the number of bales of cotton produced in the South from 1792 to 1860?

6. What was the impact of the change in cotton production illustrated by the chart?

North vs. South at the Beginning of the Civil War

Categories	North	South
Population	22 million	9 million (one-third enslaved)
Experienced naval officers	75%	25%
Experienced sailors	Nearly 100%	Nearly 0%
Experienced military officers	690	313
Military colleges	1	7
Factories/industry	80% of nation's total	20% of nation's total
Railroads	Twice as many miles	Half as many miles
Finances	• Controlled the National Treasury • Expected continued tax revenues	• Small banks • Indebted planters

7. Referring to the chart above, what can you deduce about the South's financial position going into the Civil War?

8. Based on the chart and on your reading, how did the South address its financial situation during the Civil War?

NAME ______________________ DATE ______________ CLASS ____________

Lesson Quiz 2-1

networks

Settling the West

DIRECTIONS: Completion Enter the appropriate word(s) to complete the statement.

1. The Comstock strike turned the town of ____________, Nevada, into a boomtown.

2. The rapidly growing communities that appeared at the site of mineral strikes were called ____________.

3. The Texas ____________ was a breed of cattle descended from Spanish cattle that had been brought to Mexico two centuries earlier.

4. The "open range" referred to a vast area of grassland owned by ____________.

5. Many ____________ became rich when the mines they created generated huge profits.

DIRECTIONS: Multiple Choice Indicate the answer choice that best completes the statement or answers the question.

_______ 6. Early prospectors would extract shallow deposits of ore by

A. hydraulic mining.
B. placer mining.
C. quartz mining.
D. tunnel mining.

_______ 7. The Comstock Lode was a rich deposit of

A. copper.
B. diamonds.
C. gold.
D. silver.

_______ 8. Many of the first miners in the Colorado mountains did not find any minerals because

A. mining companies had claimed them.
B. the areas were too hard to reach.
C. the minerals were buried too deep.
D. there were no minerals to find.

_______ 9. Huge ranches that covered thousands of acres were called

A. barrios.
B. haciendas.
C. lariats.
D. stampedes.

_______ 10. Which of the following greatly spurred the settlement of Colorado, Arizona, and Montana?

A. the arrival of large numbers of miners
B. the availability of free land
C. the growth of the cattle industry
D. the presence of peaceful, orderly towns

NAME ______________________ DATE ______________ CLASS __________

Lesson Quiz 2-2

networks

Settling the West

DIRECTIONS: Matching Match each item with the correct statement below.

______ **1.** a tract of public land available for settlement

______ **2.** often brought their owners big profits

______ **3.** productive farm area that began at the eastern edge of the Great Plains

______ **4.** explored the Great Plains in 1819

______ **5.** planting seeds deep in the ground where there was enough moisture for them to grow

A. bonanza farms

B. Stephen Long

C. Wheat Belt

D. dry farming

E. homestead

DIRECTIONS: Multiple Choice Indicate the answer choice that best completes the statement or answers the question.

______ **6.** Threshing machines were used for

A. clearing homesteads.
B. harvesting wheat.
C. improving irrigation.
D. planting crops.

______ **7.** Settlement of the Great Plains was promoted by the railroads and supported by

A. cattle ranchers.
B. the government.
C. the mining industry.
D. plow manufacturers.

______ **8.** Large landholders on the Great Plains were able to

A. determine their own prices.
B. grow any crops they wanted.
C. invest in the tools they needed.
D. prevent droughts from happening.

______ **9.** One approach to farming on the Great Plains was "dry farming," in which farmers

A. cooperated to build community irrigation ditches.
B. dug out depressions to create ponds for irrigation.
C. grew crops that could withstand long periods without rain.
D. planted seeds deep in the ground.

______ **10.** The Homestead Act gave land to homesteaders if they __________ for five years.

A. cut down trees on it
B. fenced it off
C. lived on it
D. planted crops on it

NAME ______________________ DATE ______________ CLASS ____________

Lesson Quiz 2-3

networks

Settling the West

DIRECTIONS: Modified True/False In the blank, indicate whether the statement is true (T) or false (F). If false, edit the statement to make it a true statement.

_______ **1.** The Dawes Act succeeded in achieving its goals of assimilating Native Americans into American society as landowners and citizens.

____

_______ **2.** After losing many of his people in a series of battles, Chief Joseph and the remaining Nez Perce under him were exiled to California in 1877.

____

_______ **3.** The Indian Peace Commission plan was doomed to failure because the Native Americans were forced to sign the treaty.

____

_______ **4.** Many Native American nations on the Great Plains had lived as nomads.

____

DIRECTIONS: Multiple Choice Indicate the answer choice that best completes the statement or answers the question.

_______ **5.** The Dawes Act attempted to help Native Americans by

A. giving them land for farming.
B. reintroducing the buffalo to native lands.
C. returning them to their native lands.
D. sustaining their previous way of life.

_______ **6.** The army encouraged the killing of buffalo in order to

A. force Native Americans onto reservations.
B. make way for new railroad lines.
C. protect crops.
D. starve Native Americans.

_______ **7.** What was the effect of the Indian Reorganization Act of 1934?

A. A "waiting period" for citizenship was established.
B. Land was given to Native American households for farming.
C. Reservations were expanded in many states.
D. The previous policy of assimilation was reversed.

_______ **8.** The Dakota Sioux uprising occurred as a result of

A. fear, caused by the continued loss of buffalo herds.
B. greed, caused by an outlawed Native American group.
C. jealousy, caused by anger at the presence of white settlers.
D. poverty, caused by annuity payments that were not received.

NAME ______________________ DATE ______________ CLASS ____________

Chapter 2 Test, Form A

networks

Settling the West

DIRECTIONS: Matching Match each item with the correct statement below.

_______ **1.** author of *A Century of Dishonor*

_______ **2.** destination for the first cattle drive

_______ **3.** supply point for mining areas in the Rocky Mountains

_______ **4.** leader of the Cheyenne who were massacred at Sand Creek

_______ **5.** one destination for the "long drive"

_______ **6.** cavalry commander at Little Bighorn

_______ **7.** Lakota Sioux chief killed at Wounded Knee

_______ **8.** Nez Perce chief who surrendered after a flight of 1,300 miles

_______ **9.** cattle that roamed wild on the grasslands of Texas

_______ **10.** war chief who lured an army detachment into an ambush

A. Black Kettle

B. Helen Hunt Jackson

C. Sedalia

D. George Custer

E. Sitting Bull

F. Abilene

G. Crazy Horse

H. Denver

I. longhorns

J. Chief Joseph

DIRECTIONS: Multiple Choice Indicate the answer choice that best completes the statement or answers the question.

_______ **11.** In the early 1800s, Americans did not think cattle ranches on the Great Plains were practical because

A. eastern cattle could not survive on tough prairie grasses.

B. there was no demand for beef in the eastern states.

C. there was not enough grass to support large cattle herds.

D. wagon trains had stripped the land of needed resources.

_______ **12.** The "long drive" was when

A. cowboys herded cattle hundreds of miles to a railroad line.

B. Lewis and Clark mapped their journey to the Pacific Ocean.

C. Native Americans traveled on their forced westward migration.

D. wagon trains traveled through the Rocky Mountains.

_____ **13.** What effect did the use of barbed wire to fence off land on the open range have on cattle ranching?

A. It harmed cattle, reducing the number that made it to market.
B. It blocked cattle trails, making it difficult to get cattle to market.
C. It prevented cattle from finding food, reducing the number of cattle that survived each year.
D. It required too much effort to maintain, so ranchers abandoned their ranches.

_____ **14.** In the 1890s, some farmers tried to survive by mortgaging their land because

A. a glut of wheat on the world market caused prices to drop.
B. a series of floods destroyed several years of crops.
C. prices for wheat dropped when demand for corn grew.
D. they needed money to grow cotton instead of wheat.

_____ **15.** After ore deposits near the surface dwindled, mining corporations began using

A. placer mining.
B. quartz mining.
C. strip mining.
D. tunnel mining.

_____ **16.** People using the phrase "Pikes Peak or Bust!" were

A. cattle ranchers.
B. dry farmers.
C. gold miners.
D. mountain climbers.

_____ **17.** Which of the following was a hardship faced by settlers on the Great Plains?

A. flooding
B. plague
C. prairie fires
D. too many trees

_____ **18.** Before the Sand Creek Massacre, the Cheyenne had come to Fort Lyon to

A. attack.
B. defend their land.
C. negotiate.
D. surrender.

_____ **19.** The confrontation at Wounded Knee occurred because the chief's followers

A. continued hunting buffalo.
B. left their reservation.
C. performed a ritual.
D. raided nearby farms.

_____ **20.** Many Mexican Americans lost their lands in the West because

A. American courts would not recognize Spanish land grants.
B. Mexican courts forced them to sell to American settlers.
C. they decided to leave the area before new settlers arrived.
D. they fought against U.S. troops during the War with Mexico.

Chapter 2 Test, Form A *cont.*

Settling the West

DIRECTIONS: Short Answer Answer each of the following questions.

21. Describe the agreement the Dakota Sioux had made with the U.S. government and the reason for their uprising.

____

____

____

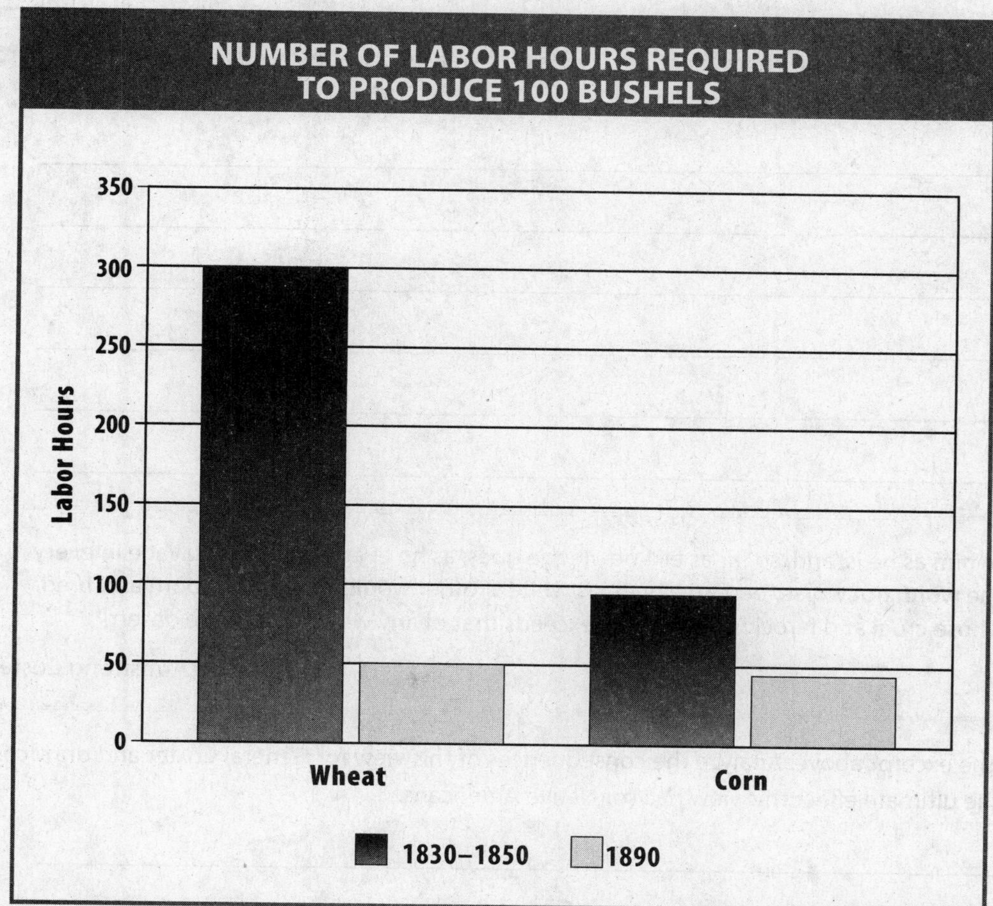

22. Analyze the chart above and explain what conclusion you can draw from its details. Hypothesize about how the Industrial Revolution was dependent on the Agricultural Revolution.

____

____

____

Native American Population and the Railroad					
Year	**1860**	**1870**	**1880**	**1890**	**1900**
Approximate miles of railroad track in U.S.	30,000	53,000	116,000	208,000	259,000
Approximate Native American population	351,000	323,000	318,000	265,000	248,000

23. Examine the figures in the chart. What are the possible reasons for the trends shown on this chart? Cite evidence that supports your conclusion.

"... We see him as he is, and, so far as all knowledge goes, as he ever has been, a savage in every sense of the word; not worse, perhaps, than his white brother would be similarly born and bred, but one whose cruel and ferocious nature far exceeds that of any wild beast of the desert."

—George Armstrong Custer

24. Assess the excerpt above. Analyze the consequences of this view for General Custer and draw conclusions about the ultimate effect this view had for Native Americans.

NAME ______________________ DATE ____________ CLASS ____________

Chapter 2 Test, Form B

networks

Settling the West

DIRECTIONS: Short Answer Answer each of the following questions on a separate piece of paper.

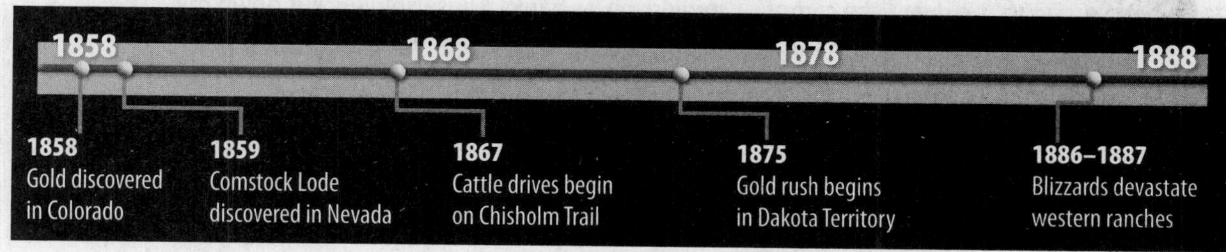

1. Study the time line and describe what drew people to the West during this period.

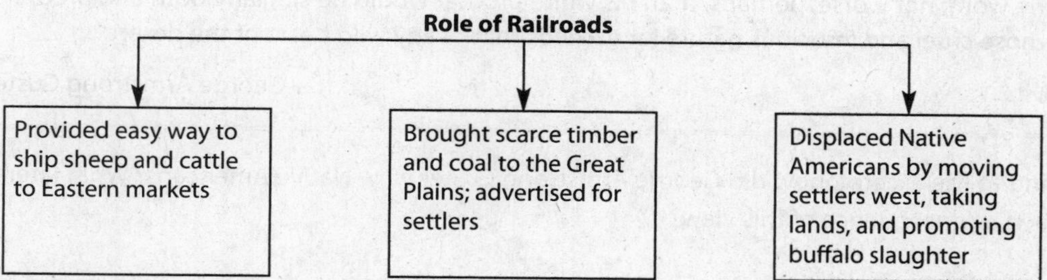

Role of Railroads
Provided easy way to ship sheep and cattle to Eastern markets
Brought scarce timber and coal to the Great Plains; advertised for settlers
Displaced Native Americans by moving settlers west, taking lands, and promoting buffalo slaughter

2. What positive effects did the railroads have for Western settlers?

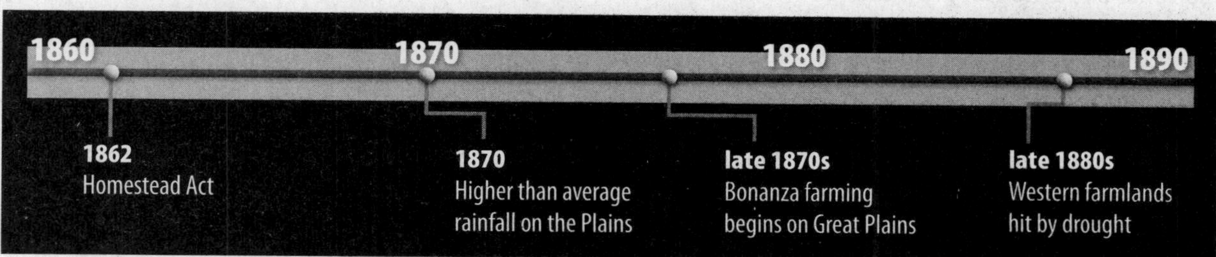

3. After studying the time line, describe how the events that occurred between the late 1870s and the late 1880s might have affected settlers on the Great Plains.

". . . when I go up to the river I see camps of soldiers on its banks. These soldiers cut down my timber; they kill my buffalo. . . . Has the white man become like a child that he should recklessly kill and not eat? When the red men slay game, they do so that they may live and not starve."

—Satanta, chief of the Kiowa

4. After reading the quote, describe two ways Satanta felt the soldiers were behaving like children.

". . . We see him as he is, and, so far as all knowledge goes, as he ever has been, a savage in every sense of the word; not worse, perhaps, than his white brother would be similarly born and bred, but one whose cruel and ferocious nature far exceeds that of any wild beast of the desert."

—George Armstrong Custer

5. According to the excerpt, how did George Armstrong Custer view Native Americans? What later event may have been a consequence of this view?

". . . such a house is somewhat cold in winter, as the crevices between the sods admit some cold air; so some of the houses are plastered with a kind of 'native lime,' made of sand and a very sticky native clay. This plaster is very good unless it happens to get wet."

—Kansas homesteader, 1877

6. After reading the excerpt, explain the best reason a settler on the Great Plains would choose to build a sod house to live in.

"By the end of the three-day blizzard we were in fine shape to take care of our stock. Many others did not fare so well; but that's life. After all, we said to each other, this was a new country and folks had to learn how to look after themselves."

—Charley O'Kieffe, settler

7. After reading the quote, describe personal characteristics that new settlers needed to adapt to life on the Western frontier.

DIRECTIONS: Essay Answer the following question on a separate piece of paper.

8. Assess how the growth of railroads transformed America during the nineteenth century.

NAME ______________________ DATE ______________ CLASS __________

Lesson Quiz 3-1

networks

Industrialization

DIRECTIONS: Modified True/False In the blank, indicate whether the statement is true (T) or false (F). If false, edit the statement to make it a true statement.

_______ **1.** Supporters of laissez-faire economics believe the government should not interfere in the economy other than to protect private property rights and maintain peace.

____

_______ **2.** The United States lacked the natural resources upon which industrialization in the 1800s depended, including water, timber, coal, iron, and copper.

____

_______ **3.** Thomas Alva Edison stood as a symbol of the emerging age of technology with his invention of the telephone.

____

_______ **4.** Machines could mass-produce shoes more cheaply and efficiently than local cobblers, so shoe production moved from small shops to large factories.

____

_______ **5.** The growth of the population between 1860 and 1910 provided industrialists with a large workforce and also created greater demand for the consumer goods factories produced.

____

DIRECTIONS: Multiple Choice Indicate the answer choice that best completes the statement or answers the question.

_______ **6.** Who began the first modern research laboratory, resulting in many new inventions, including the battery and the motion picture?

A. Alexander Graham Bell
B. Edwin Drake
C. George Pullman
D. Thomas Alva Edison

_______ **7.** Supporters of laissez-faire generally favor

A. free trade.
B. government protections.
C. high prices.
D. tariffs.

_______ **8.** The first oil well was drilled near Titusville, Pennsylvania, by

A. Alexander Graham Bell.
B. Edwin Drake.
C. Elisha Otis.
D. Thomas Alva Edison.

_______ **9.** One reason for the country's industrial success was its vast abundance of natural

A. resources.
B. gross national product.
C. technology.
D. enterprise.

NAME ________________ DATE ________________ CLASS ________________

Lesson Quiz 3-2

networks

Industrialization

DIRECTIONS: Matching Match each item with the correct statement below.

_____ **1.** implicated in the Crédit Mobilier scandal

_____ **2.** made a fortune from the Central Pacific Railroad

_____ **3.** notoriously corrupt railroad owner

_____ **4.** built the Great Northern Railroad

_____ **5.** chief engineer of the Union Pacific Railroad

A. Leland Stanford

B. James J. Hill

C. Grenville Dodge

D. Oakes Ames

E. Jay Gould

DIRECTIONS: Multiple Choice Indicate the answer choice that best completes the statement or answers the question.

_____ **6.** The government offered each railroad company building the Transcontinental Railroad _____ along its right-of-way.

A. railroad stations
B. natural resources
C. land
D. free housing

_____ **7.** A shortage of workers in California forced the Central Pacific Railroad to hire about 10,000 workers from

A. China.
B. Ireland.
C. Japan.
D. Mexico.

_____ **8.** To build their railroads, railroad companies raised most of the money they needed from

A. hauling freight to market.
B. private investors.
C. selling government land grants.
D. subsidies from tax revenues.

_____ **9.** The two railroad corporations that built the transcontinental railroad were the

A. Southern Railway and Great Northern.
B. Southern Railway and Union Pacific.
C. Union Pacific and Central Pacific.
D. Union Pacific and Great Northern.

_____ **10.** To make rail service more reliable, in 1883 the American Railway Association

A. divided the country into standardized time zones.
B. drew latitude and longitude lines for the country.
C. set a maximum number of cars that a train could pull.
D. set standards for materials used in the construction of railroad lines.

NAME ______________________ DATE ______________ CLASS ____________

Lesson Quiz 3-3

networks

Industrialization

DIRECTIONS: Matching Match each item with the correct statement below.

_____ **1.** owns stock in companies that produce goods

_____ **2.** specialized in helping sell large blocks of stock to investment bankers

_____ **3.** founder of a steel company in Pittsburgh

_____ **4.** manages property for others

_____ **5.** operated Standard Oil

A. Andrew Carnegie

B. J. P. Morgan

C. trust

D. John D. Rockefeller

E. holding company

DIRECTIONS: Multiple Choice Indicate the answer choice that best completes the statement or answers the question.

_____ **6.** When a single company achieves control of an entire market, it is known as

A. a corporation.
B. a monopoly.
C. an integration.
D. an oligarchy.

_____ **7.** Department stores changed the idea of shopping by

A. bringing together a huge array of different products.
B. coming together to form shopping malls.
C. locating in rural areas.
D. offering low prices instead of elaborate service.

_____ **8.** In contrast to department stores, which offered many services, chain stores focused on offering

A. an elegant atmosphere.
B. low prices.
C. mail-order catalogs.
D. more fashionable goods.

_____ **9.** How did N. W. Ayer and Son, the first advertising company, try to attract customers?

A. by placing ads only in newspapers
B. by printing a catalog
C. by putting up billboards
D. by using large illustrated ads

_____ **10.** What is an organization owned by many people but treated by law as though it were a single person?

A. a corporation
B. a holding company
C. a trust
D. an organized pool

NAME ______________________ DATE ______________ CLASS ________

networks

Lesson Quiz 3-4

Industrialization

DIRECTIONS: Modified True/False In the blank, indicate whether the statement is true (T) or false (F). If false, edit the statement to make it a true statement.

______ **1.** As industrialism brought more machines into the workplace, jobs became more complex and required more skills.

____

______ **2.** Most unions in the late 1800s excluded women.

____

______ **3.** In the late 1800s, large trade unions generally failed, but industrial unions prospered.

____

______ **4.** In the late 1800s, workers' buying power generally decreased.

____

______ **5.** Some labor supporters were anarchists, who believed that society did not need any government.

____

DIRECTIONS: Multiple Choice Indicate the answer choice that best completes the statement or answers the question.

______ **6.** A __________ was a technique for breaking a union through which the company refused to allow workers onto their property.

A. blacklist
B. lockout
C. sit-down
D. strike

______ **7.** When a union called a strike, employers would often hire replacements, called

A. blacklists.
B. lockouts.
C. strikebreakers.
D. troublemakers.

______ **8.** Employers generally viewed unions as

A. conspiracies that interfered with property rights.
B. groups that helped increase productivity.
C. organizations that were necessary for protecting workers.
D. secret societies planning to overthrow the government.

______ **9.** The Knights of Labor suffered a steady decline in membership and influence due to lost strikes and

A. its refusal to use arbitration.
B. its support of Marxism.
C. the Haymarket Riot.
D. the Homestead Strike.

NAME ______________________ DATE ______________ CLASS __________

Chapter 3 Test, Form A

networks

Industrialization

DIRECTIONS: Matching Match each item with the correct statement below.

_______ **1.** wages, shipping charges, and supplies

_______ **2.** Iron Molders' International Union, for example

_______ **3.** represented all workers in a particular industry

_______ **4.** began the railroad boom

_______ **5.** loans, mortgages, and taxes

_______ **6.** allowed cloth to be made more quickly

_______ **7.** enabled longer and heavier trains

_______ **8.** saw capitalism as a struggle between workers and owners

_______ **9.** belief that the government should not interfere in the economy

_______ **10.** head of the American Railway Union

A. fixed costs

B. Karl Marx

C. industrial union

D. air brakes

E. operating costs

F. trade union

G. automatic loom

H. Pacific Railway Act

I. Eugene V. Debs

J. laissez-faire

DIRECTIONS: Multiple Choice Indicate the answer choice that best completes the statement or answers the question.

_______ **11.** Even before the invention of the automobile, petroleum was in high demand because it could

A. be made into plastics.

B. be turned into kerosene.

C. lubricate moving parts in a machine.

D. power locomotives.

_______ **12.** Laissez-faire relies on __________ to regulate prices and wages.

A. supply and demand

B. businesses

C. government

D. the GNP

_______ **13.** During the early days of industrialization, many members of Congress believed that tariffs were necessary to

A. entice European consumers to buy American goods.

B. increase the prices Europeans paid for American products.

C. protect new industries from foreign competition.

D. entice American consumers to buy European goods.

NAME ______________________ DATE ______________ CLASS ____________

Chapter 3 Test, Form A *cont.*

networks

Industrialization

_____ **14.** In the late 1800s, workers' buying power generally increased because

A. factories often increased prices.

B. factories often increased wages.

C. prices fell faster than wages.

D. wages increased faster than prices.

_____ **15.** People who risk their own money to organize and run businesses are known as

A. capitalists.

B. entrepreneurs.

C. robber barons.

D. investors.

_____ **16.** In the Crédit Mobilier scandal, Union Pacific investors got rich by

A. accepting bribes from business owners to route railroad tracks through their towns.

B. achieving a monopoly in hauling freight along their railroads' tracks.

C. conspiring with other railroads to set high prices.

D. paying inflated bills from a construction company they controlled.

_____ **17.** The total value of all goods and services that a country produces is its

A. distribution chain.

B. economy of scale.

C. gross national product.

D. supply of natural resources.

_____ **18.** Issuing stock allows a corporation to raise large amounts of money for big projects while

A. cutting prices to increase sales.

B. decreasing fixed costs.

C. lending money to investors.

D. spreading out the financial risk.

_____ **19.** The American Federation of Labor pushed for closed shops, meaning that companies

A. could only hire union workers.

B. could not try to prevent strikes.

C. would agree to collective bargaining.

D. would not hire African Americans.

Chapter 3 Test, Form A *cont.*

Industrialization

_______ **20.** What is one advantage that big corporations had over small businesses?

A. Their products were more expensive.

B. They could hire more workers.

C. They had higher operating costs.

D. They could produce goods more cheaply and efficiently.

DIRECTIONS: Short Answer Answer each of the following questions.

21. What is a corporation, who owns it, and how does it raise money?

____

____

____

____

____

Cattle → Slaughterhouse → Meat Packing Plants → Ace Meat Industries

22. What type of economic strategy does the graph illustrate? Describe how Andrew Carnegie utilized this strategy during the Industrial Revolution.

____

____

____

____

____

____

____

____

Chapter 3 Test, Form A *cont.*

Industrialization

"The capitalist class is organized economically and politically to keep the working class in subjection and perpetuate its power as a ruling class. They do not support a working class union nor a working-class party. They are not so foolish. They wisely look out for themselves."

—Eugene Debs, 1912

23. Explain the struggle described in the above quote. Apply the quote in the context of the conditions facing workers during the Industrial Revolution.

NAME ______________________ DATE ______________ CLASS ______________

Chapter 3 Test, Form B

networks

Industrialization

DIRECTIONS: Short Answer Answer each of the following questions on a separate piece of paper.

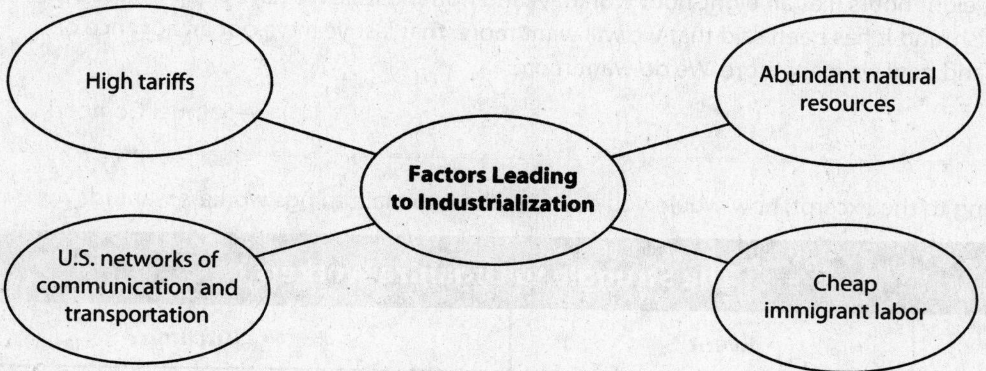

1. Which of the factors in the growth of industrialization in the United States was not influenced by government policies?

> "We sat and looked and the lamp continued to burn and the longer it burned the more fascinated we were. None of us could go to bed and there was no sleep for over 40 hours; we sat and just watched it with anxiety growing into elation."
>
> —Thomas Edison

2. Identify the emotions that Thomas Edison and his team of workers probably experienced as they watched the first electric lamp burn.

> "Men who continue hoarding great sums all their lives, the proper use of which for public ends would work good to the community, should be made to feel that the community . . . cannot thus be deprived of its proper share. By taxing estates heavily at death the state marks its condemnation of the selfish millionaire's unworthy life."
>
> —Andrew Carnegie

3. According to the excerpt, what is Carnegie's justification for the state to tax a millionaire's estate at death?

> "We want eight hours [i.e., an eight-hour workday] and nothing less. We have been accused of being selfish, and it has been said that we will want more; that last year we got an advance of ten cents and now we want more. We do want more."
>
> —Samuel Gompers

4. According to the excerpt, how would you describe the two main things workers wanted?

The Struggle to Organize Workers

Date	Event	Outcome
1877	Great Railroad Strike	After railroads announce wage cuts, the nationwide strike that follows involves 80,000 railroad workers. President Hayes orders the army to Philadelphia, Pittsburgh, and Chicago. Troops restore order, but more than 100 people are killed and millions of dollars of property is destroyed.
1886	Haymarket Riot	Seven police officers and four workers are killed in Chicago's Haymarket Square after a bomb goes off following a clash between strikers and police.
1894	Pullman Strike	A strike is called by the American Railway Union after the Pullman Company cuts wages. President Cleveland calls on federal troops to keep the railroads moving. A formal court order ends the strike.

5. According to the chart, how did the government react to disgruntled railroad employees in 1877?

DIRECTIONS: Essay Answer the following question on a separate piece of paper.

6. Draw conclusions about how the expansion of railroads spurred America's industrial growth, changed the lives of Americans, and shaped the nation's future.

NAME ______________________ DATE ____________ CLASS ____________

Lesson Quiz 4-1

networks

Urban America

DIRECTIONS: Matching Match each item with the correct statement below.

_______ **1.** ethnic neighborhood in New York City

_______ **2.** an anti-immigrant organization

_______ **3.** factor that caused an increase in Chinese immigration

_______ **4.** location of a barracks in California to accommodate immigrants from Asia

_______ **5.** an extreme dislike for foreigners by native-born people

A. Angel Island

B. Little Italy

C. American Protective Association

D. nativism

E. Taiping Rebellion

DIRECTIONS: Multiple Choice Indicate the answer choice that best completes the statement or answers the question.

_______ **6.** By the 1890s, more than half of all immigrants in the United States were

A. European and Russian Jews.
B. Eastern and Southern Europeans.
C. Chinese.
D. Japanese.

_______ **7.** Many immigrants came to the United States in part to escape from poverty and

A. Europe's class system.
B. the social ladder.
C. Europe's labor laws.
D. urban political machines.

_______ **8.** The vast majority of immigrants arriving on the East Coast passed through a processing center located where?

A. Angel Island
B. Ellis Island
C. Staten Island
D. Long Island

_______ **9.** What law prevented Chinese immigrants already in the United States from becoming citizens?

A. Workingmen's Act
B. Chinese Immigration Act
C. Taiping Act
D. Chinese Exclusion Act

_______ **10.** At the end of the nineteenth century, immigrants made up a significant percentage of some of the country's largest

A. plantations.
B. farms.
C. cities.
D. suburbs.

NAME ______________________ DATE ____________ CLASS ____________

networks

Lesson Quiz 4-2

Urban America

DIRECTIONS: True/False Indicate whether the statement is true or false.

_____ **1.** The rising value of land in some cities encouraged the building of tall, steel framed buildings called skyscrapers.

_____ **2.** During the last half of the 1800s, the wealthiest families established fashionable districts in "streetcar suburbs."

_____ **3.** Threats from crime and violence, fire, disease, and pollution were part of city life in the late 1800s—especially for the working poor.

_____ **4.** In the late 1800s, drinking water in American cities was often contaminated because of the lack of flush toilets.

_____ **5.** The famous New York City Democratic political machine was known as Tammany Hall.

DIRECTIONS: Multiple Choice Indicate the answer choice that best completes the statement or answers the question.

_____ **6.** In the late 1800s, many rural Americans moved to big cities in search of

A. better-paying jobs.
B. political power.
C. high society.
D. shorter work hours.

_____ **7.** Most urban working-class families lived in multifamily apartment buildings called

A. suburbs.
B. skyscrapers.
C. tenements.
D. work houses.

_____ **8.** In response to urban congestion, Boston and New York City built the first

A. tunnels.
B. trolley cars.
C. overpasses.
D. subway systems.

_____ **9.** America's industrialization made some people wealthy and created a growing

A. federal government.
B. political machine.
C. middle class.
D. agricultural system.

_____ **10.** Who rose to become one of New York City's most powerful party bosses?

A. Thomas Pendergast
B. George Plunkitt
C. Cornelius Vanderbilt
D. Zalmen Yoffeh

NAME _______________ DATE _______________ CLASS _______________

Lesson Quiz 4-3

networks

Urban America

DIRECTIONS: Completion Enter the appropriate word(s) to complete the statement.

1. The belief that people can rise as far as their talents will take them, no matter how humble their origins, was called _______________.

2. American artists and writers of the 1800s who tried to capture the world as they saw it were known as _______________.

3. Scott Joplin was one of the most important African American _______________ composers.

4. Jane Addams established a(n) _______________ called Hull House in Chicago.

5. The _______________ was a reform-minded organization that tried to help the urban poor by offering practical aid and religious counseling.

DIRECTIONS: Multiple Choice Indicate the answer choice that best completes the statement or answers the question.

_______ 6. By calling their era the "Gilded Age," authors Mark Twain and Charles Warner were

A. praising industrial advances.
B. warning against realism.
C. criticizing corruption.
D. pleading for individualism.

_______ 7. The application of the theory of evolution and natural selection to human society was known as

A. Naturalism.
B. Social Darwinism.
C. Dynamic Sociology.
D. the Social Gospel.

_______ 8. The Gospel of Wealth was a philosophy that wealthy Americans had a responsibility to

A. build their wealth through investment.
B. help high culture grow in America.
C. support laissez-faire policies.
D. engage in philanthropy.

_______ 9. Formed in 1869, the Cincinnati Red Stockings were the nation's first

A. sports team affiliated with a city.
B. professional baseball team.
C. World Series champion.
D. college football team.

_______ 10. Which of the following social reformers believed that the best way to help the urban poor was to redeem their souls and reform their characters?

A. Dwight L. Moody
B. Lester Frank Ward
C. Lillian Wald
D. Henry George

NAME ______________________ DATE ______________ CLASS ________

networks

Lesson Quiz 4-4

Urban America

DIRECTIONS: Matching Match each item with the correct statement below.

_____ **1.** campaigned for the free coinage of silver in the 1896 election

_____ **2.** popular name for the Patrons of Animal Husbandry

_____ **3.** Republicans that supported Cleveland against Blaine

_____ **4.** marketing organizations that worked for the benefit of their members

_____ **5.** a movement to increase the political power of farmers

A. cooperatives

B. People's Party

C. Mugwumps

D. Populism

E. the Grange

DIRECTIONS: Multiple Choice Indicate the answer choice that best completes the statement or answers the question.

_____ **6.** Under the Pendleton Act of 1883, some government jobs were filled by

A. appointments made by members of Congress.

B. people who raised money for a political party's election campaign.

C. job applicants who performed well on competitive written examinations.

D. a quota system that balanced the number of jobs going to each party's supporters.

_____ **7.** In the late 1800s, new technology helped farmers produce more crops, which tended to

A. lower prices.

B. raise prices.

C. raise quality.

D. lower quality.

_____ **8.** Farmers were hurt economically by high tariffs, high shipping rates, and

A. falling interest rates.

B. inflation.

C. increased regulation.

D. deflation.

_____ **9.** Which of the following did the People's Party—also known as the Populists—call for in 1892?

A. tax breaks for businesses

B. a new tariff law

C. a graduated income tax

D. gold-based currency

_____ **10.** The Populist Party declined after the election of 1896, when

A. pro-silver Democrats did not vote with the Populists.

B. Populists supported losing candidate William Jennings Bryan.

C. many Democrats promised to support Populist programs.

D. Populists won control of several state legislatures.

NAME ______________________ DATE ______________ CLASS ____________

Lesson Quiz 4-5

networks

Urban America

DIRECTIONS: Completion Enter the appropriate word(s) to complete the statement.

1. After Reconstruction, most African Americans in the rural South lived in poverty and chronic debt as ______________, landless farmers who gave their landlords a large portion of their crops as rent.

2. In 1892 an African American named Homer ______________ challenged a Louisiana law that forced him to ride in a separate railroad car from whites.

3. The statutes enforcing segregation in the South were known as ______________ laws.

4. One of the most prominent African American leaders of the late 1800s was Booker T. ______________.

5. ______________, a leader of a new generation of African American activists born after the Civil War, argued that African Americans had to demand their rights.

DIRECTIONS: Multiple Choice Indicate the answer choice that best completes the statement or answers the question.

______ **6.** In the mid-1870s, a former enslaved person named Benjamin "Pap" Singleton helped set in motion

A. the spread of vocational education for African Americans.
B. a nationwide campaign for civil rights.
C. the establishment of the Colored Farmers' National Alliance.
D. a mass migration of African Americans.

______ **7.** Mississippi took the first step to prohibit African Americans from voting when it required that all citizens registering to vote pay a

A. literacy fee.
B. poll tax.
C. head tax.
D. voting fee.

______ **8.** The stage was set for legalized segregation in 1883, when the Supreme Court overturned which of the following?

A. the Civil Rights Act of 1875
B. the Fourteenth Amendment
C. Reconstruction
D. the Fifteenth Amendment

______ **9.** Ida B. Wells was an African American journalist who launched a campaign against

A. voting restrictions.
B. segregation.
C. poverty.
D. lynching.

NAME ______________________ DATE ______________ CLASS ______________

Chapter 4 Test, Form A

networks

Urban America

DIRECTIONS: Matching Match each item with the correct statement below.

_______ **1.** a Republican president who opposed patronage

_______ **2.** composer who was called the "King of Ragtime"

_______ **3.** founder of the Tuskegee Institute

_______ **4.** believed wealthy Americans should use their wealth to help people help themselves

_______ **5.** argued that society progressed because only the fittest people survived

_______ **6.** journalist who launched a crusade against lynching

_______ **7.** perhaps the best-known American realist painter

_______ **8.** Populist and Democratic presidential nominee in 1896

_______ **9.** wrote that "color discrimination is barbarism"

_______ **10.** opened Hull House in Chicago

A. Andrew Carnegie

B. W.E.B. Du Bois

C. James A. Garfield

D. Thomas Eakins

E. Jane Addams

F. Scott Joplin

G. William Jennings Bryan

H. Ida B. Wells

I. Herbert Spencer

J. Booker T. Washington

DIRECTIONS: Multiple Choice Indicate the answer choice that best completes the statement or answers the question.

_______ **11.** Nativists reacted to immigration in the late 1800s by

A. grouping immigrants into their own sections of cities.
B. urging immigrants to assimilate into American society.
C. pressuring the government to limit or cut off immigration.
D. seeking to convert Catholic immigrants to Protestantism.

_______ **12.** Some Chinese immigrants opened their own businesses in part because

A. native-born Americans kept them out of many businesses.
B. they settled mainly in Western cities.
C. demand for railroad workers increased in the 1860s.
D. they lived in city neighborhoods separated by ethnic group.

Chapter 4 Test, Form A *cont.*

networks

Urban America

______ **13.** In Boston, Chicago, and New York City, elevated railroads and subway systems were developed to

A. transport people away from cities.

B. carry people from one city to another.

C. eliminate polluted air in the cities.

D. relieve congestion on city streets.

______ **14.** Political machines provided new city dwellers with necessities such as jobs, housing, and police protection in exchange for

A. graft.

B. votes.

C. kickbacks.

D. wages.

______ **15.** Popular culture changed in the late 1800s because industrialization improved the standard of living for many people, enabling them to

A. spend money on entertainment.

B. travel across the country.

C. buy mass-produced clothing.

D. own houses with more amenities.

______ **16.** In one of the major economic debates of the late 1800s, Republicans in Congress blocked Democratic efforts to

A. regulate the railroad industry.

B. lower tariffs.

C. prohibit the formation of trusts.

D. raise tariffs.

______ **17.** Passed by Congress in response to the assassination of President James A. Garfield, the Pendleton Act

A. brought an end to patronage and the spoils system.

B. marked the beginning of a professional civil service.

C. attempted to regulate rates charged by railroads.

D. increased tariffs on textiles and many other goods.

______ **18.** The People's Party, also known as the ______________, was formed in 1890 to elect candidates who would fight for the interests of farmers.

A. Grange

B. Farmers' Alliance

C. Populists

D. Cross of Gold

NAME ______________________ DATE ______________ CLASS ____________

Chapter 4 Test, Form A *cont.*

networks

Urban America

_______ **19.** Beginning in the late 1800s, Southern states used a loophole in the wording of the Fifteenth Amendment to impose restrictions that

A. allowed private groups to discriminate against African Americans.

B. prevented African Americans from owning their own farms.

C. barred African Americans from voting in elections.

D. required African Americans to use separate facilities.

_______ **20.** Which of the following set out the doctrine of "separate but equal," establishing a legal basis for segregation that would last more than 50 years?

A. the Supreme Court's decision in *Plessy* v. *Ferguson*

B. the Pendleton Act

C. the Supreme Court's decision in *Wabash* v. *Illinois*

D. the Chinese Exclusion Act

DIRECTIONS: Short Answer Answer each of the following questions.

21. Describe the problems of urban living in the late 1800s and explain their causes.

> "To provide a center for higher civic and social life; to institute and maintain educational and philanthropic enterprises, and to investigate and improve the conditions in the industrial districts of Chicago."
>
> —Charter adopted by Hull House Association

22. Explain what Hull House was and describe how the settlement house movement attempted to solve social problems.

Chapter 4 Test, Form A *cont.*

Urban America

23. Describe several reasons why Europeans immigrated to the United States in the late 1800s.

____

____

____

24. Define "deflation" and explain why it hurts farmers.

____

____

____

"The wisest among my race understand that . . . the enjoyment of all the privileges that will come to us must be the result of severe and constant struggle rather than of artificial forcing. . . . It is important and right that all privileges of the law be ours, but it is vastly more important that we be prepared for the exercise of these privileges."

—Booker T. Washington, *Address to the Atlanta Cotton States and International Exposition ("The Atlanta Compromise")*, 1895

"[T]he way for a people to gain their reasonable rights is not by voluntarily throwing them away and insisting that they do not want them . . . on the contrary, Negroes must insist continually, in season and out of season, that voting is necessary to modern manhood, [and] that color discrimination is barbarism."

—W.E.B. Du Bois, *The Souls of Black Folk*, 1903

25. Summarize the ideas of Booker T. Washington and W.E.B. Du Bois on how to address discrimination against African Americans.

____

____

____

____

____

NAME ______________________ DATE ______________ CLASS ______________

Chapter 4 Test, Form B

networks

Urban America

DIRECTIONS: Short Answer Answer each of the following questions on a separate piece of paper.

Immigration Settlement Patterns, c. 1900

	China	Germany	Ireland	Italy	Poland	Russia	Scandinavia
California	40,000	72,000	44,000				
Illinois		332,000	129,000	23,000	64,000	28,000	129,000
Massachusetts			249,000	28,000		26,000	32,000
New York		480,000	425,000	182,000	66,000	165,000	42,000
Ohio		204,000	55,000				
Pennsylvania		212,000	205,000	66,000	72,000	50,000	
Wisconsin		242,000	61,000		23,000		30,000

1. What does the table above demonstrate about immigration and the settlement patterns of immigrants in the late 1800s?

2. Based on the table, compare immigration from China to immigration from Europe during this period.

> "Society does not owe any man a living. . . . The fact that a man is here is no demand upon other people that they shall keep him alive and sustain him. He has got to fight the battle with nature as every other man has; and if he fights it with the same energy and enterprise and skill and industry as any other man, I cannot imagine his failing—that is, misfortune apart."
>
> —William Graham Sumner, testimony before the U.S. House of Representatives, 1879

3. Describe the theory of Social Darwinism as it is reflected in the statements above.

4. How is Sumner's Social Darwinism paralleled by the economic doctrine of laissez-faire?

Chapter 4 Test, Form B *cont.*

Urban America

> "The farmers of the United States are up in arms . . . (T)hey are getting, they say, the smallest share (of the nation's wealth) for themselves. The American farmer is steadily losing ground."
>
> —Washington Gladden, "The Embattled Farmers"

5. What caused farmers to feel as though they were "steadily losing ground" in the late 1800s?

6. Describe how farmers responded to their situation, both politically and economically.

DIRECTIONS: Essay Answer the following question on a separate piece of paper.

7. What processes and patterns caused many people to settle in American cities in the late 1800s? How did people address the new challenges of urban society?

NAME ________________ DATE ________________ CLASS ________________

Lesson Quiz 5-1

networks

Becoming a World Power

DIRECTIONS: Matching Match each item with the correct statement below.

________ **1.** helped build public support for a strong navy		**A.** Pan-Americanism
________ **2.** the economic and political domination of a strong nation over weaker nations		**B.** Alfred T. Mahan
		C. imperialism
________ **3.** the idea that Latin America and the United States should work together		**D.** Matthew C. Perry
________ **4.** the idea that English-speaking nations were superior to other nations		**E.** Anglo-Saxonism
________ **5.** took a naval expedition to Japan in order to negotiate a trade treaty		

DIRECTIONS: Multiple Choice Indicate the answer choice that best completes the statement or answers the question.

________ **6.** Economic and military competition from ________________ helped to convince many Americans that the United States should become a world power.

A. Canada
B. Europe
C. China
D. Latin America

________ **7.** John Fiske, a historian in the late 1800s, argued that English-speaking nations had superior character, ideas, and systems of government. His ideas convinced many Americans

A. that the United States needed to build a large, modern navy.
B. to support the annexation of Hawaii.
C. that the United States should be dominant in the Western Hemisphere.
D. to support the expansion of American civilization.

________ **8.** In the 1880s, Secretary of State James G. Blaine led efforts to

A. open trade between Japan and the United States.
B. overthrow the Hawaiian monarchy.
C. expand American influence into Latin America.
D. increase support for American expansion.

________ **9.** The Commercial Bureau of the American Republics was formed in order to promote

A. limits on trade with European nations.
B. cooperation among the nations of the Western Hemisphere.
C. democracy in the Western Hemisphere.
D. widespread use of the United States dollar in Latin America.

NAME _______________ DATE _______________ CLASS _______________

networks

Lesson Quiz 5-2

Becoming a World Power

DIRECTIONS: Completion Enter the appropriate word(s) to complete the statement.

1. Reporters who published sensationalized stories about Spanish atrocities were called _______________.

2. As tensions were building against the Spanish in Cuba, President McKinley was faced with strong _______________, or aggressive nationalism, within the Republican Party.

3. On April 19, 1898, Congress declared Cuba _______________ and demanded that Spain withdraw from the island; five days later, Spain declared war on the United States.

4. The "_______________," a volunteer cavalry unit made up of cowboys, miners, and law officers, played an important role in the battle for Cuba.

5. Congress passed the Foraker Act in 1900, establishing a civil government for _______________.

DIRECTIONS: Multiple Choice Indicate the answer choice that best completes the statement or answers the question.

_____ **6.** In 1898 President William McKinley sent the American battleship USS *Maine* to Havana to

A. put down the Cuban rebellion.
B. negotiate peace with Spain.
C. evacuate Americans if necessary.
D. put down riots by Spanish loyalists.

_____ **7.** When the *Maine* exploded, whom did many Americans hold responsible?

A. Cuba
B. Japan
C. the Philippines
D. Spain

_____ **8.** On April 11, 1898, President McKinley asked Congress to authorize the use of force to end the conflict in

A. Mexico.
B. Cuba.
C. Colombia.
D. the Philippines.

_____ **9.** Under the terms of the Treaty of Paris, Cuba became an independent nation, the United States agreed to pay Spain $20 million for the Philippines, and the United States acquired Puerto Rico and

A. Guam.
B. Hawaii.
C. the Bahamas.
D. Panama.

_____ **10.** The Platt Amendment effectively made Cuba into an American

A. protectorate.
B. colony.
C. territory.
D. state.

Lesson Quiz 5-3

networks

Becoming a World Power

DIRECTIONS: True/False Indicate whether the statement is true or false.

_______ **1.** As president, Theodore Roosevelt opposed the Open Door policy in China and worked to establish an American trade monopoly there.

_______ **2.** The United States first applied the Roosevelt Corollary in the Dominican Republic, which had fallen behind on its debt payments to European nations.

_______ **3.** The United States constructed the Panama Canal after a French company had abandoned its own efforts to do so.

_______ **4.** President William Howard Taft's "dollar diplomacy" placed less emphasis on military force and more on helping Latin American industry.

_______ **5.** Woodrow Wilson wanted Victoriano Huerta to be in power in Mexico, but he was murdered by the forces of Francisco Madero.

DIRECTIONS: Multiple Choice Indicate the answer choice that best completes the statement or answers the question.

_______ **6.** In 1899 the United States was a major power in

A. Africa.
B. Asia.
C. the Mediterranean.
D. the Middle East.

_______ **7.** Under the Open Door policy promoted by Secretary of State John Hay,

A. all countries would be allowed to trade with China.
B. China would be broken up into European colonies.
C. more countries would be given leaseholds in China.
D. America's sphere of influence in China would grow.

_______ **8.** In 1903 the United States negotiated with ________________ for the right to build a canal through its province of Panama.

A. Spain
B. Mexico
C. Nicaragua
D. Colombia

_______ **9.** Which of the following was an effect of Wilson's policies in Mexico between 1914 and 1917?

A. The U.S. became a respected international peacekeeping force.
B. The U.S. successfully established a stable government in Mexico.
C. Wilson's policies were ridiculed and U.S. foreign relations were damaged.
D. Trade between the U.S. and Latin America was halted for several years.

NAME ______________________ DATE ______________ CLASS ____________

Chapter 5 Test, Form A

networks

Becoming a World Power

DIRECTIONS: Matching Match each item with the correct statement below.

______ **1.** belief that if U.S. business leaders supported Latin American development, everyone would benefit	**A.** sphere of influence
______ **2.** ensured that Cuba would remain tied to the United States	**B.** Roosevelt Corollary
______ **3.** the United States would intervene in Latin American affairs when necessary	**C.** Pan-Americanism
______ **4.** controlled mosquito populations to minimize disease during construction of the Panama Canal	**D.** Anglo-Saxonism
______ **5.** area where a foreign nation controlled economic development	**E.** William Crawford Gorgas
______ **6.** established a civil government for Puerto Rico	**F.** yellow journalism
______ **7.** the U.S. had a duty to shape "less civilized" parts of the world	**G.** Platt Amendment
______ **8.** idea that the U.S. and Latin America should work together	**H.** Foraker Act
______ **9.** local rulers had to accept advice from an imperial power	**I.** protectorate
______ **10.** sensational reporting in which writers often exaggerated or even invented stories	**J.** dollar diplomacy

DIRECTIONS: Multiple Choice Indicate the answer choice that best completes the statement or answers the question.

______ **11.** In 1852 President Millard Fillmore sent a naval expedition to Japan to

A. convince Japan to become an American protectorate.
B. force Japan to trade with the United States.
C. bring Western civilization to Japan.
D. conquer the islands around Japan.

______ **12.** In the 1880s, economic and military competition from other nations and a growing feeling of cultural superiority convinced many Americans that

A. European-style imperialism violated American principles.
B. the United States should be more isolated.
C. European influence in the Americas should be reduced.
D. the United States should be a world power.

Chapter 5 Test, Form A *cont.*

networks

Becoming a World Power

_______ **13.** At the first Pan-American Conference in 1889, the United States hoped to strengthen trade and diplomacy with Latin American nations in part to

A. provide the American navy with new bases.

B. increase tariffs on manufactured products from Europe.

C. keep European powers from meddling in the Americas.

D. protect American manufacturers from competition.

_______ **14.** In the United States, public support for Cuban rebels was fueled in large part by which of the following?

A. the desire to protect American sugar interests on the island

B. popular interest in starting an American empire

C. sensational stories published by rival newspapers

D. the fear of having a Spanish colony so close to the United States

_______ **15.** During the Spanish-American War, American victory in the San Juan Heights led the Spanish to

A. surrender colonies in Guam and the Philippines.

B. protect Santiago Harbor with shore-based guns.

C. evacuate the Spanish fleet from Cuba.

D. launch a military campaign against Cuban rebels.

_______ **16.** The Treaty of Paris of 1898, which formally ended the Spanish-American War, granted independence to which of the following?

A. Guam

B. Cuba

C. Puerto Rico

D. the Philippines

_______ **17.** Supporters of annexing the Philippines after the Spanish-American War believed that

A. the islands would provide the United States with a naval base.

B. the Philippines would become a military rival otherwise.

C. the islands had no potential as a market for American goods.

D. Filipino culture was similar to that of the United States.

_______ **18.** What was the purpose of the Open Door policy in China?

A. to end the Boxer Rebellion

B. to win leaseholds in China

C. to establish a sphere of influence

D. to ensure trading rights with China

_______ **19.** When Panamanian forces revolted against Colombia, the United States quickly

A. sent ten warships to put down the rebellion and reestablish Colombian control.

B. recognized Panama's independence and signed a treaty to build the Panama Canal.

C. withdrew American workers who had begun construction on the Panama Canal.

D. decided to build a canal in Nicaragua because Panama was dangerously unstable.

_______ **20.** U.S. foreign relations were damaged by President Woodrow Wilson's intervention in

A. Honduras.

B. Mexico.

C. Haiti.

D. Nicaragua.

DIRECTIONS: Short Answer Answer each of the following questions on a separate piece of paper.

21. Explain the major economic, cultural, and military factors that built American support for imperialist policies in the 1880s.

> "Whereas, the abhorrent conditions which have existed for more than three years in the Island of Cuba, so near our own borders, have shocked the moral sense of the people of the United States . . . culminating, as they have, in the destruction of a United States battleship, with two hundred and sixty-six of its officers and crew, while on a friendly visit in the harbor of Havana, and can not longer be endured. . . . Therefore,
>
> "Resolved, by the Senate and House of Representatives of the United States of America in Congress assembled, First. That the people of the Island of Cuba are, and of right ought to be, free and independent.
>
> "Second. That it is the duty of the United States to demand, and the Government of the United States does hereby demand, that the Government of Spain at once relinquish its authority and government in the Island of Cuba, and withdraw its land and naval forces from Cuba and Cuban waters. . . ."
>
> —from Congress's Joint Resolution for the Recognition of the Independence of the People of Cuba, April 1898

22. What does the congressional resolution excerpted above suggest about why the United States went to war with Spain in 1898?

Chapter 5 Test, Form A *cont.*

networks

Becoming a World Power

"The rule of liberty that all just government derives its authority from the consent of the governed, applies only to those who are capable of self-government. . . . Would not the people of the Philippines prefer the just, humane, civilizing government of this Republic to the savage, bloody rule of pillage and extortion from which we have rescued them?"

—U.S. Senator Albert J. Beveridge, from *The Meaning of the Times*

"It is not necessary to own people in order to trade with them. We carry on trade today with every part of the world, and our commerce has expanded more rapidly than the commerce of any European empire. . . . A harbor and coaling station in the Philippines would answer every trade and military necessity and such a concession could have been secured at any time without difficulty."

—William Jennings Bryan, from *Speeches of William Jennings Bryan*

23. Describe the major arguments in the debate over annexing the Philippines, as represented by the statements above.

24. Explain Theodore Roosevelt's "big stick" policy and give an example of how it was applied.

25. What factors contributed to President Wilson's intervention in Mexico in 1916?

Chapter 5 Test, Form B

networks

Becoming a World Power

DIRECTIONS: Short Answer Answer each of the following questions on a separate piece of paper.

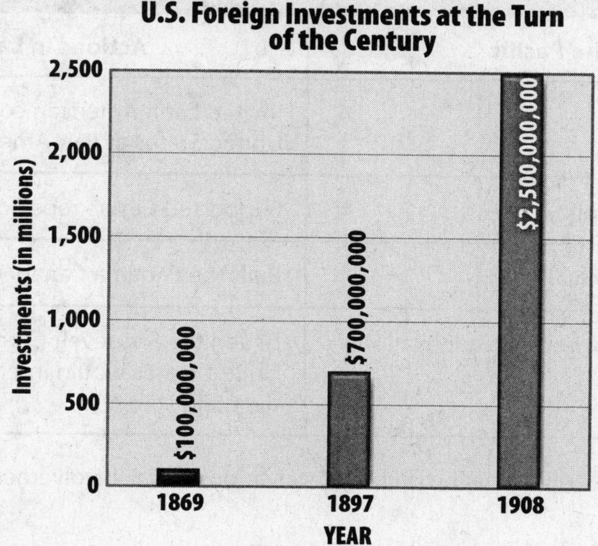

1. What were the major reasons for the increase in U.S. foreign investment illustrated by the chart above?

2. Explain the relationship between increased foreign investment and U.S. imperialism during this period.

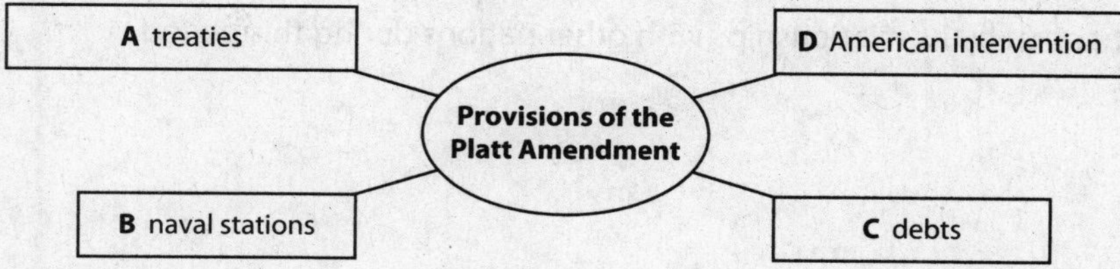

3. What was the Platt Amendment and why was it added to the Cuban constitution?

4. Explain the four major provisions of the Platt Amendment listed in the chart above.

Chapter 5 Test, Form B *cont.*

Becoming a World Power

U.S. Involvement in International Affairs, 1850–1905

Actions in the Pacific	Actions in Latin America
Opened Japanese markets	Invited Latin American countries to trade with United States at Pan-American Conference
Supported the Open Door policy	Supported Cuba's rebellion against Spain
Built coaling stations on Samoan Islands	Built the Panama Canal
Led successful campaign for Hawaiian annexation	Issued the Roosevelt Corollary, stating that the United States would intervene in Latin America to maintain stability

5. Based on the chart above, what was the primary motivation for U.S. involvement in foreign affairs in this period?

6. In what ways did U.S. actions in Latin America during this period differ from U.S. actions in the Pacific?

DIRECTIONS: Essay Answer the following question on a separate piece of paper.

7. In what ways did the United States seek to influence other nations between 1872 and 1917? How was the United States changed by its relationships with other nations during this period?

NAME ______________________ DATE ______________ CLASS ______________

Lesson Quiz 6-1

networks

The Progressive Movement

DIRECTIONS: Completion Enter the appropriate word(s) to complete the statement.

1. On August 26, 1920, after three-fourths of the states had voted to ratify it, the Nineteenth Amendment guaranteeing ______________ the right to vote went into effect.

2. One reason progressives believed people could improve society was because they had a strong faith in ______________ and technology.

3. Progressives joined union leaders to pressure states for workers' ______________ laws that would establish insurance funds for injured workers.

4. To counter Senate corruption, progressives called for the ______________ election of senators by all state voters rather than election by the state legislatures.

5. Progressives supported proposals to reform city government, including a commission plan that put city departments under a(n) ______________ commissioner's control.

DIRECTIONS: Multiple Choice Indicate the answer choice that best completes the statement or answers the question.

______ **6.** Progressivism was partly a reaction against ______________ economics, which emphasized an unregulated free market.

A. conservative
B. free trade
C. laissez-faire
D. Social Darwinist

______ **7.** Alice Paul was arrested after picketing the White House, an example of her attempts to

A. start a women-only political party.
B. support Woodrow Wilson.
C. use protests to force suffrage.
D. use violence to force suffrage.

______ **8.** What did progressives think needed to play a more active role in solving society's problems?

A. big business
B. social welfare organizations
C. the churches
D. the government

______ **9.** Wisconsin became a model of political reform under the leadership of

A. Charles Edward Russell.
B. Frederick W. Taylor.
C. Jacob Riis.
D. Robert M. La Follette.

______ **10.** Which progressive government reform allowed voters to demand a special election to remove an elected official from office before his or her term had expired?

A. direct primary
B. initiative
C. recall
D. referendum

NAME ______________________ DATE ______________ CLASS __________

Lesson Quiz 6-2

networks

The Progressive Movement

DIRECTIONS: True/False Indicate whether the statement is true or false.

_______ **1.** William Howard Taft brought many more antitrust cases during his term than Theodore Roosevelt did during his presidency.

_______ **2.** Progressives were pleased with William Howard Taft for pushing through the Payne-Aldrich Tariff.

_______ **3.** Theodore Roosevelt believed that most trusts benefited the economy and breaking them up would do more harm than good.

_______ **4.** In international affairs, Theodore Roosevelt was a Social Darwinist.

_______ **5.** By intervening in the labor dispute surrounding the coal strike of 1902, Roosevelt took the first step toward establishing the federal government as an honest broker between powerful groups in society.

DIRECTIONS: Multiple Choice Indicate the answer choice that best completes the statement or answers the question.

_______ **6.** Theodore Roosevelt supported the Republican nomination of William Howard Taft in the 1908 election after Taft had served as his

A. secretary of state.
B. attorney general.
C. secretary of war.
D. secretary of defense.

_______ **7.** Theodore Roosevelt warned William Howard Taft that tariff reform would

A. anger powerful business leaders.
B. anger progressives.
C. divide the Republican Party.
D. increase spending.

_______ **8.** In the coal strike of 1902, the United Mine Workers agreed to accept ______________, a settlement negotiated by an outside party, but the mine owners refused.

A. regulation
B. recall
C. arbitration
D. prohibition

_______ **9.** In what area did Taft's contributions equal or surpass Roosevelt's?

A. conservation
B. muckraking
C. prohibition
D. suffrage

_______ **10.** Taft set up the Bureau of Mines to monitor the activities of mining companies, protect waterpower sites from private development, and

A. create national seashores.
B. curb industrial pollution.
C. encourage hunting laws.
D. expand the national forests.

NAME ______________________ DATE ______________ CLASS ____________

Lesson Quiz 6-3

networks

The Progressive Movement

DIRECTIONS: Modified True/False In the blank, indicate whether the statement is true (T) or false (F). If false, edit the statement to make it a true statement.

_______ **1.** By the end of the Progressive Era, Americans expected the government, particularly the federal government, to play a more active role in regulating the economy and solving social problems.

____

_______ **2.** Woodrow Wilson entered politics as a firm conservative.

____

_______ **3.** The most conspicuous limit to progressivism came in its failure to address economic reform issues.

____

_______ **4.** Woodrow Wilson wanted the Federal Trade Commission to break up big business.

____

_______ **5.** In the election of 1912, Woodrow Wilson called his program the New Freedom.

____

DIRECTIONS: Multiple Choice Indicate the answer choice that best completes the statement or answers the question.

_______ **6.** To restore public confidence in the banking system, Wilson supported the establishment of a

A. federal reserve system.
B. Federal Trade Commission.
C. gold-based currency system.
D. loan system.

_______ **7.** The Keating-Owen Act was passed in order to regulate

A. child labor.
B. farm loans.
C. price discrimination.
D. railroad workdays.

_______ **8.** What law reduced the average tariff on imported goods to about 30 percent of the value of the goods?

A. Payne-Aldrich Tariff
B. Clayton Antitrust Act
C. Keating-Owen Act
D. Underwood Tariff

_______ **9.** One provision of the Clayton Antitrust Act banned

A. child labor.
B. income tax.
C. price discrimination.
D. racial discrimination.

NAME ______________________ DATE ______________ CLASS __________

Chapter 6 Test, Form A

networks

The Progressive Movement

DIRECTIONS: Matching Match each item with the correct statement below.

_____ **1.** provided for the direct election of U.S. senators	**A.** Richard A. Ballinger
_____ **2.** made it legal for the federal government to tax the income of individuals directly	**B.** Ida Tarbell
_____ **3.** guaranteed women the right to vote	**C.** Children's Bureau
_____ **4.** established five new national parks and 51 wildlife reservations	**D.** Meat Inspection Act
_____ **5.** banned the manufacture, sale, and consumption of alcohol	**E.** Sixteenth Amendment
_____ **6.** tried to open nearly a million acres of public land to private development	**F.** Theodore Roosevelt
_____ **7.** as governor of New Jersey, he introduced many progressive reforms	**G.** Woodrow Wilson
_____ **8.** wrote articles criticizing Standard Oil	**H.** Seventeenth Amendment
_____ **9.** passed in response to *The Jungle*	**I.** prohibition
_____ **10.** investigated and publicized problems with child labor	**J.** Nineteenth Amendment

DIRECTIONS: Multiple Choice Indicate the answer choice that best completes the statement or answers the question.

_____ **11.** In the *Northern Securities* v. *United States* case, the Supreme Court ruled that Northern Securities

A. violated the Clayton Antitrust Act.

B. violated the Sherman Antitrust Act.

C. would be supervised by the Department of Labor and Commerce.

D. would be supervised by the Interstate Commerce Commission.

_____ **12.** By 1920 the Interstate Commerce Commission had moved away from its original purpose and had started

A. imposing fees on goods transported by rail across state lines.

B. setting rates to help ensure railroads' profits.

C. suing railroads for competing unfairly.

D. taking an active role in operating railroads.

_______ **13.** The Underwood Tariff Act included a provision for

A. banning tying agreements.

B. levying an income tax.

C. negotiating tariffs with other nations.

D. starting a new national bank.

_______ **14.** Through scientific management, a company could become efficient by

A. breaking tasks down into small parts and using standardized tools.

B. keeping staff to a minimum and breaking tasks down into small parts.

C. keeping staff to a minimum and treating the employees well.

D. using standardized tools and treating employees well.

_______ **15.** Tragedy at the Triangle Shirtwaist Company led to

A. building codes requiring fire escapes.

B. child labor laws.

C. laws against harmful fumes.

D. standards for safe use of machines.

_______ **16.** The laissez-faire argument for the best way to preserve public land was to

A. keep it under government control and not allow companies to use it.

B. keep it under government control, but allow its use for land development projects.

C. sell it to lumber companies, who would conserve it as a source of profits.

D. sell it to private individuals, who would conserve it because it belonged to them.

_______ **17.** What were crusading journalists who investigated social conditions and political corruption called?

A. efficiency progressives

B. muckrakers

C. reformers

D. suffragists

_______ **18.** The Constitution originally specified that, in each state, U.S. senators would be elected by

A. leaders of the majority party.

B. the legislature of each state.

C. the majority party in each state.

D. the voters of each state.

NAME ______________________ DATE ______________ CLASS ____________

Chapter 6 Test, Form A *cont.*

networks

The Progressive Movement

_______ **19.** In early 1902, Roosevelt ordered his attorney general to file a lawsuit under the Sherman Antitrust Act against

A. Northern Securities.

B. the Burlington Railroad.

C. the New York Stock Exchange.

D. the Union Pacific Railroad.

_______ **20.** A meeting in 1905 that included W.E.B. Du Bois and other African American leaders to demand full political rights and responsibilities for African Americans resulted in the launching of the

A. Colored Farmers' National Alliance.

B. Federal Trade Commission.

C. Niagara Movement.

D. Progressive Party.

DIRECTIONS: Short Answer Answer each of the following questions.

21. Describe the situation with patent medicines that led to the passage of the Pure Food and Drug Act, and describe the protections the new law provided.

____

____

____

____

22. Compare the personalities of Theodore Roosevelt and William Howard Taft.

____

____

____

____

23. Refer to the charts above. How does the council-manager form of government reflect the goals of government reform during the Progressive Era?

____

____

____

____

24. Compare the views on trusts expressed by Theodore Roosevelt and Woodrow Wilson during the election campaign of 1912.

____

____

____

____

NAME ______________________ DATE ____________ CLASS ____________

Chapter 6 Test, Form B

networks

The Progressive Movement

DIRECTIONS: Short Answer Answer each of the following questions on a separate piece of paper.

Muckrakers' Focus		
Large Corporations	**Government**	**Social Problems**
Ida Tarbell writes series of articles critical of Standard Oil.	Charles Edward Russell describes influence of money in the Senate.	Jacob Riis writes *How the Other Half Lives,* a book that discusses poverty, disease, and crime.
Upton Sinclair writes about the meatpacking industry.	Lincoln Steffens writes report on vote stealing.	Muckraker articles lead to public debates on social and economic problems.

1. Based on the information provided in this chart, describe how muckrakers such as Ida Tarbell and Jacob Riis exposed corruption and societal problems.

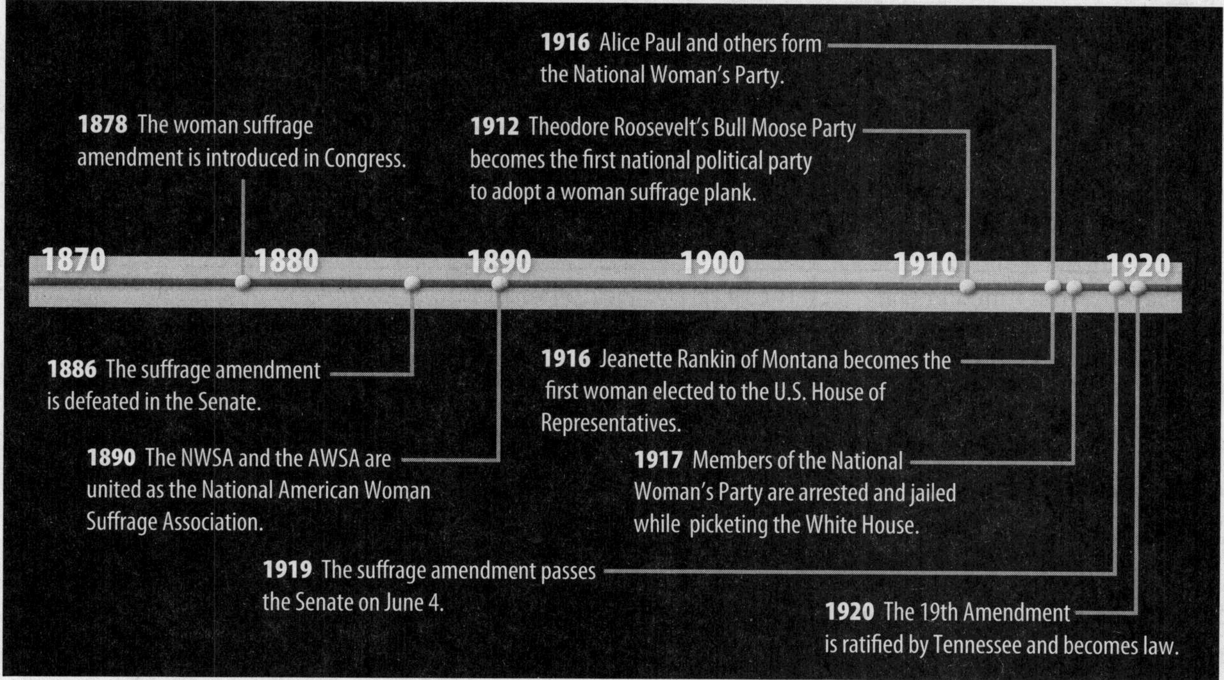

2. Which party does the above diagram indicate included woman suffrage as part of its platform?

"Two years ago, I saw 150 children working illegally at 20 minutes past 10 o'clock at night in a perfectly reputable dry goods store in the city of New York on the Saturday night before Christmas. If one of those children had stolen any small article . . . the heavy hand of the law would have carried that child promptly into the Juvenile Court. But 150 children were robbed of sleep in violation of the law."

—Florence Kelley, National Consumers' League, "Obstacles to the Enforcement of Child Labor Legislation"

3. What does the excerpt reveal about the New York dry goods store referred to by Florence Kelley?

"Added to this, the spread of lawless attacks upon the Negro, North, South and West—even in the Springfield made famous by Lincoln—often accompanied by revolting brutalities, sparing neither sex, or age nor youth, could not but shock the author of the sentiment that 'government of the people, by the people, for the people shall not perish from the earth.'"

—*The Founding of the NAACP*

4. What major societal issue is the author referring to in this passage?

Progressives Support . . .

Government Reforms	Business Regulation	Social Reforms
Commission and city- manager forms of government	Consumer protection laws	Child labor laws
The Seventeenth Amendment, which gave voters the right to elect senators directly	The Federal Trade Commission, which was set up to regulate business	Worker's compensation legislation
The Nineteenth Amendment, which gave women the right to vote	The Federal Reserve system, which was set up to control the money supply	The temperance movement, which worked to ban alcohol

5. What does the table indicate about progressive reformers?

DIRECTIONS: Essay Answer the following question on a separate piece of paper.

6. The Progressive Era was a time of reform in American society. Who were the progressives? What kinds of problems did they see in society?

NAME ______________________ DATE ______________ CLASS ____________

Lesson Quiz 7-1

networks

World War I and Its Aftermath

DIRECTIONS: Completion Enter the appropriate word(s) to complete the statement.

1. By 1871 after launching a series of wars, the German kingdom of ______________ had united various German states into one nation.

2. The Serbs, Bosnians, Croats, and Slovenes all lived in a region in southeastern Europe called the ______________.

3. German submarines that attacked ships bound for Britain were called ______________.

4. President Wilson declared the United States to be neutral concerning the war in Europe, but in general, American public opinion favored the ______________ rather than the Central Powers.

5. The issue of Germany attacking civilian ships reached a crisis on May 7, 1915, when a submerged German submarine fired on the British passenger liner ______________.

DIRECTIONS: Multiple Choice Indicate the answer choice that best completes the statement or answers the question.

_______ **6.** One reason for the tension between the European powers was their intense pride in their homelands, called

A. imperialism.
B. nationalism.
C. progressivism.
D. socialism.

_______ **7.** The event that touched off the first declaration of war in World War I was

A. the assassination of the archduke of Germany.
B. the assassination of the heir to the throne of Austria-Hungary.
C. the German invasion of Belgium.
D. the German invasion of Russia.

_______ **8.** According to the Zimmermann telegram, if Mexico allied with Germany, Germany would

A. help Mexico regain territory in Texas, New Mexico, and Arizona.
B. help Mexico take control of Central America.
C. prevent the United States from taking control of Mexico.
D. send troops to support the Huerta government.

_______ **9.** The Triple Entente included

A. Britain, France, and Russia.
B. Britain, France, and the U.S.
C. Germany, Bulgaria, and Italy.
D. Germany, Turkey, and Russia.

NAME _______________ DATE _______________ CLASS _______________

networks

Lesson Quiz 7-2

World War I and Its Aftermath

DIRECTIONS: Modified True/False In the blank, indicate whether the statement is true (T) or false (F). If false, edit the statement to make it a true statement.

_______ **1.** To help prevent strikes from disrupting the war effort, the government established the Committee on Public Information in April 1918.

____

_______ **2.** The War Industries Board worked closely with women and African Americans to help them gain civil rights.

____

_______ **3.** A new government agency, the Committee on Public Information, had the task of establishing penalties and prison terms for anyone who gave aid to the enemy.

____

_______ **4.** To help fund the war effort, Congress raised income tax rates.

____

DIRECTIONS: Multiple Choice Indicate the answer choice that best completes the statement or answers the question.

_______ **5.** Perhaps the most successful government agency during this time was the Food Administration, which was run by

A. Bernard Baruch.
B. George Creel.
C. Herbert Hoover.
D. William Howard Taft.

_______ **6.** Realizing a draft was necessary, Congress created a new system of conscription called

A. local draft boards.
B. lotteries.
C. selective service.
D. selective volunteers.

_______ **7.** To conserve energy, the Fuel Administration shortened workweeks for factories that did not make war materials and introduced

A. conscription.
B. daylight saving time.
C. flexible hours.
D. time zones.

_______ **8.** During World War I, women officially served in the armed forces for the first time in

A. combat positions.
B. training operations positions.
C. officer and management positions.
D. clerical and nursing positions.

NAME ______________________ DATE ____________ CLASS ____________

Lesson Quiz 7-3

networks

World War I and Its Aftermath

DIRECTIONS: Completion Enter the appropriate word(s) to complete the statement.

_______ **1.** In April 1915, the Germans first used ______________ gas.

_______ **2.** President Wilson's plan for peace was known as the ______________ Points and was based on "the principle of justice to all peoples and nationalities."

_______ **3.** World War I saw the first use of ______________ in combat, first as a way to observe enemy actions and later to drop small bombs.

_______ **4.** Critics of the League of Nations feared that it might supersede the power of ______________ to declare war and thus force the United States to fight in numerous foreign conflicts.

_______ **5.** One of the conditions of the Treaty of Versailles was that ______________ must admit its guilt in causing World War I.

DIRECTIONS: Multiple Choice Indicate the answer choice that best completes the statement or answers the question.

_______ **6.** President Wilson called for the creation of a "general association of nations" known as the

A. Allies.
B. Central Powers.
C. League of Nations.
D. United Nations.

_______ **7.** In World War I, ______________ were battles in the air between aircraft with attached machine guns.

A. dogfights
B. dirigibles
C. trench warfare
D. zeppelins

_______ **8.** What was used to defend soldiers against the use of mustard gas and chlorine bombs during World War I?

A. gas masks
B. howitzer guns
C. periscopes
D. zeppelins

_______ **9.** What two new forms of warfare were introduced during World War I?

A. aerial combat and gas attacks
B. machine guns and trench warfare
C. rocket launchers and cannons
D. submarines and warships

_______ **10.** In November 1917, Vladimir Lenin's Bolshevik Party seized power in Russia and established a

A. democratic government.
B. monarchy.
C. Communist government.
D. temporary government.

NAME ______________________ DATE ______________ CLASS __________

Lesson Quiz 7-4

networks

World War I and Its Aftermath

DIRECTIONS: True/False Indicate whether the statement is true or false.

_______ **1.** After the war, people raced to buy goods that had been rationed, while businesses rapidly raised prices they had been forced to keep low during the war. This resulted in rapid deflation.

_______ **2.** In the aftermath of World War I, unions in Seattle organized a general strike.

_______ **3.** The Red Scare was a nationwide panic that arose from the fear that Communists might seize power in the United States.

_______ **4.** The Palmer Raids were in response to a series of bombs and rising tension due to The Red Scare.

_______ **5.** Calvin Coolidge's sentiments of returning to normalcy struck a chord with voters, and he won the election of 1920 in a landslide.

DIRECTIONS: Multiple Choice Indicate the answer choice that best completes the statement or answers the question.

_______ **6.** In addition to the soldiers returning from Europe who needed to find employment, many African Americans who had moved north were competing for jobs and housing, which resulted in

A. cooperation among races.
B. new industries.
C. new zoning laws.
D. race riots.

_______ **7.** Who walked off the job in Boston in what was perhaps the most famous strike of 1919?

A. hospital workers
B. shipyard workers
C. steel workers
D. the police force

_______ **8.** Americans often linked radicalism with

A. immigrants.
B. nativism.
C. progressivism.
D. reform programs.

_______ **9.** One of the largest strikes in American history began when steel workers went on strike for recognition of their union, higher pay, and

A. cost of living raises.
B. medical benefits.
C. safer working conditions.
D. shorter hours.

NAME ______________________ DATE ____________ CLASS ____________

Chapter 7 Test, Form A

networks

World War I and Its Aftermath

DIRECTIONS: Matching Match each item with the correct statement below.

_____ **1.** goods prohibited from shipment to Germany or its allies

_____ **2.** information designed to influence opinion

_____ **3.** British ship sunk by Germany, killing over 1,000 passengers

_____ **4.** gave patriotic speeches urging support of war effort

_____ **5.** Bosnian revolutionary behind assassination of Archduke Franz Ferdinand

_____ **6.** method of loaning money to the government to pay for war

_____ **7.** spying to acquire government secrets

_____ **8.** supreme commander of the Allied forces

_____ **9.** Bolshevik leader

_____ **10.** coordinated the production of war materials

A. *Lusitania*

B. Gavrilo Princip

C. War Industries Board

D. contraband

E. Ferdinand Foch

F. propaganda

G. espionage

H. Vladimir Lenin

I. Liberty Bonds

J. Four-Minute Men

DIRECTIONS: Multiple Choice Indicate the answer choice that best completes the statement or answers the question.

_____ **11.** To prevent strikes from disrupting the war effort, the government established the

A. Committee on Public Information.
B. League of Nations.
C. National War Labor Board.
D. War Industries Board.

_____ **12.** World War I was the first war in which

A. African American soldiers were not segregated from white soldiers.
B. the government officially imposed conscription.
C. the military drafted men.
D. women officially served in the armed forces.

Chapter 7 Test, Form A *cont.*

networks

World War I and Its Aftermath

_______ **13.** The Great Migration during World War I was the flow of

A. African Americans moving from the South to Northern cities.

B. European immigrants fleeing to the United States to escape the war in Europe.

C. French refugees fleeing to Britain ahead of the German onslaught.

D. Mexicans fleeing to the American Southwest to escape political turmoil.

_______ **14.** In 1908 the Serbs became furious when

A. a Slav assassinated their leader.

B. Austria-Hungary annexed Bosnia.

C. Austria-Hungary refused them independence.

D. the Ottoman Empire refused them independence.

_______ **15.** According to the Selective Service Act, the order in which men were called to service was determined by

A. age.

B. local draft boards.

C. lottery.

D. military headquarters.

_______ **16.** "Selling" the war to the American people was the task of

A. J. Edgar Hoover.

B. the Committee on Public Information.

C. the War Industries Board.

D. the War Propaganda Board.

_______ **17.** Criticism of the war at home was effectively silenced by

A. the Committee on Public Information.

B. the Espionage and Sedition Acts.

C. the Palmer Raids.

D. the Red Scare.

_______ **18.** The British entered World War I when

A. Austria-Hungary annexed Bosnia.

B. Franz Ferdinand was assassinated.

C. German troops crossed into Belgium.

D. Germany sank the *Lusitania*.

_______ **19.** What was the only group of women in the military sent overseas in World War I?

A. army nurses
B. clerical workers
C. pilots
D. volunteers

_______ **20.** During World War I, a group called the ______________ took power in Russia and established a Communist government.

A. Bolsheviks
B. Bosnians
C. Serbs
D. Slovenes

DIRECTIONS: Short Answer Answer each of the following questions.

21. Describe Woodrow Wilson's Fourteen Points plan by summarizing the main purpose of the first five points, then the next eight points, and finally the fourteenth point.

____

____

____

____

22. Explain the purpose of the War Industries Board and the National War Labor Board and describe their activities.

____

____

____

____

23. What caused the inflation after World War I, and how did inflation help cause the wave of strikes in the United States?

____

____

____

____

Chapter 7 Test, Form A *cont.*

World War I and Its Aftermath

> "In the audience was a civilian representative of the Military Intelligence Service. He had a premonition that some sort of attempt was going to be made at this meeting . . . to discredit the war and America's imminent participation there in."
>
> —"The Making of a Red" [satire], *Nation*, March 15, 1919

24. Why was a member of military intelligence at the meeting, according to the excerpt?

____

____

____

____

> ". . . in unhesitating obedience to what I deem my constitutional duty, I advise that the Congress declare the recent course of the Imperial German Government to be, in fact, nothing less than war against . . . the United States; . . . that it take immediate steps not only to put the country in a more thorough state of defense, but also to exert all its power and employ all its resources to bring the Government of the German Empire to terms and end the war."
>
> —Woodrow Wilson, speech to Congress requesting a declaration of war, April 2, 1917

25. What prompted President Wilson to ask Congress for a declaration of war against Germany?

____

____

____

____

NAME ______________________ DATE ______________ CLASS __________

Chapter 7 Test, Form B

networks

World War I and Its Aftermath

DIRECTIONS: Short Answer Answer each of the following questions on a separate piece of paper.

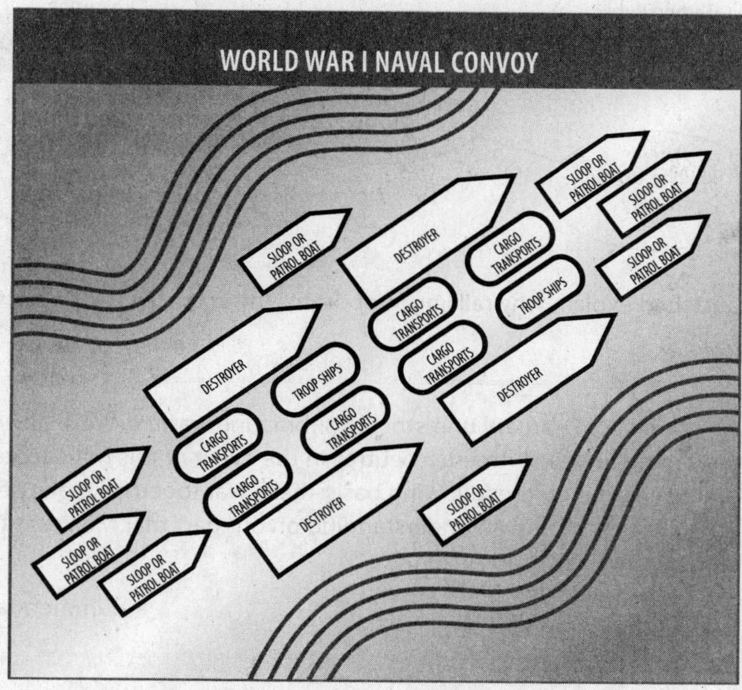

1. Based on the graphic and your knowledge of the chapter, explain the positions of the sloops or patrol boats.

"I look upon the Espionage Law as a despotic enactment in flagrant conflict with democratic principles and with the spirit of free institutions. . . . I am opposed to the social system in which we live. . . . I believe in fundamental change, but if possible by peaceful and orderly means. . . ."

—Eugene V. Debs

2. Read the above excerpt from a speech given by Eugene Debs. What did Debs think about the Espionage Law?

"Our Kaisers . . . have lackeys with knee pants bring them champagne while you starve, while you grow old at forty, stoking their furnaces. You pull in your belts while they banquet. They have stomachs two miles long and two miles wide and you fill them. . . . What we want is a little leisure, time for music, playgrounds, a decent home, books, and things that make life worthwhile."

—"Mother" Jones, speech to striking steelworkers, 1919

3. In the above quotation, how does Mother Jones compare the lives of the wealthy "Kaisers," or industrialists, to the lives of workers?

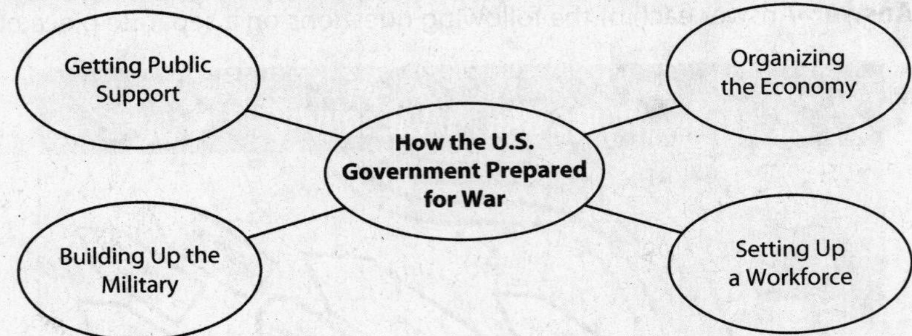

4. Study the graphic and then explain why rallying support for the war from the public was important for the U.S. government.

> "We intend to begin on the first of February unrestricted submarine warfare. We shall endeavor in spite of this to keep the United States of America neutral. In the event of this not succeeding, we make Mexico a proposal or alliance on the following basis: make war together, make peace together, generous financial support and an understanding on our part that Mexico is to reconquer the lost territory in Texas, New Mexico, and Arizona. . . ."
>
> —Zimmermann telegram

5. Read the excerpt from the Zimmermann telegram. What did Germany plan to propose to Mexico?

DIRECTIONS: Essay Answer the following question on a separate piece of paper.

6. Describe two events that pushed the United States toward entering World War I.

NAME ______________________ DATE ______________ CLASS __________

Lesson Quiz 8-1

networks

The Jazz Age

DIRECTIONS: True/False Indicate whether the statement is true or false.

_____ **1.** In his policies, Calvin Coolidge aligned himself and the government with big business.

_____ **2.** During the 1920s, the national debt increased due to greater government spending.

_____ **3.** Charles R. Forbes sold scarce medical supplies from veterans' hospitals and kept the money for himself.

_____ **4.** Robert M. La Follette, a successful banker and industrialist, became secretary of the treasury under President Harding.

_____ **5.** President Harding gave many cabinet posts and other high-level jobs to friends and political allies from Iowa.

DIRECTIONS: Multiple Choice Indicate the answer choice that best completes the statement or answers the question.

_____ **6.** The chief architect of economic policy in the United States during the 1920s was

A. Andrew Mellon.
B. Charles Evan Hughes.
C. Herbert Hoover.
D. Warren Harding.

_____ **7.** President Harding's secretary of the interior, Albert B. Fall, secretly allowed private interests to lease lands containing U.S. Navy oil reserves, causing a scandal that came to be known as the

A. Daugherty scandal.
B. Fall scandal.
C. Forbes scandal.
D. Teapot Dome scandal.

_____ **8.** Attorney General Harry Daugherty resigned in disgrace after being investigated for taking bribes in exchange for allowing

A. a private company to drill for oil on public lands.
B. immunity to wealthy businessmen accused of insider trading.
C. someone to acquire a valuable German-owned company seized during the war.
D. two powerful corporations to merge.

_____ **9.** The Ohio Gang was a

A. group of Harding's friends.
B. group of notorious bank robbers.
C. nickname for the Veterans' Bureau.
D. powerful crime network.

NAME ______________________ DATE ______________ CLASS ____________

Lesson Quiz 8-2

networks

The Jazz Age

DIRECTIONS: Completion Enter the appropriate word(s) to complete the statement.

1. Many consumers in the 1920s began to feel confident they could buy now and pay later, so many bought everything from radios to cars on the ________________ plan.

2. In 1926, NBC set up a network of stations to broadcast ________________.

3. ________________ linked products with qualities associated with the modern era and preyed on consumers' fears and anxieties.

4. The system of manufacturing adopted by Henry Ford was known as the ________________.

5. American ________________ did not share in the prosperity of the 1920s, earning less than one-third of the average income for workers in the rest of the economy.

DIRECTIONS: Multiple Choice Indicate the answer choice that best completes the statement or answers the question.

______ **6.** After entrepreneurs such as Glenn Curtiss started building practical aircraft, the federal government

A. began to restrict commercial flights.
B. began to support the airline industry.
C. ordered a fleet of new warplanes.
D. restricted flying in urban areas.

______ **7.** To attract consumers for their new products, manufacturers turned to

A. advertising.
B. mass production.
C. newspaper and magazine articles.
D. television.

______ **8.** What effect did the automobile industry of the 1920s have on American society?

A. People could live farther from their places of work.
B. People moved from the suburbs to the city.
C. The mail delivery system expanded across the country.
D. Workers did not commute anymore.

______ **9.** Commercial radio began its rise in November 1920, with news about

A. a presidential election.
B. Albert Fall.
C. Charles Lindbergh.
D. World War I.

______ **10.** Who made the first successful flight in history in 1903?

A. Charles Lindbergh
B. Glenn Curtiss
C. the Wright brothers
D. Samuel Langley

NAME ______________________ DATE ____________ CLASS ____________

Lesson Quiz 8-3

networks

The Jazz Age

DIRECTIONS: Completion Enter the appropriate word(s) to complete the statement.

1. The National Origins Act of 1924 placed permanent limits on immigration based on a ______________ system.

2. Stylish, unconventional American women of the 1920s who wore sleeveless dresses and short skirts were called ______________.

3. In the name of preserving traditional moral standards, religious fundamentalists supported passage of the ______________ banning the sale of alcohol.

4. The sharp reduction in immigrants due to new immigration laws in the late 1920s contributed to the decline of ______________.

DIRECTIONS: Multiple Choice Indicate the answer choice that best completes the statement or answers the question.

_______ **5.** What is the name of the belief that one's land needs to be protected against immigrants?

A. foreignism
B. isolationism
C. nativism
D. racism

_______ **6.** What did many of the groups that wanted to restrict immigration and preserve what they considered traditional values fear was taking over the nation?

A. a "new morality"
B. a "new religion"
C. anarchists
D. Communists

_______ **7.** Many people viewed Sacco and Vanzetti with suspicion because

A. Sacco owned a gun similar to the murder weapon.
B. the bullets used in a murder matched Sacco's gun.
C. they were Italian immigrants and anarchists.
D. they were members of the Ku Klux Klan.

_______ **8.** Many Americans feared that the country was losing its traditional values and responded by joining a religious movement known as

A. Catholicism.
B. Fundamentalism.
C. Protestantism.
D. Quakerism.

_______ **9.** A major element of the new morality was

A. a decrease in the use of automobiles.
B. an increase in stay-at-home mothers.
C. an increase in support for women's independence.
D. an increase in traditional values in marriage.

NAME ______________________ DATE ______________ CLASS __________

Lesson Quiz 8-4

networks

The Jazz Age

DIRECTIONS: True/False Indicate whether the statement is true or false.

_______ **1.** Several writers of this time, such as Gertrude Stein, had an important impact on the literary culture.

_______ **2.** T. S. Eliot's fiction presented a new literary style characterized by direct, simple, and concise prose, as shown in his novel *A Farewell to Arms*.

_______ **3.** One of the most innovative playwrights of the time was Eugene O'Neill, whose modern themes portrayed realistic characters and situations, offering a vision of life that sometimes touched on the tragic.

_______ **4.** *The Birth of a Nation* was the first "talking" motion picture.

DIRECTIONS: Multiple Choice Indicate the answer choice that best completes the statement or answers the question.

_______ **5.** The golden age of Hollywood began in 1927 with the release of the first

A. animated film.
B. feature-length film.
C. full-length motion picture.
D. "talking" motion picture.

_______ **6.** American modern artists were greatly influenced by the art movements of

A. Africa.
B. Asia.
C. Australia.
D. Europe.

_______ **7.** The emergence of mass media helped make which baseball star a national hero?

A. Babe Ruth
B. Bill Tilden
C. Jack Dempsey
D. Red Grange

_______ **8.** The _______________, including radio, movies, newspapers, and magazines, fostered a sense of a shared experience that helped unify the nation.

A. mass media
B. bohemian life
C. "new morality"
D. fundamentalist movement

_______ **9.** What artist applied the influence of photography and the geometric forms of Cubism to his paintings of urban and rural American landscapes?

A. Charles Sheeler
B. Eugene O'Neill
C. John Marin
D. Paul Cézanne

NAME ______________________ DATE ______________ CLASS ____________

Lesson Quiz 8-5

networks

The Jazz Age

DIRECTIONS: Matching Match each item with the correct statement below.

_______ **1.** first important writer of the Harlem Renaissance

_______ **2.** the "Empress of the Blues"

_______ **3.** the first musical written, produced, and performed by African Americans

_______ **4.** the site of a flowering of African American arts

_______ **5.** author whose work featured African American women as central characters

A. Zora Neale Hurston

B. Claude McKay

C. *Shuffle Along*

D. Bessie Smith

E. Harlem

DIRECTIONS: Multiple Choice Indicate the answer choice that best completes the statement or answers the question.

_______ **6.** What style of music was influenced by Dixieland and ragtime?

A. classical
B. country
C. jazz
D. soul

_______ **7.** Claude McKay's poetry expressed two striking characteristics of Harlem Renaissance writing—a proud defiance and a bitter contempt of

A. anarchists.
B. Communists.
C. nationalism.
D. racism.

_______ **8.** The flowering of African American arts in the 1920s became known as the

A. Glory Days.
B. Great Awakening.
C. Great Migration.
D. Harlem Renaissance.

_______ **9.** The Cotton Club was a

A. Chicago speakeasy where gangsters, artists, and politicians congregated.
B. fictitious nightclub featured in the famous picture *The Jazz Singer*.
C. Harlem nightspot where many African American entertainers got their start.
D. Hollywood nightspot frequented by the stars of the silver screen.

_______ **10.** The Universal Negro Improvement Association was formed to

A. elect African Americans to Congress.
B. promote black pride and unity.
C. promote integration.
D. protest the horrors of lynching.

NAME ______________________ DATE ______________ CLASS ____________

Chapter 8 Test, Form A

networks

The Jazz Age

DIRECTIONS: Matching Match each item with the correct statement below.

______ **1.** writer who became a leading voice of the African American experience in the United States

______ **2.** first built by the Ford Company in 1908

______ **3.** leader of the "back to Africa" movement

______ **4.** pilot of the first solo nonstop transatlantic flight

______ **5.** composer, pianist, and bandleader whose sound was a blend of improvisation and orchestration

______ **6.** payments Germany was required to make as punishment for starting World War I

______ **7.** attempted to outlaw war

______ **8.** agreement to halt production on warships

______ **9.** enormously increased manufacturing efficiency

______ **10.** singer who seemed to symbolize soul

A. Bessie Smith

B. Marcus Garvey

C. Charles Lindbergh

D. Kellogg-Briand Pact

E. Model T

F. Langston Hughes

G. assembly line

H. Duke Ellington

I. Five Power Naval Limitation Treaty

J. reparations

DIRECTIONS: Multiple Choice Indicate the answer choice that best completes the statement or answers the question.

______ **11.** Warren G. Harding won the presidency by appealing to Americans' desire to

A. become a world power.

B. reform society.

C. repeal Prohibition.

D. return to life as it was before the war.

______ **12.** Coolidge believed part of his job as president was to make sure the government

A. became involved in social reform.

B. interfered with business and industry as little as possible.

C. participated regularly in world affairs.

D. regulated big business in order to stabilize the economy.

______ **13.** Henry Ford's system for making cars increased efficiency by

A. assigning a team to each car.

B. dividing operations into simple tasks.

C. reducing the number of parts needed.

D. training each worker to do every task.

Chapter 8 Test, Form A *cont.*

networks

The Jazz Age

______ **14.** In the early 1920s, the Ku Klux Klan added to its membership by

A. avoiding scandals and power struggles.

B. hiring professional promoters.

C. opening membership to all whites, regardless of religion.

D. publicizing their support of legitimate political goals.

______ **15.** John T. Scopes was put on trial for

A. accepting bribes.

B. being a leader of the Ku Klux Klan.

C. teaching evolution.

D. violating Prohibition laws.

______ **16.** After World War I, most Americans wanted to avoid future wars by

A. avoiding involvement in world affairs.

B. disbanding the League of Nations.

C. excluding Germany from the League of Nations.

D. forbidding Germany to rebuild its armed forces.

______ **17.** The purpose of the Volstead Act was to

A. ban the teaching of evolution.

B. enforce Prohibition.

C. limit immigration.

D. prohibit lynching.

______ **18.** In 1922, the NAACP's lobbying efforts influenced the House of Representatives to pass

A. anti-lynching legislation.

B. anti-segregation legislation.

C. equal opportunity legislation.

D. voting rights legislation.

______ **19.** Henry Ford was able to cut daily work hours and increase wages due to the success of

A. the airline industry.

B. negotiating with unions.

C. public transportation.

D. mass production.

______ **20.** In 1925 Congress passed the Kelly Act which

A. trained new pilots.

B. provided federal aid to build airports.

C. allocated funds to support Charles Lindbergh.

D. authorized postal officials to hire private pilots.

DIRECTIONS: Short Answer Answer each of the following questions.

21. Describe the factors that prevented farmers from sharing in the prosperity of the 1920s.

____

____

____

____

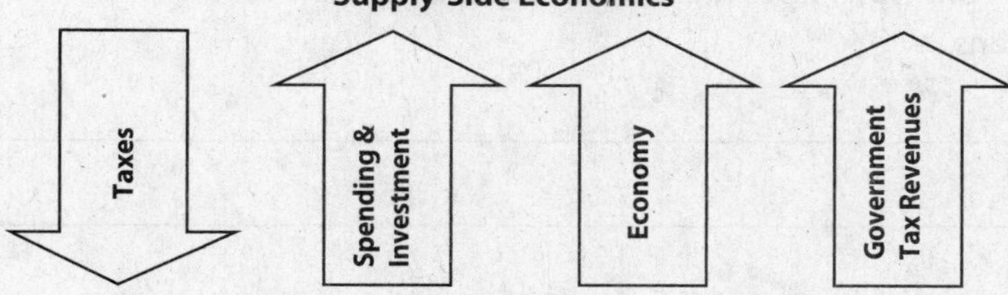

22. Use the diagram to help you explain how supporters of supply-side economics believed that lower tax rates would actually result in more tax money collected.

____

____

____

____

Cause:		Effect:
Prohibition	→	Rise of organized crime

23. Explain the relationship depicted in the diagram.

____

____

____

24. Describe the changes in women's lives in the 1920s.

____

____

____

25. Explain how Henry Ford was able to make automobiles affordable for the majority of Americans.

____

____

____

NAME ______________________ DATE ______________ CLASS __________

Chapter 8 Test, Form B

networks

The Jazz Age

DIRECTIONS: Short Answer Answer each of the following questions on a separate piece of paper.

> "The small, unattractive and often unsafe halls which served well enough in the earlier years . . . now developed into gorgeous and gigantic theaters designed especially for the purpose, equipped with pipe-organ and symphony-size orchestra. . . . The turning point in this development . . . may be dated as 1914 when Samuel L. Rothafel, known to millions as 'Roxy,' . . . opened the Strand Theater in New York and developed a form of entertainment more akin to the opera than the old 'nickelodeon.'"
>
> —from *The Great Crusade and After, 1914–1928*

1. Why would it have been profitable to build new and improved theaters as described in this quotation?

> "There are now more than 500 broadcasting stations. . . . The amateur listener is unfortunate, indeed who cannot hear any one that he chooses among half a dozen, while the more patient or skillful person can pick up one after another a score of stations."
>
> —from "Listening In" (1923)

2. Describe the technological development being described in the quotation. Why are amateur listeners less fortunate than skilled listeners?

Invented This Decade

How did we live without . . .

- push-button elevators
- neon signs
- oven thermostats
- electric razors
- tissues
- spiral-bound notebooks
- motels
- dry ice
- zippers
- pop-up toasters
- flavored yogurt
- car radios
- adhesive tape
- food disposals
- water skiing
- automatic potato peeler
- self-winding wristwatch

3. Based on the title of the graphic, what you know of the 1920s, and the items in the list above, how can you describe this decade?

"It was hot weather when they tried the infidel Scopes at Dayton, Tenn., but I went down there very willingly. . . . The Scopes jury . . . was composed mostly of [country folk], with a few Dayton sophisticates added to leaven the mass. . . . [After a preacher delivered a sermon], there arose out of the darkness a woman with her hair pulled back into a little tight knot. . . . She was denouncing the reading of books. . ."

—H. L. Mencken

4. Based on the excerpt from Mencken's account of events, predict how you think the mostly traditionalist jury would decide the case against Scopes.

"We [Sacco and Vanzetti] were tried during a time that has now passed into history . . . a time when there was a hysteria of resentment and hate against the people of our principles, against the foreigner, against slackers. . . ."

—Bartolomeo Vanzetti

5. According to the quotation, list three reasons that Vanzetti gives for his murder conviction.

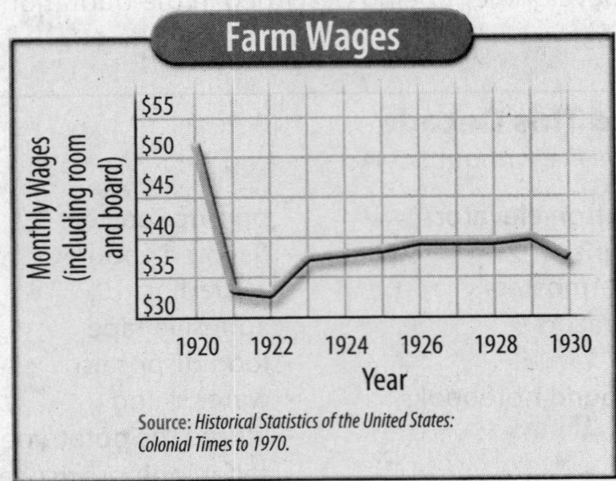

6. What effect did the Fordney-McCumber Act have on the change in farm wages shown in the graph?

7. In the 1920s, automobiles became affordable for the majority of Americans. How did automobiles affect life in America in the 1920s?

NAME ______________________ DATE ______________ CLASS ____________

Lesson Quiz 9-1

networks

The Great Depression Begins

DIRECTIONS: Matching Match each item with the correct statement below.

_______ **1.** if they remain too low, banks make risky loans and companies expand too much

_______ **2.** companies make more goods than people can buy, causing a decrease in sales

_______ **3.** when many depositors decide to withdraw their money at one time

_______ **4.** making investments in hope that prices will go up, yielding a quick windfall

_______ **5.** a long period of rising stock prices

A. bank run

B. interest rates

C. speculation

D. bull market

E. overproduction

DIRECTIONS: Multiple Choice Indicate the answer choice that best completes the statement or answers the question.

_______ **6.** Buying on margin was a method of buying stocks

A. with mostly borrowed money.
B. without using a broker.
C. by pooling money with others.
D. without any risk.

_______ **7.** Stockbrokers who made loans that allowed investors to buy stocks could issue a _______________ to protect their loans.

A. collateral call
B. credit call
C. margin call
D. foreclosure call

_______ **8.** The stock market took its steepest dive on October 29, 1929, the day now known as

A. Red Thursday.
B. Black Tuesday.
C. Black Friday.
D. Bloody Sunday.

_______ **9.** As a result of the stock market crash, some banks suffered more losses than they could absorb and

A. tried to attract more depositors.
B. had to approve more loans.
C. needed to increase interest rates.
D. were forced to close.

_______ **10.** At the time of the stock market crash, the government did not insure bank deposits, so

A. banks kept only a fraction of depositors' money in reserve.
B. customers lost their savings if a bank collapsed.
C. banks had to make money by making loans and investing.
D. customers turned to their stockbrokers for help.

NAME ______________________ DATE ______________ CLASS ____________

Lesson Quiz 9-2

networks

The Great Depression Begins

DIRECTIONS: Modified True/False In the blank, indicate whether the statement is true (T) or false (F). If false, edit the statement to make it a true statement.

_____ **1.** The Depression improved steadily during President Hoover's administration.

____

_____ **2.** Blaming the president for their plight, newly homeless people established shantytowns they called Hoovervilles.

____

_____ **3.** The Dust Bowl occurred primarily because plowed land was left uncultivated and there was a terrible drought.

____

_____ **4.** During the early 1930s, dust storms blackened the skies of the Great Plains for hundreds of miles.

____

_____ **5.** "Okies" were usually farmers who sold their land and used the profits to travel to California and begin new lives.

____

DIRECTIONS: Multiple Choice Indicate the answer choice that best completes the statement or answers the question.

_____ **6.** During the Depression, charities set up ______________ to give poor people meals.

A. soup kitchens
B. communities
C. public works
D. dust bowls

_____ **7.** In search of work or a better life, many unemployed people

A. moved to big cities.
B. became farmers.
C. became homeless.
D. rode the rails.

_____ **8.** During the Depression, many people were able to enjoy which two popular forms of entertainment?

A. theater and radio
B. theater and sports
C. movies and television
D. movies and radio

_____ **9.** The first feature-length animated film was

A. *Animal Crackers.*
B. *The Wizard of Oz.*
C. *Snow White and the Seven Dwarfs.*
D. *Mr. Smith Goes to Washington.*

NAME ______________________ DATE ______________ CLASS ____________

Lesson Quiz 9-3

networks

The Great Depression Begins

DIRECTIONS: Completion Enter the appropriate word(s) to complete the statement.

1. After the Federal ________________ Board refused to put more money into circulation, President Hoover set up the National Credit Corporation to create a pool of money for troubled banks.

2. The Reconstruction Finance Corporation marked the first time the federal government established an agency to stimulate the ________________ during peacetime.

3. Though Hoover was reluctant to sign it, Congress passed the Emergency ________________ Act, which called for $1.5 billion for public works and $300 million in loans to the states for direct relief.

4. The group of World War I veterans who marched on Washington in 1932 was called the ________________.

DIRECTIONS: Multiple Choice Indicate the answer choice that best completes the statement or answers the question.

______ **5.** President Herbert Hoover did not want the government to create as many new jobs as the millions of unemployed people needed because that would require

A. much lower unemployment.
B. increased government regulation.
C. reform of federal taxes.
D. increased government spending.

______ **6.** In 1932 President Hoover asked Congress to set up the Reconstruction Finance Corporation to allow the government to

A. expand the money supply.
B. make loans to businesses.
C. provide relief to the unemployed.
D. create jobs in public works.

______ **7.** As creditors foreclosed on nearly one million farms between 1930 and 1934, some farmers destroyed their crops in a desperate attempt to

A. retaliate against their creditors.
B. raise prices by reducing supply.
C. call public attention to their plight.
D. find ways to feed their families.

______ **8.** When the Senate voted down a bill that promised the immediate payment of the $1,000 bonus to each veteran of World War I, some veterans

A. burned down public buildings.
B. marched to Oregon.
C. camped in vacant buildings in Washington, D.C.
D. demonstrated in front of the White House.

______ **9.** President Hoover's image was tarnished by the rout of the Bonus Marchers as well as by the

A. lingering Depression.
B. public works funding.
C. emergency loans to states.
D. National Credit Corporation.

NAME _______________ DATE _______________ CLASS _______________

Chapter 9 Test, Form A

networks

The Great Depression Begins

DIRECTIONS: Matching Match each item with the correct statement below.

_____ **1.** reluctantly signed by President Hoover to supply relief funds to states

_____ **2.** led the troops that dispersed the Bonus Army

_____ **3.** painter of the 1930s who was part of the regionalist school

_____ **4.** stockbroker's demand for immediate repayment of a loan used to buy stock

_____ **5.** the result when the government spends more than it collects in taxes

_____ **6.** many depositors withdrawing their money at once

_____ **7.** the biggest drop of the 1929 stock market crash

_____ **8.** writer who showed what characters were thinking before they spoke

_____ **9.** migrants from the Great Plains heading west in search of better lives

_____ **10.** set up in 1932 to allow the government to make loans to businesses

A. Black Tuesday

B. bank run

C. Okies

D. budget deficit

E. Douglas MacArthur

F. William Faulkner

G. margin call

H. Reconstruction Finance Corporation

I. Emergency Relief and Construction Act

J. Grant Wood

DIRECTIONS: Multiple Choice Indicate the answer choice that best completes the statement or answers the question.

_____ **11.** _______________ invested in stocks, betting that the market would continue to climb so they could make a quick profit.

A. Speculators
B. Okies
C. Bailiffs
D. Stockbrokers

_____ **12.** Stock prices first began to decline in late 1929 because

A. stockbrokers stopped margin loans.
B. company earnings declined.
C. several companies went bankrupt.
D. investors began to sell their stock.

Chapter 9 Test, Form A *cont.*

The Great Depression Begins

_______ **13.** The stock market crash weakened the nation's banks because

A. banks had invested their deposits in the stock market.

B. investors no longer had money to deposit in banks.

C. banks depended on their stock for operating funds.

D. investors could no longer afford to take out loans from banks.

_______ **14.** The Depression had deep roots in the economy of the 1920s, including overproduction, high tariffs, missteps by the Federal Reserve, and

A. the uneven distribution of income.

B. an inadequate money supply.

C. deficit spending by the government.

D. excessive reliance on export sales.

_______ **15.** During the Depression, newly homeless people put up communities of shacks they called

A. hobo towns.

B. Hoovervilles.

C. Bonus Armies.

D. Okie towns.

_______ **16.** Farmers on the Great Plains began to lose their crops during the Depression because

A. the soil lost its fertility.

B. frequent rains eroded the soil.

C. a fungus depleted the soil of nutrients.

D. a terrible drought dried the soil.

_______ **17.** During the 1930s, many Americans preferred movies, radio programs, and other forms of popular entertainment that

A. focused on the homeless and unemployed.

B. evoked indignation at social injustice.

C. provided a release from daily worries.

D. created thrills with new special effects.

_______ **18.** President Herbert Hoover hoped that increasing government funding for public works projects would

A. reduce the budget deficit.

B. spur the construction industry.

C. provide jobs lost in the private sector.

D. help reduce farm foreclosures.

Chapter 9 Test, Form A *cont.* networks

The Great Depression Begins

______ **19.** President Hoover opposed direct federal relief to the unemployed because he believed

A. only state and city governments should dole out relief.

B. federal relief would only shorten the Depression.

C. charities could provide sufficient relief.

D. individuals are responsible for taking care of themselves.

______ **20.** Thousands of World War I veterans came to Washington, D.C., in 1932 to lobby Congress to

A. give bonus payments to war veterans and their families.

B. pass legislation giving veterans their promised bonuses early.

C. provide public works jobs for unemployed veterans.

D. provide military jobs for family members of veterans.

DIRECTIONS: Short Answer Answer each of the following questions.

21. Explain how buying stocks on margin worked in the late 1920s, and describe the risks and rewards of this investment practice.

______

______

______

"[Groucho Marx's broker] was sitting in front of the now-stilled ticker-tape machine, with his head buried in his hands. Ticker tape was strewn around him on the floor, and the place . . . looked as if it hadn't been swept out in a week.

"Groucho tapped [him] on the shoulder and said, 'Aren't you the fellow who said nothing could go wrong—that we were in a world market?'

"'I guess I made a mistake,' the broker wearily replied.

"'No, I'm the one who made a mistake,' snapped Groucho. 'I listened to you.'"

—quoted in *1929: The Year of the Great Crash*

22. What mistake did Groucho Marx believe he had made, and why did he feel that way, according to the excerpt?

______

______

______

NAME ______________________ DATE ____________ CLASS ____________

23. Discuss three major root causes of the Great Depression that were at work before the stock market crash of 1929.

____

____

____

____

____

____

> "Maybe he [the owner of the fields] needs two hunderd men, so he talks to five hunderd, an' they tell other folks, an' when you get to the place, they's a thousan' men. This here fella says, 'I'm payin' twenty cents an hour.' An' maybe half the men walk off. But they's still five hunderd that's so . . . hungry they'll work for nothin' but biscuits. Well, this here fella's got a contract to pick them peaches or—chop that cotton. You see now? The more fellas he can get, an' the hungrier, less he's gonna pay. An' he'll get a fella with kids if he can."
>
> —John Steinbeck, from *The Grapes of Wrath*

24. Based on the excerpt above, describe the circumstances faced by Great Plains farmers who migrated to California during the Depression.

____

____

____

____

____

____

DIRECTIONS: Essay Answer the following question on a separate piece of paper.

25. Describe the art and popular culture of the 1930s, including movies, radio, literature, and visual art.

NAME ______________________ DATE ______________ CLASS ______________

Chapter 9 Test, Form B

networks

The Great Depression Begins

DIRECTIONS: Short Answer Answer each of the following questions on a separate piece of paper.

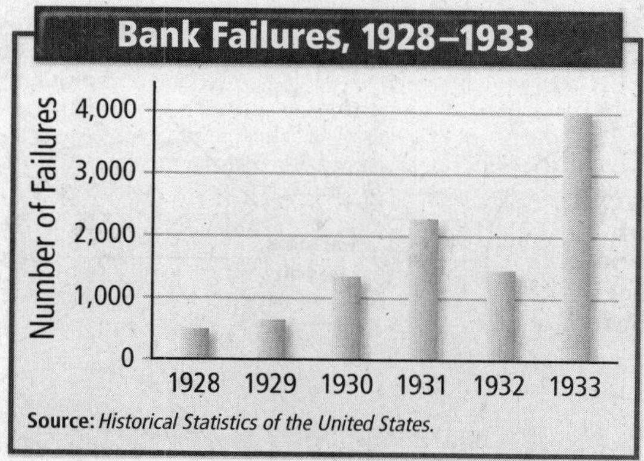

Source: *Historical Statistics of the United States.*

1. Describe the effects of the stock market crash of 1929 on American banks.
2. Based on the graph above, did banks begin closing as an immediate result of the crash?

"Walking through an American city, you might find few signs of the Depression. . . . You might notice that a great many shops were untenanted . . . ; that few factory chimneys were smoking; that the streets were not so crowded with trucks. . . . Otherwise things might seem to you to be going on much as usual. The major phenomena of the depression were mostly negative and did not assail the eye."

—Frederick Lewis Allen, *Since Yesterday*

3. According to the excerpt, what signs of the Depression might one notice while walking through an American city?
4. Name two visible signs of the Depression that Frederick Lewis Allen does not mention in this excerpt.

"You cannot extend the mastery of the government over the daily working life of a people without at the same time making it the master of the people's souls and thoughts. . . . Free speech does not live many hours after free industry and free commerce die."

—Herbert Hoover, speech delivered October 22, 1928

5. Based on the excerpt above, what was Herbert Hoover's philosophy of government?
6. In what ways did President Hoover's philosophy of government hinder the recovery?

Chapter 9 Test, Form B *cont.*

The Great Depression Begins

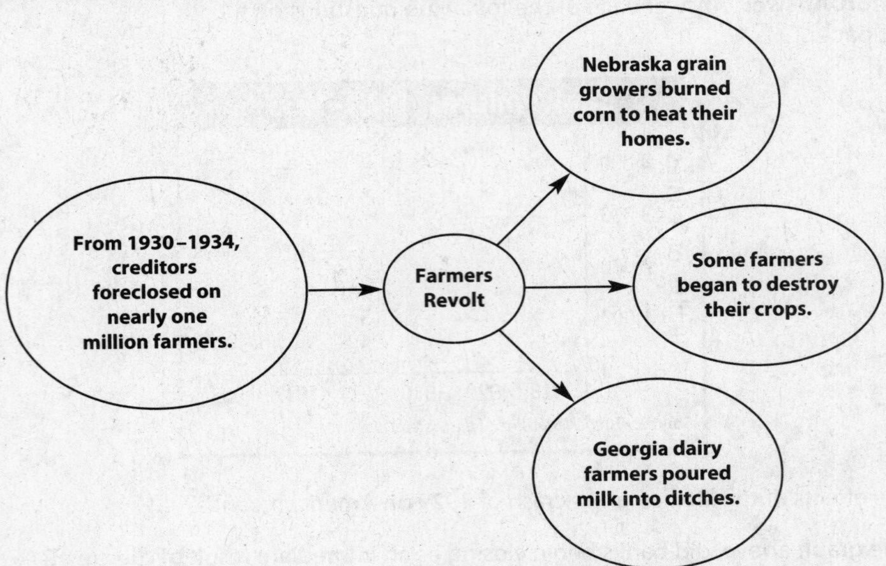

7. Why did creditors foreclose on nearly one million farmers between 1930 and 1934?

8. Explain how farmers hoped that destroying their crops, as described in the graphic, would ultimately help them.

DIRECTIONS: Essay Answer the following question on a separate piece of paper.

9. Describe how the U.S. economy changed as a result of the stock market crash of 1929 and the Depression. What effects did these economic changes have on the lives of American citizens?

NAME ______________________ DATE ____________ CLASS ____________

Lesson Quiz 10-1

networks

Roosevelt and the New Deal

DIRECTIONS: Completion Enter the appropriate word(s) to complete the statement.

1. President Roosevelt's energy, serenity, confidence, and ________________ gave many Americans hope despite the tough times of the Depression.

2. The Agricultural Adjustment Act that Roosevelt asked Congress to pass was based on the idea that prices for farm goods were low because farmers grew too ________________ food.

3. President Roosevelt and his advisers did not want to simply give money to the unemployed, so they established a series of government agencies that would organize ________________ programs for the unemployed.

4. The Federal Emergency ________________ Administration attempted to help unemployed Americans by channeling money to state and local agencies.

DIRECTIONS: Multiple Choice Indicate the answer choice that best completes the statement or answers the question.

________ **5.** The period between March 9 and June 16, 1933, when Congress passed 15 major acts to meet the economic crisis of the Depression, was called the

A. First New Deal.
B. New Nationalism.
C. Hundred Days.
D. New Freedom.

________ **6.** The Emergency Banking Relief Act helped solve the banking crisis by

A. putting all banks under government operation.
B. declaring that the gold standard would not be abandoned.
C. issuing licenses to banks that federal examiners found financially sound.
D. closing the banks long enough for the Federal Reserve to replenish them.

________ **7.** To regulate the stock market, Congress created the

A. Federal Trade Commission.
B. Securities and Exchange Commission.
C. National Recovery Administration.
D. Federal Deposit Insurance Corporation.

________ **8.** Perhaps the most important result of President Franklin Roosevelt's First New Deal was a noticeable change in

A. the spirit of the American people.
B. how many Americans remained unemployed.
C. the level of debt carried by most Americans.
D. how Americans viewed the banks.

NAME ________________ DATE ________ CLASS ________

Lesson Quiz 10-2

networks

Roosevelt and the New Deal

DIRECTIONS: Matching Match each item with the correct statement below.

_____ **1.** funded the construction of roadways, buildings, and parks

_____ **2.** union organizing tactic in which employees stopped work inside a factory and refused to leave

_____ **3.** law providing modest payments to older Americans and the unemployed

_____ **4.** guaranteed workers the right to organize unions and to bargain collectively

_____ **5.** government practice of borrowing money to pay for programs and not balancing the budget

A. National Labor Relations Act

B. deficit spending

C. Social Security Act

D. Works Progress Administration

E. sit-down strike

DIRECTIONS: Multiple Choice Indicate the answer choice that best completes the statement or answers the question.

_____ **6.** After the New Deal had been in effect for two years, the U.S. economy

A. demonstrated robust growth.

B. had slipped more deeply into the Depression.

C. had recovered from the Depression almost completely.

D. showed only slight improvement.

_____ **7.** Father Coughlin, a former New Deal supporter with a popular radio show, called for the government to

A. nationalize the banking system.

B. engineer a massive redistribution of wealth.

C. distribute a pension to elderly citizens.

D. end union and labor organizing.

_____ **8.** In *Schechter Poultry Corporation* v. *United States*, the Supreme Court struck down

A. most New Deal programs.

B. the authority of the NRA.

C. Roosevelt's deficit spending.

D. the Glass-Steagall Act.

_____ **9.** What did the bold series of programs and reforms that President Franklin Roosevelt launched in 1935 come to be called?

A. the Wagner Act

B. the Townshend plan

C. the Second New Deal

D. the American Liberty plan

NAME ______________________ DATE ______________ CLASS ____________

Lesson Quiz 10-3

networks

Roosevelt and the New Deal

DIRECTIONS: True/False Indicate whether the statement is true or false.

______ **1.** Women and African Americans made modest gains because of the support of Eleanor Roosevelt.

______ **2.** African American voters turned away from the Republican Party in 1936 to support Roosevelt's reelection.

______ **3.** The New Deal coalition was made up of President Roosevelt's supporters in Congress, as well as the Supreme Court justices who upheld New Deal programs and agencies.

______ **4.** The term "broker state" is used to refer to New Deal agencies and programs that regulate and police the stock market.

______ **5.** President Roosevelt's programs succeeded in creating a safety net for average Americans, in the form of safeguards and relief programs that protected them against economic disaster.

DIRECTIONS: Multiple Choice Indicate the answer choice that best completes the statement or answers the question.

______ **6.** Which figure in the Roosevelt administration was most active in bringing African Americans and women into the New Deal coalition?

A. Frances Perkins
B. First Lady Eleanor Roosevelt
C. Henry Morganthau
D. President Franklin Roosevelt

______ **7.** President Roosevelt's desire to change the political balance on the Supreme Court led to the ______________, which proved to be Roosevelt's first serious political mistake.

A. recession of 1937
B. court-packing plan
C. embrace of Keynesian economics
D. end of the New Deal

______ **8.** The Fair Labor Standards Act abolished child labor, limited the workweek to 44 hours for most workers, and

A. provided labor mediation for disputes.
B. implemented a fair-hiring provision.
C. gave workers the right to join a union.
D. set the first federal minimum wage.

______ **9.** In terms of its main goal of ending the Depression, the New Deal was only a limited success, but it

A. enabled more Americans to own their own homes.
B. limited the role of the government in economic life.
C. gave many Americans a sense of security and stability.
D. protected the courts from interference by the executive.

NAME _______________ DATE _______________ CLASS _______________

Chapter 10 Test, Form A

networks

Roosevelt and the New Deal

DIRECTIONS: Matching Match each item with the correct statement below.

_______ **1.** hired workers directly, including thousands of women, to build or improve airports, roads, and playgrounds

_______ **2.** caused industrial production to fall and was declared unconstitutional in 1935

_______ **3.** organized secret ballots at factories to see if workers wanted unions

_______ **4.** required companies that sell stocks and bonds to provide complete and truthful information to investors

_______ **5.** awarded contracts to construction companies to build highways, dams, schools, and other facilities

_______ **6.** guaranteed workers the right to organize unions and bargain collectively

_______ **7.** prohibited commercial banks from speculating on the stock market

_______ **8.** offered unemployed young men work planting trees, fighting forest fires, and building reservoirs

_______ **9.** sponsored the Federal Number One program for artists, musicians, theater people, and writers

_______ **10.** covered the money that people save in banks against loss

A. Glass-Steagall Banking Act

B. Civilian Conservation Corps

C. Wagner Act

D. Works Progress Administration

E. Public Works Administration

F. National Labor Relations Board

G. Securities Act of 1933

H. Civil Works Administration

I. National Recovery Administration

J. Federal Deposit Insurance Corporation

DIRECTIONS: Multiple Choice Indicate the answer choice that best completes the statement or answers the question.

_______ **11.** President Franklin Roosevelt entered office with no clear agenda or strong political ideology, but his administration favored government

A. involvement in health care.

B. intervention in the economy.

C. promotion of competition.

D. assistance to small businesses.

Chapter 10 Test, Form A *cont.*

networks

Roosevelt and the New Deal

____ **12.** President Roosevelt's policies for ending the Depression became known as the

A. fireside chats.
B. Glass-Steagall Act.
C. gold standard.
D. New Deal.

____ **13.** To fight the Depression, the first thing President Roosevelt set out to do was to

A. provide direct relief to the unemployed.
B. set up massive public works programs.
C. restore confidence in the nation's banking system.
D. provide mortgage assistance to farmers.

____ **14.** By 1934 Senator Huey Long of Louisiana began criticizing the New Deal from the left and calling for

A. a massive redistribution of wealth.
B. the government to balance the budget.
C. a pension for all citizens over the age of 60.
D. the government to stop interfering with business.

____ **15.** President Roosevelt launched the bold new programs that came to be known as the Second New Deal primarily because

A. the Supreme Court struck down key elements of New Deal programs.
B. Roosevelt faced strong criticism from the right over the New Deal.
C. the first New Deal programs had not generated an economic recovery.
D. Roosevelt wanted to undermine potential threats to his reelection.

____ **16.** The Social Security Act established the principle that the federal government should be responsible for

A. ensuring that employers treat their workers fairly.
B. citizens who, through no fault of their own, were unable to work.
C. protecting the rights of women and of African Americans.
D. people who, as a result of the Depression, had lost their jobs.

____ **17.** The New Deal helped establish a new voting coalition for President Roosevelt and the Democratic Party by

A. creating safeguards and relief programs to protect Americans from economic disaster.
B. responding to New Deal critics on both the right and the left with bold new programs.
C. creating numerous federal agencies and programs that still exist today.
D. addressing the needs of groups such as women, African Americans, and laborers.

_______ **18.** President Roosevelt's "court-packing plan" was a serious mistake because

A. it appeared to interfere with the Constitution's separation of powers.

B. the angry judges struck down the plan as unconstitutional.

C. many Americans opposed the idea of forced retirement.

D. the angry judges reacted by striking down much of the New Deal legislation.

_______ **19.** President Roosevelt triggered a new economic downturn in 1937 by

A. launching new programs.

B. decreasing government spending.

C. breaking up trusts.

D. decreasing taxes.

_______ **20.** In taking on a mediating role among competing economic interests—such as business leaders, farmers, workers, and homeowners—the New Deal established what some have called

A. binding arbitration.

B. the safety net.

C. welfare capitalism.

D. the broker state.

DIRECTIONS: Short Answer Answer each of the following questions.

> "This is preeminently the time to speak the truth, the whole truth, frankly and boldly. Nor need we shrink from honestly facing conditions in our country today. This great Nation will endure as it has endured, will revive and will prosper. So, first of all, let me assert my firm belief that the only thing we have to fear is fear itself—nameless, unreasoning, unjustified terror which paralyzes needed efforts to convert retreat into advance. . . . This Nation asks for action, and action now."
>
> —Franklin Delano Roosevelt, first Inaugural Address, March 4, 1933

21. Describe Franklin Roosevelt's personality and approach to the nation's problems as they are expressed in the excerpt above.

____

____

22. Describe the provisions of the National Labor Relations Act and the work of the board it created.

____

____

Chapter 10 Test, Form A *cont.*

networks

Roosevelt and the New Deal

> "Old people who are in need, unemployables, children, mothers and the sightless, will find systematic regular provisions for needs. The Act limits the Federal aid to not more than $15 per month for the individual, provided the State in which he resides appropriates a like amount."
>
> —Secretary of Labor Frances Perkins, "The Social Security Act"

23. Explain how the Social Security system described in the excerpt initially worked, who benefited from it, and who did not.

____

____

____

____

24. Discuss the New Deal's legacy, including its effectiveness in dealing with the Depression and its lasting effects on the role of government.

____

____

____

____

NAME _______________ DATE _______________ CLASS _______________

Chapter 10 Test, Form B

networks

Roosevelt and the New Deal

DIRECTIONS: Short Answer Answer each of the following questions on a separate piece of paper.

The First New Deal, 1933–1935		
Agency	**Established**	**Function**
Civilian Conservation Corps (CCC)	March 1933	Employed single men, ages 18–25, for natural resource conservation
Tennessee Valley Authority (TVA)	May 1933	Built hydroelectric plants and dams aimed at improving seven Southern states and attracting industry to the South
Agricultural Adjustment Act (AAA)	May 1933	Reduced agricultural surplus and raised prices for struggling farmers
Federal Emergency Relief Administration (FERA)	May 1933	Granted federal money to state and local governments to be used to help the unemployed
National Recovery Administration (NRA)	June 1933	Controlled industrial production and prices with industry-created codes of fair competition
Federal Deposit Insurance Corporation (FDIC)	June 1933	Guaranteed bank deposits up to $2,500
Public Works Administration (PWA)	June 1933	Provided employment in construction of airports, parks, schools, and roads
Civil Works Administration (CWA)	November 1933 (canceled 1934)	
Securities and Exchange Commission (SEC)	June 1934	Regulated the stock market to avoid dishonest practices

1. Explain why the Federal Deposit Insurance Corporation (FDIC) and the Securities and Exchange Commission (SEC) were so important in light of the causes of the Depression.

2. Based on information in the chart above, how could relief programs such as FERA, the CCC, and the CWA and recovery programs such as the AAA and the NRA work together to help lift the country out of the Depression?

NAME ______________________ DATE ______________ CLASS ____________

Chapter 10 Test, Form B *cont.*

networks

Roosevelt and the New Deal

The Second New Deal, 1935	
Agency/Legislation	**Function**
Works Progress Administration (WPA)	Combated unemployment; created jobs throughout economy
Social Security Act	Created unemployment system, disability insurance, old-age pension, and child welfare benefits
Wagner Act (National Labor Relations Act)	Guaranteed workers right to organize unions and to bargain collectively

3. Explain how the agencies and legislation shown in the table above helped better protect American citizens.

4. In what ways did the programs of the Second New Deal differ from those of the First New Deal?

> "Last Thursday, I described the American form of Government as a three-horse team provided by the Constitution. . . . The three horses are . . . the three branches of government—the Congress, the Executive, and the Courts. Two of the horses are pulling in unison today. The third is not. . . . The Court has been acting not as a judicial body but as a policymaking body."
>
> —Franklin Roosevelt, March 9, 1937

5. Which "horse," according to Roosevelt, is not pulling its weight, and why?

6. Explain why Roosevelt's plan to change the political balance on the Supreme Court proved to be a mistake.

DIRECTIONS: Essay Answer the following question on a separate piece of paper.

7. Explain how the crisis of the Depression led to Franklin Roosevelt's election in 1932. How did President Roosevelt's efforts to solve the problems caused by the Depression trigger a historic political realignment by 1936?

NAME ______________________ DATE ______________ CLASS ______________

Lesson Quiz 11-1

networks

A World in Flames

DIRECTIONS: True/False Indicate whether the statement is true or false.

________ **1.** Fascism was an aggressive form of nationalism that emphasized the supreme importance of individualism and free enterprise.

________ **2.** By 1932 the Nazis were the largest party in the Reichstag, or the lower house of the German parliament.

________ **3.** When German troops entered Austria, Hitler announced the *Anschluss*, or unification, of Austria and Germany.

________ **4.** At the Munich Conference, Britain and France informed Czechoslovakia's leaders that they must give up the Sudetenland.

________ **5.** In September of 1939, Germany invaded Russia, leading to declarations of war by Britain and France.

DIRECTIONS: Multiple Choice Indicate the answer choice that best completes the statement or answers the question.

________ **6.** Mussolini exploited the public's fears by portraying fascism as a bulwark against

A. militaristic expansion. **C.** communism.
B. democracy. **D.** economic depression.

________ **7.** One of the new political parties to rise during the political and economic chaos in Germany after World War I was the National Socialist German Workers' Party, also known as the

A. Socialist Party. **C.** Fascist Party.
B. Nazi Party. **D.** Bolshevik Party.

________ **8.** Many military officers in Japan believed Japan was destined to dominate

A. North America. **C.** East Asia.
B. the Soviet Union. **D.** the Pacific.

________ **9.** At first Britain and France gave in to Hitler's demands, a policy known as

A. appeasement. **C.** nationalism.
B. militarization. **D.** unification.

________ **10.** The Nazi-Soviet non-aggression pact contained a secret deal between Germany and the Soviet Union to divide which country?

A. Lithuania **C.** Yugoslavia
B. Hungary **D.** Poland

NAME ______________________ DATE ______________ CLASS ____________

Lesson Quiz 11-2

networks

A World in Flames

DIRECTIONS: Completion Enter the appropriate word(s) to complete the statement.

1. European refusal to repay loans from World War I and the findings of the ______________ Committee, which documented the huge profits arms factories had made during the war, turned even more Americans to isolationism.

2. The ______________ Act of 1935 made it illegal for Americans to sell arms to any country at war.

3. President Roosevelt supported ______________, the idea that trade between nations creates prosperity and helps prevent war.

4. The ______________ Act allowed the United States to send weapons to Britain if Britain promised to return them or pay rent for them when the war ended.

5. President Roosevelt and British Prime Minister Winston Churchill developed the ______________, which committed the United States and Britain to a postwar world of democracy, free trade, nonaggression, economic advancement, and freedom of the seas.

DIRECTIONS: Multiple Choice Indicate the answer choice that best completes the statement or answers the question.

______ **6.** President Franklin Roosevelt sent destroyers to Britain in exchange for

- **A.** cash and manufactured goods.
- **B.** a promise to pay at the war's end.
- **C.** the use of British bases in the Atlantic.
- **D.** a new agreement on trade.

______ **7.** The Neutrality Act of 1939 permitted the United States to sell arms to warring countries, but only

- **A.** on a cash-and-carry basis.
- **B.** to Britain and its allies.
- **C.** in exchange for military bases.
- **D.** to nations in the Pacific.

______ **8.** In 1940 which group pushed for stronger action against Germany and the repeal of all neutrality laws?

- **A.** the America First Committee
- **B.** the Fight for Freedom Committee
- **C.** the Committee to Defend America
- **D.** the Four Freedoms Committee

______ **9.** In July of 1940, Congress gave President Roosevelt the power to put economic pressure on Japan by

- **A.** attacking Japanese submarines.
- **B.** building up American defenses in the Philippines.
- **C.** sending lend-lease aid to China.
- **D.** blocking the sale of strategic materials to Japan.

NAME _______________ DATE _______________ CLASS _______________

Lesson Quiz 11-3

networks

A World in Flames

DIRECTIONS: Matching Match each item with the correct statement below.

_______ **1.** Hebrew word for "catastrophe," used specifically to refer to the Holocaust

_______ **2.** revoked landing certificates for those aboard the SS *St. Louis*

_______ **3.** extermination camp where 1,600,000 people died

_______ **4.** German government's secret police under the Nazis

_______ **5.** took citizenship away from Jewish Germans and banned marriage between Jews and other Germans

A. Nuremberg Laws

B. Auschwitz

C. Cuba

D. *Shoah*

E. Gestapo

DIRECTIONS: Multiple Choice Indicate the answer choice that best completes the statement or answers the question.

_______ **6.** The Nazis reserved their strongest hatred for Jews, although they also held other groups in contempt, including homosexuals, the disabled, Gypsies, and

A. Russians.
B. Scandinavians.
C. Slavic peoples.
D. the Japanese.

_______ **7.** What event in 1938 marked a significant escalation of the Nazi policies of persecution against Jews?

A. *Kristallnacht*
B. Nuremberg Laws
C. Wannsee Conference
D. *Anschluss*

_______ **8.** Following the unification of Austria and Germany, around 3,000 Austrian Jews

A. died from horrible living conditions every month.
B. applied for American visas each day.
C. escaped to the United States in a few weeks.
D. were deported by the Nazis every week.

_______ **9.** Many of the Jewish refugees aboard the SS *St. Louis*

A. immigrated to the United States.
B. disembarked in Havana.
C. were given refuge in Mexico.
D. died in the Nazis' "final solution."

_______ **10.** The Nazis' "final solution" referred to their plans to

A. defeat France and Britain.
B. deport Jews to the Soviet Union.
C. conquer and rule over Europe.
D. exterminate European Jews.

NAME ____________________ DATE ____________ CLASS ____________

Chapter 11 Test, Form A

networks

A World in Flames

DIRECTIONS: Matching Match each item with the correct statement below.

_____ **1.** staunchly isolationist group that opposed any American intervention or aid to the Allies

_____ **2.** Nazi extermination camp where an estimated 1,600,000 people died

_____ **3.** dictator who rose to power in Germany in the 1930s

_____ **4.** idea that trade between nations creates prosperity and helps prevent war

_____ **5.** unification, used specifically to describe Germany's takeover of Austria

_____ **6.** Fascist leader who established a dictatorship in Italy

_____ **7.** agreement that committed the signing nations to a postwar world of democracy, nonaggression, and free trade

_____ **8.** basis on which warring nations could buy arms from the United States under the Neutrality Act of 1939

_____ **9.** policy that stopped all sales of fuel and scrap iron from the United States to Japan

_____ **10.** British leader who promised "peace for our time"

A. internationalism

B. Benito Mussolini

C. Neville Chamberlain

D. America First Committee

E. Auschwitz

F. Adolf Hitler

G. embargo

H. cash-and-carry

I. *Anschluss*

J. Atlantic Charter

DIRECTIONS: Multiple Choice Indicate the answer choice that best completes the statement or answers the question.

_____ **11.** Two major causes of the rise of dictatorships after World War I were

A. the Treaty of Versailles and economic depression.

B. the emergence of new political ideas and economic depression.

C. the Treaty of Versailles and a lack of strong leadership after the war.

D. the emergence of new political ideas and a lack of strong leadership after the war.

_____ **12.** Which of the following was a reason European nations did not deal more aggressively with Adolf Hitler when the Nazi regime in Germany was still weak?

A. They considered Nazi Germany to be a bulwark against Stalin and the Soviet Union.

B. They believed Germany's military was far stronger than it actually was.

C. They feared Fascist movements would come to power in other European nations.

D. They believed the Nazis would want peace once they gained more territory.

Chapter 11 Test, Form A *cont.*

networks

A World in Flames

_______ **13.** At the Munich Conference in 1938, Britain and France

A. told Hitler they would declare war if Germany invaded Czechoslovakia.

B. gave in to Hitler's demands for the Sudetenland.

C. allowed Czechoslovakia to become a German protectorate.

D. told Hitler they would declare war if Germany invaded Poland.

_______ **14.** In 1934 the Nye Committee report created the impression that America's entry into World War I was influenced by

A. attacks on American merchant ships.

B. militarism in Europe.

C. American arms manufacturers.

D. European Communists.

_______ **15.** President Franklin Roosevelt believed the United States should try to preserve peace in the world, but many Americans supported ______________ and wanted the United States to avoid involvement in international conflicts.

A. fascism

B. isolationism

C. communism

D. internationalism

_______ **16.** The Lend-Lease Act allowed President Roosevelt to supply arms to Great Britain without

A. exposing American ships to attack by German submarines.

B. forcing Britain to return the arms after the war.

C. requesting Congress approve deficit spending for the war.

D. requiring financially strapped Britain to pay cash.

_______ **17.** President Roosevelt developed the idea of a hemispheric defense zone to

A. protect British cargo ships in the Atlantic from German submarines.

B. allow the transfer of old American destroyers to Britain.

C. prevent Japan from seizing Britain's colonial possessions in Asia.

D. expand the United States's role in the war against Japan and Germany.

_______ **18.** The Hebrew term for the Holocaust is

A. *Shoah.*

B. *Auschwitz.*

C. *Grynszpan.*

D. *Kristallnacht.*

_______ **19.** ____________________ was a carefully planned night of violence against Jews in Germany and Austria that was staged by the Nazis to seem like a spontaneous outpouring of popular anger.

A. *Anschluss*

B. Wannsee

C. *Kristallnacht*

D. The "final solution"

_______ **20.** In 1939 Mexico, Paraguay, Argentina, Costa Rica, and the United States all

A. welcomed many refugees from war-torn Europe.

B. denied entry to European Jews fleeing the Holocaust.

C. raised immigration quotas to accommodate refugees.

D. offered hope to Jews that they might escape the Holocaust.

DIRECTIONS: Essay Answer the following questions on a separate piece of paper.

21. Describe fascism and the beliefs of its followers and explain how Fascist ideology contributed to global warfare.

22. Describe Adolf Hitler's beliefs and explain how his nationalism and his views on race contributed to World War II and the Holocaust.

". . . In the future days, which we seek to make secure, we look forward to a world founded upon four essential human freedoms.

"The first is freedom of speech and expression—everywhere in the world.

"The second is freedom of every person to worship God in his own way—everywhere in the world.

"The third is freedom from want—which, translated into world terms, means economic understandings which will secure to every nation a healthy peacetime life for its inhabitants—everywhere in the world.

"The fourth is freedom from fear—which, translated into world terms, means a world-wide reduction of armaments to such a point and in such a thorough fashion that no nation will be in a position to commit an act of physical aggression against any neighbor—anywhere in the world."

—Franklin Delano Roosevelt, 1941 State of the Union Address

23. Describe the vision for the world that President Roosevelt suggests in this excerpt and explain what Roosevelt wanted the United States to do to achieve that vision.

24. Why were many German Jews and Jews in other parts of Europe unable to flee and immigrate to the United States when the Nazis took power?

NAME ______________________ DATE ______________ CLASS ______________

Chapter 11 Test, Form B

networks

A World in Flames

DIRECTIONS: Short Answer Answer each of the following questions on a separate piece of paper.

1938
• Hitler sends troops into Austria, declares Austrian *Anschluss*
• Munich Conference, where Britain and France agree to Hitler's demand for Sudetenland
• Hitler demands city of Danzig
1934
1935
1936
1937
1938
1939
1934
• Hitler becomes president of Germany
1935
• Germany builds a new air force; begins military draft
1939
• Hitler sends troops into Czechoslovakia
• Britain and France announce they will defend Poland
• Germany and USSR sign nonaggression pact

1. What examples of appeasement are listed on the time line above?

2. Based on the time line above, in what way did the policy of appeasement toward Hitler allow Germany to rapidly achieve its military goals in 1938 and 1939?

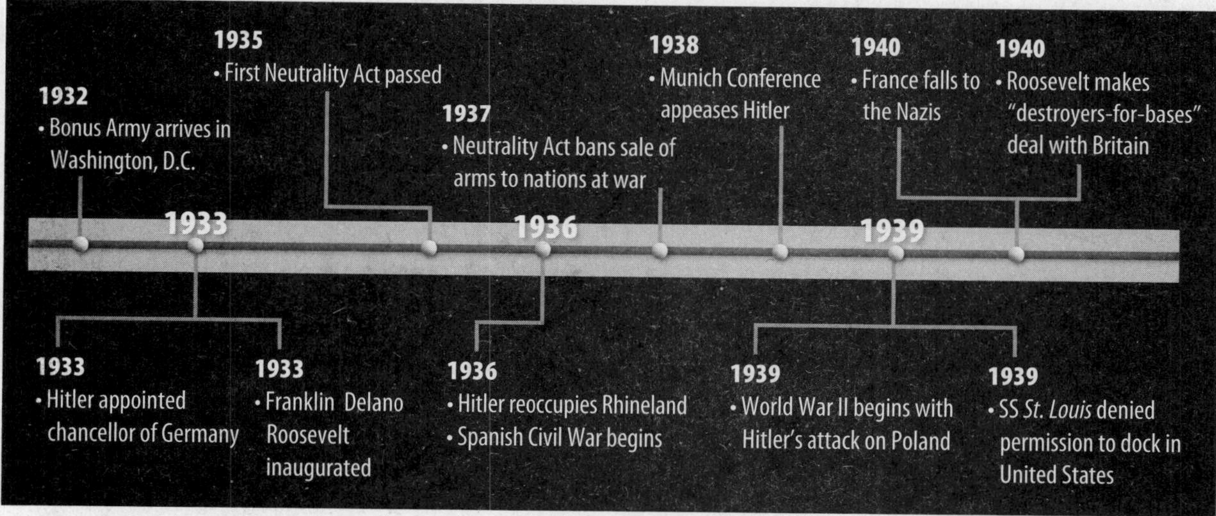

3. Which events listed on the time line were most likely factors leading to the passage of Neutrality Acts in 1935 and 1937?

4. Why did President Roosevelt make a "destroyers-for-bases" deal with Britain in 1940?

A World in Flames

"... In the future days, which we seek to make secure, we look forward to a world founded upon four essential human freedoms.

"The first is freedom of speech and expression—everywhere in the world.

"The second is freedom of every person to worship God in his own way—everywhere in the world.

"The third is freedom from want—which, translated into world terms, means economic understandings which will secure to every nation a healthy peacetime life for its inhabitants—everywhere in the world.

"The fourth is freedom from fear—which, translated into world terms, means a world-wide reduction of armaments to such a point and in such a thorough fashion that no nation will be in a position to commit an act of physical aggression against any neighbor—anywhere in the world."

—Franklin Delano Roosevelt, 1941 State of the Union Address

5. In what ways did Nazi actions during World War II violate each of the "four freedoms" described by President Roosevelt?

6. How does Roosevelt propose preserving the freedom from fear?

"The snow fell thickly. We were forbidden to sit down or even to move. The snow began to form a thick layer over our blankets. They brought us bread—the usual ration. We threw ourselves upon it. Someone had the idea of appeasing his thirst by eating the snow. Soon the others were imitating him. As we were not allowed to bend down, everyone took out his spoon and ate the accumulated snow off his neighbor's back. A mouthful of bread and a spoonful of snow. The SS who were watching laughed at this spectacle."

—*Night* by Elie Wiesel. Copyright © 1960 by Hill and Wang.

7. Why did the prisoners described in the excerpt eat snow off each other's backs?

8. Using information from the passage and your knowledge of the chapter, describe the conditions faced by prisoners of the Nazis during the Holocaust.

DIRECTIONS: Essay Answer the following question on a separate piece of paper.

9. Explain how leaders in Europe and the United States failed to respond to Nazi Germany's military aggression and persecution of Jews and other groups. In what ways did leaders such as Franklin Roosevelt and Winston Churchill rally their nations to take action?

NAME ______________________ DATE ______________ CLASS ____________

Lesson Quiz 12-1

networks

America and World War II

DIRECTIONS: Matching Match each item with the correct statement below.

______ **1.** agreements the government made to produce military equipment, instead of asking companies for bids

______ **2.** stated that the relocation of Japanese Americans living in most of the West Coast was constitutional

______ **3.** first allowed women in the military in 1942

______ **4.** symbol of the campaign to hire women during World War II

______ **5.** mass-produced basic cargo transport used during the war

A. Women's Army Auxiliary Corps

B. cost-plus contracts

C. "Rosie the Riveter"

D. Liberty ship

E. *Korematsu* v. *United States*

DIRECTIONS: Multiple Choice Indicate the answer choice that best completes the statement or answers the question.

______ **6.** During World War II, the army enlisted women for the first time, although they were barred from

A. basic training.
B. combat.
C. the barracks.
D. clerical positions.

______ **7.** The *Pittsburgh Courier* argued that African Americans should join the war effort to achieve victory over Hitler's racism and over racism at home, in a campaign called

A. "Double V."
B. "Tuskegee Airmen."
C. "Fight for Right."
D. "Victory Suit."

______ **8.** The automobile industry was uniquely suited to the mass production of

A. "Government Issue" clothing.
B. ships and submarines.
C. military equipment.
D. buildings to house soldiers.

______ **9.** A difficulty facing cities with war industries was

A. rationing.
B. relocating Japanese Americans.
C. finding housing for new workers.
D. calming racial tensions.

______ **10.** The growth of southern California and cities in the Deep South created a new industrial region known as what?

A. the Sunbelt
B. the Southwest
C. the Rust Belt
D. the Military Zone

NAME ______________________ DATE ______________ CLASS __________

networks

Lesson Quiz 12-2

America and World War II

DIRECTIONS: Completion Enter the appropriate word(s) to complete the statement.

1. American troops on the ____________ Peninsula surrendered in April 1942, and although a small force held out on the island of Corregidor in Manila Bay until May, the Philippines fell to the Japanese.

2. The ____________ Raid convinced Japanese leaders to change their strategy and to attack Midway Island, the farthest American base in the North Pacific west of Hawaii.

3. American naval attacks in the Coral Sea prevented the Japanese from landing on ____________ and kept the American supply lines to Australia open.

4. Fought in June 1942, the Battle of ____________ was a turning point in the war that stopped the Japanese advance in the Pacific.

DIRECTIONS: Multiple Choice Indicate the answer choice that best completes the statement or answers the question.

_______ **5.** On April 18, 1942, American bombs fell on Japan for the first time when American aircraft carriers' usual short-range bombers were replaced with

A. paratroopers.
B. radio transmitters.
C. code breakers.
D. B-25 bombers.

_______ **6.** Why were the Japanese unable to decipher the messages of the Navajo code talkers?

A. The code talkers used a code that consisted of a series of whistle-like noises.
B. The code talkers had an advanced code machine that was an early computer.
C. The code talkers used the Navajo language, which had no written alphabet.
D. The code talkers used a mathematical code based on the Navajo numeric system.

_______ **7.** A key to the American success at the Battle of Midway was

A. the use of new sonar and radar technology.
B. breaking the Japanese navy's secret code.
C. the use of long-range B-25 bombers.
D. the superior capabilities of American submarines.

_______ **8.** One part of the American plan for the defeat of Japan called for General Douglas MacArthur's troops to advance through the Solomon Islands, capture the north coast of New Guinea, and then retake

A. the Philippines.
B. Manchuria.
C. Indonesia.
D. Australia.

NAME ______________________ DATE ____________ CLASS ____________

Lesson Quiz 12-3

networks

America and World War II

DIRECTIONS: True/False Indicate whether the statement is true or false.

_______ **1.** President Franklin Roosevelt agreed with Prime Minister Winston Churchill's plan to attack the periphery of the German Empire, and in July 1942 ordered the invasion of Morocco and Algeria.

_______ **2.** In May of 1943, German troops in North Africa succeeded in pushing American and British forces out of Tunisia.

_______ **3.** Before D-Day, the Allies placed dummy equipment along the coast of Britain to convince the Germans that the Allies planned to land their invasion forces in Pas-de-Calais.

_______ **4.** The invasion of France had to begin at night to hide the ships crossing the English Channel.

_______ **5.** On D-Day, the American landing at Omaha Beach went very well, unlike the landing at Gold Beach.

DIRECTIONS: Multiple Choice Indicate the answer choice that best completes the statement or answers the question.

_______ **6.** In the spring and summer of 1942, the Battle of the Atlantic slowly turned in favor of the Allies, due in part to new technology such as depth charges, radar, and

A. B-25 bombers.
B. mass production.
C. convoy systems.
D. sonar.

_______ **7.** In November 1942, the American invasion of North Africa began under the command of which general?

A. Dwight D. Eisenhower
B. George Patton
C. Douglas MacArthur
D. Chester Nimitz

_______ **8.** Capturing Stalingrad was the key to Hitler's strategy to

A. eradicate communism from the world.
B. force Stalin to sign a treaty.
C. destroy the Soviet Union's economy.
D. draw China into the war.

_______ **9.** At the Tehran Conference, President Roosevelt, Prime Minister Churchill, and Soviet leader Joseph Stalin agreed

A. to name the invasion of France "Operation Overlord."
B. that the Soviet Union would help fight Japan after Germany was defeated.
C. to return Mussolini to power in Italy.
D. that Allied forces would not land in Pas-de-Calais.

NAME ______________________ DATE ____________ CLASS ____________

Lesson Quiz 12-4

networks

America and World War II

DIRECTIONS: Completion Enter the appropriate word(s) to complete the statement.

1. General Leslie R. Groves organized a team of engineers and scientists to build an atomic bomb, a program code named the ______________ Project.

2. General ______________ led troops that broke through the German line at the Battle of the Bulge.

3. The use of firebombs filled with ______________, a kind of jellied gasoline, was very controversial because the fires would kill civilians.

4. On August 9, 1945, the United States dropped an atomic bomb codenamed "Fat Man" on the city of ______________.

DIRECTIONS: Multiple Choice Indicate the answer choice that best completes the statement or answers the question.

_____ **5.** The Germans' goal in the Battle of the Bulge was to cut off Allied supplies coming through the port of

A. Antwerp, Belgium.
B. Odense, Denmark.
C. Helsinki, Finland.
D. Nice, France.

_____ **6.** Invading Iwo Jima proved difficult for American troops because of the island's rugged terrain and

A. kamikaze attacks on American supply ships.
B. a vast network of bunkers built by the Japanese.
C. large waves that swamped American landing craft.
D. a coral reef surrounding the island.

_____ **7.** General Curtis LeMay attempted to destroy Japan's war production by

A. invading Japan.
B. island hopping in the Pacific.
C. firebombing Japanese cities.
D. dropping an atomic bomb.

_____ **8.** In order to stockpile supplies and build up troops for an invasion of Japan, American military planners chose to first invade where?

A. Hiroshima
B. Iwo Jima
C. Nagasaki
D. Okinawa

_____ **9.** The purpose of the Nuremberg Trials was to

A. test the newly developed atomic bomb.
B. determine how the Holocaust had happened.
C. punish German leaders for war crimes.
D. remove the emperor of Japan from power.

NAME ______________________ DATE ______________ CLASS ____________

Chapter 12 Test, Form A

networks

America and World War II

DIRECTIONS: Matching Match each item with the correct statement below.

_______ **1.** American general in overall command of the Allied invasion of France

_______ **2.** area of France where the Allied invasion force landed

_______ **3.** led the American team of engineers and scientists building the atomic bomb

_______ **4.** American general in command of forces landing at Omaha Beach

_______ **5.** commander of the U.S. Navy in the Pacific

_______ **6.** highest-ranking African American officer in the U.S. military

_______ **7.** turning point in the war that stopped the Japanese advance in the Pacific

_______ **8.** the date chosen to begin Operation Overlord

_______ **9.** American general who said "I shall return" upon evacuating the Philippines

_______ **10.** American general who helped turn the German lines back during the Battle of the Bulge

A. Battle of Midway

B. Benjamin O. Davis, Sr.

C. Chester Nimitz

D. Robert Oppenheimer

E. D-Day

F. George S. Patton

G. Normandy

H. Omar Bradley

I. Douglas MacArthur

J. Dwight D. Eisenhower

DIRECTIONS: Multiple Choice Indicate the answer choice that best completes the statement or answers the question.

_______ **11.** During World War II, women were recruited into the U.S. military to

A. serve in light combat.

B. serve as nurses.

C. ensure men were available for combat.

D. entertain the troops.

_______ **12.** Nearly one-third of all American military equipment made during World War II was manufactured by the

A. steel industry.

B. automobile industry.

C. ship-building industry.

D. aircraft industry.

NAME ________________ DATE ________________ CLASS ________________

Chapter 12 Test, Form A *cont.*

networks

America and World War II

_______ **13.** Mobilizing the American economy for World War II created almost 19 million new jobs and

A. flooded the home front with new products.

B. finally ended the Great Depression.

C. lowered prices on food, clothing, and other goods.

D. limited opportunities for women and minorities.

_______ **14.** Japan's goal in attacking Midway Island was to

A. gain a base from which to attack Hawaii.

B. cut American supply lines to Australia.

C. lure and destroy the American fleet.

D. gain control of resources on the island.

_______ **15.** How did Navajo soldiers help the Allies regain islands in the Pacific during the war?

A. Navajo soldiers used their native language to code messages the Japanese could not decipher.

B. Navajo fighter pilots escorted bombers to Nagasaki and Hiroshima.

C. Navajo fighter pilots firebombed Japanese cities once the Allies controlled Iwo Jima.

D. Navajo soldiers were part of a tank battalion that halted the Axis forces at the Battle of the Bulge.

_______ **16.** In 1942 Prime Minister Churchill and President Roosevelt agreed to attack the edges of the German empire because they believed

A. if they defeated Germany in North Africa, the Germans would surrender.

B. invading North Africa was the best way to take pressure off of the Soviet Union.

C. the German commander in Egypt, General Erwin Rommel, was a poor leader.

D. their countries were not ready to launch a full-scale invasion of Europe.

_______ **17.** Why was the Battle of Stalingrad important?

A. It put the Germans on the defensive for the rest of the war.

B. It led to the development of radar and other new technologies.

C. It allowed the British to recapture the Suez Canal.

D. It was the first victory for the Allies in Europe.

_______ **18.** The last, desperate German offensive of the war became known as

A. D-Day.
B. the Nuremberg Trials.
C. V-E Day.
D. the Battle of the Bulge.

_______ **19.** Iwo Jima was an important objective for the American military because

A. the Japanese were using it as a base to attack the U.S. fleet.
B. the main Japanese naval force was stationed there.
C. U.S. planes could bomb Japan from there.
D. the islands were an important link in the Japanese supply lines.

_______ **20.** The secret American program to build an atomic bomb was called

A. the Manhattan Project.
B. Operation Overlord.
C. V-J Day.
D. the *Enola Gay* project.

DIRECTIONS: Essay Answer the following questions on a separate piece of paper.

> "It should be noted, to begin with, that all legal restrictions which curtail the civil rights of a single racial group are immediately suspect. That is not to say that all such restrictions are unconstitutional. It is to say that courts must subject them to the most rigid scrutiny. Pressing public necessity may sometimes justify the existence of such restrictions; racial antagonism never can."
>
> —*Korematsu* v. *United States* 323 U.S. 214 (1944), Justice Black, Opinion of the Court, Supreme Court of the United States.

21. What government action was being challenged in the case of *Korematsu* v. *United States*? What was the Supreme Court's ruling in the case?

> "There shall be no discrimination in the employment of workers in defense industries and in Government, because of race, creed, color, or national origin."
>
> —Executive Order 8802: Prohibition of Discrimination in the Defense Industry (1941). National Archive and Records Administration.

22. Explain the changes in the workforce brought about by Executive Order 8802. Why was this order necessary?

23. What were some of the difficulties the Allies faced when planning Operation Overlord? How did they attempt to overcome these difficulties?

NAME _________________________ DATE ______________ CLASS ____________

Chapter 12 Test, Form B

networks

America and World War II

DIRECTIONS: Short Answer Answer each of the following questions on a separate piece of paper.

> "The greatest advantage the United States enjoyed on the ground in the fighting was . . . the jeep and the two-and-a-half ton truck. These are the instruments that moved and supplied United States troops in battle, while the German army . . . depended on animal transport. . . . The United States, profiting from the mass production achievements of its automotive industry . . . had mobility that completely outclassed the enemy."
>
> —General George Marshall

1. What does the excerpt above suggest about modern warfare and about how the Allies were able to win World War II?

2. Identify examples of U.S. economic and industrial mobilization that helped to give the Allies the advantages described by General Marshall in the excerpt above.

> "This is not . . . a case of temporary exclusion of a citizen from an area for his own safety or that of the community, nor a case of offering him an opportunity to go temporarily out of an area where his presence might cause danger to himself or to his fellows. On the contrary, it is the case of convicting a citizen as a punishment for not submitting to imprisonment in a concentration camp, based on his ancestry, and solely because of his ancestry, without evidence or inquiry concerning his loyalty and good disposition towards the United States. . . . I need hardly labor the conclusion that Constitutional rights have been violated."
>
> —Justice Owen J. Roberts, dissenting in *Korematsu* v. *United States*

3. Explain what the Supreme Court decided in *Korematsu* v. *United States*.

4. Explain why Justice Roberts dissented from the Court's decision in *Korematsu* v. *United States*.

Chapter 12 Test, Form B *cont.*

America and World War II

How Many People Died in World War II?		
Country	**Military Deaths**	**Civilian Deaths**
Soviet Union	11,000,000	6,700,000
Germany	3,250,000	2,350,000
Japan	1,740,000	393,000
China	1,400,000	8,000,000
Poland	110,000	5,300,000
United States	405,000	2,000
Great Britain	306,000	61,000
Italy	227,000	60,000
France	122,000	470,000

5. Based on the chart above, what conclusions can you draw about the impact of World War II on the Allied and Axis nations?

6. What do you think were some of the reasons World War II caused such a large number of civilian casualties?

DIRECTIONS: Essay Answer the following question on a separate piece of paper.

7. Explain how World War II can be seen as a clash between the militaristic, antidemocratic values of the Axis powers and the democratic values of nations such as the United States. In what ways did the political values of the United States change as a result of the war?

NAME ______________________ DATE ______________ CLASS __________

Lesson Quiz 13-1

networks

The Cold War Begins

DIRECTIONS: Matching Match each item with the correct statement below.

______ **1.** organization formed at the end of World War II to promote international peace and security

______ **2.** location near Berlin where Truman and Stalin met to work out a deal on Germany

______ **3.** declared "the right of all people to choose the form of government under which they will live"

______ **4.** Soviet resort on the Black Sea where Roosevelt, Churchill, and Stalin met to plan the postwar world

______ **5.** era of confrontation and competition between the United States and the Soviet Union

A. Declaration of Liberated Europe

B. United Nations

C. Cold War

D. Potsdam

E. Yalta

DIRECTIONS: Multiple Choice Indicate the answer choice that best completes the statement or answers the question.

______ **6.** By 1945 what did President Franklin Roosevelt and his advisers think was the key to keeping the world at peace?

A. economic growth
B. military strength
C. a strong United Nations
D. a willingness to compromise

______ **7.** Roosevelt, Churchill, and Stalin agreed to divide Germany into four zones controlled by the United States, Great Britain, the Soviet Union, and

A. Italy.
B. Switzerland.
C. Canada.
D. France.

______ **8.** Among the major causes of the Cold War were arguments between the United States and the Soviet Union over reparations and

A. control of Japan.
B. the use of the atomic bomb.
C. economic policy in Germany.
D. immigration to the United States.

______ **9.** The presence of the Soviet army in Eastern Europe at the end of World War II ensured that ______________________ would be established in Poland, Romania, Bulgaria, Hungary, and Czechoslovakia.

A. a system for free elections
B. pro-Soviet Communist governments
C. a system for reparations
D. heavily industrialized economies

NAME ______________________ DATE ______________ CLASS __________

Lesson Quiz 13-2

networks

The Cold War Begins

DIRECTIONS: True/False Indicate whether the statement is true or false.

______ **1.** In 1946 Turkey demanded joint control of the straits of the Dardanelles with the Soviet Union.

______ **2.** By agreeing to come to the aid of any member of the North Atlantic Treaty Organization (NATO) that was attacked, the United States committed itself for the first time in its history to maintaining peace in Europe.

______ **3.** In June 1950, North Korean troops invaded the south, rapidly driving back the poorly equipped South Korean forces.

______ **4.** During the Korean War, the Communist Chinese government saw the United Nations troops in North Korea as a threat, but the Chinese military did not enter the war.

DIRECTIONS: Multiple Choice Indicate the answer choice that best completes the statement or answers the question.

______ **5.** When the United States, Britain, and France merged their zones of Germany in 1948, the Soviet Union responded by

A. threatening to declare war.

B. trying to undermine Germany's economy.

C. blockading West Berlin.

D. organizing a military alliance.

______ **6.** President Harry Truman saw the Communist invasion of South Korea as a test of the ______________ and ordered U.S. naval and air power into action.

A. Truman Doctrine **C.** containment policy

B. Marshall Plan **D.** NATO alliance

______ **7.** After the Korean War began, the United States embarked on a major

A. military buildup. **C.** economic expansion.

B. treaty negotiation. **D.** expansion of foreign aid.

______ **8.** President Truman fired General Douglas MacArthur in 1951 when MacArthur

A. failed to win the Korean War.

B. refused to carry out an invasion of China.

C. transmitted military secrets to the Soviet Union.

D. publicly criticized the president's policy of limited war.

NAME ______________________ DATE ______________ CLASS __________

Lesson Quiz 13-3

networks

The Cold War Begins

DIRECTIONS: Completion Enter the appropriate word(s) to complete the statement.

1. Alger Hiss—a diplomat who had served in Roosevelt's administration, attended the Yalta Conference, and helped organize the United Nations—was accused of being a Communist spy and later convicted of ______________.

2. After winning the 1946 Senate election in Wisconsin by accusing his opponent of being "communistically inclined," ______________ continued to proclaim that Communists were a danger both at home and abroad.

3. The ______________ Act required all Communist Party and "Communist-front" organizations to register with the United States attorney general and publish their records.

4. Julius and Ethel ______________ were convicted of espionage and executed in June 1953, although many people believed that they were victims caught in a wave of anti-Communist frenzy.

DIRECTIONS: Multiple Choice Indicate the answer choice that best completes the statement or answers the question.

______ 5. What did President Harry Truman establish in early 1947 to screen all federal employees?

A. HUAC
B. Project Verona
C. the loyalty review program
D. the subcommittee on investigations

______ 6. What impact did the House Un-American Activities Committee (HUAC) hearings have on Hollywood?

A. Actors were required to swear that they were not Communists.
B. Many actors were denied passports and could not travel abroad.
C. Ronald Reagan was accused of being a Communist sympathizer.
D. Producers blacklisted anyone who was believed to be a Communist.

______ 7. The tactic of damaging reputations with vague, unfounded charges became known as

A. subversion.
B. the Red Scare.
C. McCarthyism.
D. censure.

______ 8. In 1953 Americans were shocked when the Soviet Union tested the

A. hydrogen bomb.
B. first fallout shelters.
C. *Sputnik* satellite.
D. spy code.

NAME ______________________ DATE ______________ CLASS __________

networks

Lesson Quiz 13-4

The Cold War Begins

DIRECTIONS: Matching Match each item with the correct statement below.

_____ **1.** type of American spy plane that was shot down by the Soviet Union

_____ **2.** policy of threatening to use nuclear weapons if a Communist state tried to seize territory by force

_____ **3.** countries with primarily agricultural economies, where many covert operations took place

_____ **4.** a relationship that developed between the military establishment and the defense industry

_____ **5.** secret; not in the open

A. massive retaliation

B. developing nations

C. military-industrial complex

D. covert

E. U-2

DIRECTIONS: Multiple Choice Indicate the answer choice that best completes the statement or answers the question.

_____ **6.** The policy of massive retaliation allowed President Dwight D. Eisenhower to

A. prevent an arms race with the Soviets.
B. significantly reduce military spending.
C. vastly expand the scale of the Cold War.
D. focus on negotiations with the Soviets.

_____ **7.** Critics described President Eisenhower's willingness to threaten nuclear war in the interest of maintaining peace as which of the following policies?

A. massive retaliation
B. containment
C. brinkmanship
D. covert

_____ **8.** To prevent Communist revolutions in other countries, President Eisenhower decided to use covert operations conducted by the

A. Central Intelligence Agency.
B. National Aeronautics and Space Administration.
C. Federal Bureau of Investigation.
D. Special Forces.

_____ **9.** U.S. covert operations in developing nations included

A. extending the policy of containment to new regions.
B. providing financial aid to help industrialize their economies.
C. encouraging leaders to nationalize foreign companies.
D. organizing riots and providing weapons to opposition groups.

NAME ______________________________ DATE ______________ CLASS ____________

Chapter 13 Test, Form A

networks

The Cold War Begins

DIRECTIONS: Matching Match each item with the correct statement below.

_____ **1.** drills performed by American school children in preparation for a Soviet attack

_____ **2.** wrote the novel *Tomorrow!* to educate the public about the horrors of atomic war

_____ **3.** seized by the Egyptians, who intended to use its profits to fund other projects

_____ **4.** deadly radiation left over after a nuclear blast

_____ **5.** military alliance formed in Eastern Europe by the Soviet Union

_____ **6.** FBI director who urged HUAC to hold public hearings on Communist subversion

_____ **7.** type of American spy plane shot down by the Soviets in 1960

_____ **8.** general in charge of occupied Japan, fired by President Truman for insubordination

_____ **9.** Communist countries of Eastern Europe that were dependent on the Soviet Union

_____ **10.** separated North Korea and South Korea after the armistice that ended the Korean War

A. J. Edgar Hoover

B. fallout

C. Suez Canal

D. demilitarized zone

E. U-2

F. duck-and-cover

G. satellite nations

H. Douglas MacArthur

I. Warsaw Pact

J. Philip Wylie

DIRECTIONS: Multiple Choice Indicate the answer choice that best completes the statement or answers the question.

_____ **11.** The United Nations was officially organized in 1945 with a Security Council responsible for international peace and security. The Security Council could ask its members to

A. take military action to uphold a UN resolution.

B. choose members for the General Assembly.

C. contain Communist expansion.

D. negotiate agreements on trade and development.

_______ **12.** At the Potsdam Conference in July 1945, President Harry Truman took a firm stand against heavy reparations and insisted that

A. Europe's economy had to be rebuilt.

B. Germany's industry had to be allowed to recover.

C. the Soviets' concerns about security were unreasonable.

D. the United States had a right to use the atomic bomb.

_______ **13.** In 1946 what did Winston Churchill describe as an "iron curtain" falling across Eastern Europe?

A. the formation of the North Atlantic Treaty Organization (NATO)

B. the adoption of the Declaration of Liberated Europe

C. the establishment of pro-Soviet Communist governments in Eastern Europe

D. the industrialization of Eastern European nations under the Marshall Plan

_______ **14.** In the document known as the Long Telegram, U.S. diplomat George Kennan expressed his opinion that the Soviet Union had major economic and political weaknesses and proposed a policy of

A. confrontation with the Soviets.

B. providing aid to European nations.

C. containment of Soviet expansion.

D. engaging in covert operations.

_______ **15.** In response to Communist aggression in Greece and Turkey, President Truman outlined a policy known as the _______________, which pledged the United States to fight the spread of communism worldwide.

A. Marshall Plan

B. Truman Doctrine

C. North Atlantic Treaty Organization

D. Berlin Airlift

_______ **16.** The purpose of the Marshall Plan was to

A. punish Germany for its role in World War II.

B. keep Communist countries weak.

C. help Germany form a new government.

D. help Western Europe recover from World War II.

_______ **17.** The post-World War II Red Scare began in 1945, when a clerk in the Soviet Embassy in Ottawa, Canada, defected and

A. turned over documents proving that Soviets were trying to infiltrate the U.S. government.

B. started Project Venona in an attempt to crack the Soviet spy code.

C. urged the U.S. government to establish a loyalty review program and pass the McCarran Act.

D. testified before the U.S. Congress that there were Communists in Hollywood.

_______ **18.** Senator Joseph McCarthy created the media frenzy that began his anti-Communist witch hunt by

A. accusing Alger Hiss of being a Soviet spy.

B. urging the House Un-American Activities Committee (HUAC) to hold hearings.

C. saying that there were spies in the U.S. army.

D. claiming he had a list of Communists employed by the U.S. State Department.

_______ **19.** The informal relationship between the military and the defense industry that some people believe influences government policy, particularly military spending, is known as

A. massive retaliation.

B. a military-industrial complex.

C. an iron curtain.

D. a subversion.

_______ **20.** To prevent developing nations from allying themselves with the Soviet Union or falling to Communist uprisings, President Eisenhower decided to use

A. covert operations.

B. economic embargoes.

C. massive retaliation.

D. economic aid.

Chapter 13 Test, Form A *cont.*

The Cold War Begins

DIRECTIONS: Essay Answer the following questions on a separate piece of paper.

> "[The] USSR still [believes] in antagonistic 'capitalist encirclement' with which in the long run there can be no permanent peaceful coexistence. . . . [T]hey have learned to seek security only in patient but deadly struggle for total destruction of rival power, never in compacts and compromises with it. . . . In summary, we have here a political force committed fanatically to the belief that . . . it is desirable and necessary that the internal harmony of our society be disrupted, our traditional way of life be destroyed, the international authority of our state be broken, if Soviet power is to be secure."
>
> —George F. Kennan, U.S. Diplomat, Moscow Embassy Telegram #511, 1946

21. Describe the beliefs, concerns, and goals of the Soviet Union and the United States that contributed to rising tensions between the two nations after World War II. To what extent was U.S. Diplomat George F. Kennan's analysis in the excerpt above accurate?

> "You have to take chances for peace, just as you must take chances in war. Some say that we were brought to the verge of war. Of course we were brought to the verge of war. The ability to get to the verge without getting into the war is the necessary art. . . . We walked to the brink and we looked it in the face. We took strong action."
>
> —John Foster Dulles, U.S. Secretary of State, quoted in *Rise to Globalism*

22. Explain the reasoning behind "massive retaliation" and "brinkmanship" in light of the excerpt above, and describe how President Eisenhower used these concepts in his conduct of the Cold War.

> "While I cannot take the time to name all the men in the State Department who have been named as members of the Communist Party and members of a spy ring, I have here in my hand a list of 205 that were known to the Secretary of State as being members of the Communist Party and who nevertheless are still working and shaping the policy of the State Department."
>
> —Senator Joseph McCarthy, February 9, 1950

23. Describe the tactics of Senator Joseph McCarthy, including the statement excerpted above, and explain why few challenged him.

24. Describe the effects of the Cold War on American popular culture in the 1950s. What were some of the themes that writers of literature, music, film, and television used to express their thoughts about the Cold War?

NAME ______________________ DATE ______________ CLASS ____________

Chapter 13 Test, Form B

networks

The Cold War Begins

DIRECTIONS: Short Answer Answer each of the following questions on a separate piece of paper.

Key Issues at Yalta Conference		
Issue	**Resolution**	**Long-term Ramification**
Government of Poland	Communist government	Set precedent for other Communist governments established by Soviets
Rest of Europe	Declaration of Liberated Europe	Countries could decide for themselves what type of government they wanted
Division of Germany	Divided into 4 zones, governed by France, Great Britain, United States, and Soviet Union	Division weakened the German economy; arguments over reparations and economic policy continued

1. Explain what the Yalta Conference was, including when the conference was held and who attended it.

2. Why was the Yalta Conference a significant element in the history of the Cold War?

> "Our policy is directed not against any country or doctrine but against hunger, poverty, desperation and chaos. Its purpose should be the revival of a working economy in the world so as to permit the emergence of political and social conditions in which free institutions can exist."
>
> —George C. Marshall, U.S. Secretary of State, quoted in *Marshall: Hero for Our Times*

3. Identify the policy described in the excerpt above and briefly describe how this policy worked.

4. Secretary of State Marshall's statement was a response to what fear that many postwar Soviet leaders had?

NAME ______________________ DATE ____________ CLASS ____________

Chapter 13 Test, Form B *cont.*

networks

The Cold War Begins

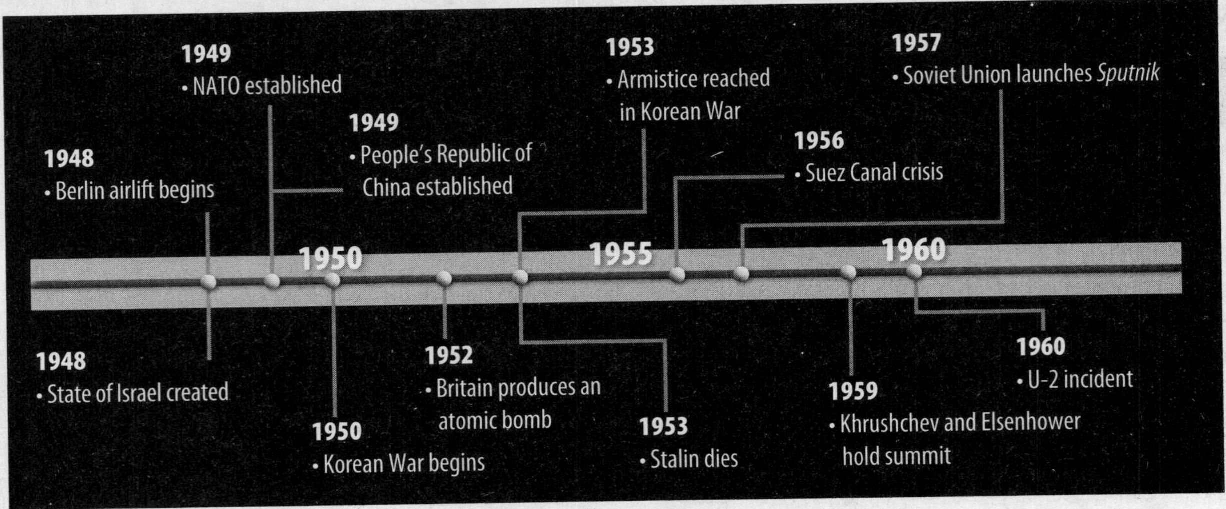

5. In what ways was the 1949 establishment of the North Atlantic Treaty Organization (NATO) significant for American foreign policy?

6. Identify two events on the time line above that shocked the American public.

DIRECTIONS: Essay Answer the following question on a separate piece of paper.

7. In what ways did tensions between the United States and the Soviet Union shape U.S. foreign policy and American society from 1945 to 1960? What effects did the Cold War have on other nations?

NAME ____________________ DATE ____________ CLASS ____________

Lesson Quiz 14-1

networks

Postwar America

DIRECTIONS: Completion Enter the appropriate word(s) to complete the statement.

1. The Servicemen's Readjustment Act, popularly called the ____________, boosted the economy by providing generous loans to veterans to help them establish businesses, buy homes, and attend college.

2. In 1947 a new and more conservative Congress set out to curb the power of organized labor by passing the ____________ Act.

3. Divisions within the Democratic Party in 1948—including the Southern Democrats who abandoned the party to form the States' Rights or ____________ Party—seemed to spell disaster for President Truman's candidacy.

4. President Eisenhower ended government price and rent ____________, which many conservatives had viewed as unnecessary federal regulation of the economy.

DIRECTIONS: Multiple Choice Indicate the answer choice that best completes the statement or answers the question.

______ **5.** A greater demand for goods after World War II led to higher prices, and this inflation soon triggered

A. public protests.
B. increased unemployment.
C. labor unrest.
D. political turmoil.

______ **6.** To the surprise of many, President Harry Truman won the election of 1948 with strong support from labor, farmers, and

A. business interests.
B. Southern Democrats.
C. the new Progressive Party.
D. African Americans.

______ **7.** Although legislators did not embrace all of President Truman's Fair Deal programs, Congress did increase Social Security benefits, extend those benefits to 10 million more Americans, and

A. raise the minimum wage.
B. provide subsidies for farmers.
C. grant federal aid to schools.
D. create national health insurance.

______ **8.** President Eisenhower took an activist role when he pushed for two large government programs, the Federal Highway Act and

A. expanded public housing.
B. the St. Lawrence Seaway.
C. the school construction bill.
D. the Tennessee Valley Authority.

NAME ________________________________ DATE ______________ CLASS ____________

Lesson Quiz 14-2

networks

Postwar America

DIRECTIONS: Matching Match each item with the correct statement below.

_____ **1.** developed an injectable polio vaccine

_____ **2.** one of the earliest suburbs, located 10 miles east of New York City

_____ **3.** period from 1945 to 1961 during which over 65 million children were born in the United States

_____ **4.** beat writer who published *On the Road* in 1957

_____ **5.** cultural separation between children and their parents

A. baby boom

B. Jonas Salk

C. Levittown

D. generation gap

E. Jack Kerouac

DIRECTIONS: Multiple Choice Indicate the answer choice that best completes the statement or answers the question.

_____ **6.** For most Americans, the 1950s was a decade of incredible

A. scarcity.
B. overconfidence.
C. prosperity.
D. turmoil.

_____ **7.** Large U.S. corporations competed with each other as the postwar economy grew, and some expanded oversees to become

A. franchises.
B. multinational corporations.
C. chain companies.
D. white-collar companies.

_____ **8.** Which trend of the 1950s did books such as *The Organization Man* and *The Lonely Crowd* criticize?

A. conformity
B. racism
C. technology
D. affluence

_____ **9.** One of the most popular shows ever to air on television was a situation comedy from the 1950s called

A. *The $64,000 Question*.
B. *I Love Lucy*.
C. *The Lone Ranger*.
D. *Dragnet*.

_____ **10.** Rock 'n' roll music, which became popular with American teenagers in the 1950s, grew out of the sounds of what other form of music?

A. jazz
B. swing
C. rhythm and blues
D. ragtime

NAME ______________________ DATE ______________ CLASS ____________

Lesson Quiz 14-3

networks

Postwar America

DIRECTIONS: True/False Indicate whether the statement is true or false.

_______ **1.** Many of the people left behind in inner cities as other residents fled to the suburbs in the 1950s were African Americans.

_______ **2.** Mexicans who came to the United States through the Bracero Program to work on farms toiled in the hot sun for long hours, but were well paid for their labor.

_______ **3.** Most Native Americans eventually concluded that termination was a good policy that helped them escape from poverty.

_______ **4.** The scenic mountains of Appalachia hid desperate poverty, high rates of nutritional deficiency and infant mortality, and failing schools.

_______ **5.** The United States saw a 45 percent rise in juvenile crime rates between 1948 and 1953, and juvenile delinquency became a major concern for many Americans.

DIRECTIONS: Multiple Choice Indicate the answer choice that best completes the statement or answers the question.

_______ **6.** The centers of numerous cities deteriorated in the postwar period as middle-class flight deprived urban areas of

A. termination policies.
B. minorities.
C. tax dollars.
D. cultural events.

_______ **7.** ______________________ programs tried to eliminate poverty by tearing down slums and erecting new high-rise buildings for poor residents.

A. Urban renewal
B. Termination
C. Bracero
D. Education reform

_______ **8.** *A Raisin in the Sun*, a play about a working-class African American family struggling against poverty and racism that opened on Broadway in 1959, was written by

A. Michael Harrington.
B. Lorraine Hansberry.
C. Fulton J. Sheen.
D. Benjamin Reifel.

_______ **9.** After the launches of *Sputnik I* and *Sputnik II* in 1957, efforts began in the United States to

A. send more juvenile delinquents to jail.
B. discourage adolescents from reading science fiction.
C. limit the amount of television that children watched.
D. improve math and science education.

NAME ______________________ DATE ______________ CLASS ____________

Chapter 14 Test, Form A

networks

Postwar America

DIRECTIONS: Matching Match each item with the correct statement below.

_______ **1.** author of the play *A Raisin in the Sun*, about a working-class African American family

_______ **2.** mountainous region of the United States that stretches from Georgia to New York

_______ **3.** African American musician who recorded hit rock 'n' roll songs in the 1950s

_______ **4.** States' Rights, or Dixiecrat, Party candidate for president in 1948

_______ **5.** beat poet who criticized modern American life for its sterility, conformity, and emptiness

_______ **6.** early computer that handled business data

_______ **7.** researcher who developed an oral vaccine for polio

_______ **8.** the largest public works program in American history

_______ **9.** work that takes place mostly in offices, instead of in factories

_______ **10.** term for the cultural separation between children and their parents

A. Federal Highway Act

B. generation gap

C. Albert Sabin

D. Strom Thurmond

E. UNIVAC

F. Lorraine Hansberry

G. white-collar jobs

H. Chuck Berry

I. Appalachia

J. Allen Ginsberg

DIRECTIONS: Multiple Choice Indicate the answer choice that best completes the statement or answers the question.

_______ **11.** A key factor that enabled the U.S. economy to continue to grow after World War II was

A. expansion of the labor market.

B. increased consumer spending.

C. inflation and higher prices.

D. government intervention.

Chapter 14 Test, Form A *cont.*

Postwar America

_______ **12.** After World War II, the Servicemen's Readjustment Act—popularly called the GI Bill—made it possible for many returning soldiers to

A. find blue-collar jobs.
B. make careers in the military.
C. buy homes.
D. move into the nation's urban centers.

_______ **13.** President Harry Truman's legislative agenda included expanding Social Security, increasing the minimum wage, and promoting employment through federal spending and investment, as well as

A. ending government price and rent controls.
B. enacting a federal highway bill.
C. abolishing the Reconstruction Finance Corporation.
D. enacting a broad civil rights bill.

_______ **14.** For President Dwight D. Eisenhower, "dynamic conservatism" meant a policy approach that balanced economic conservatism with

A. activism in areas that would benefit the country.
B. an escalation of the Korean War.
C. increases in government aid to American businesses.
D. a program to spend more on schools and public housing.

_______ **15.** According to John Kenneth Galbraith, postwar America had an "economy of abundance" because of

A. the growth of suburbs.
B. new business techniques and improved technologies.
C. the new consumer culture.
D. huge numbers of workers returning from the war.

_______ **16.** Suburbs accounted for about 85 percent of new home construction in the 1950s, and many people believed suburbs offered

A. a better life.
B. the GI Bill.
C. a departure from traditional values.
D. homes closer to their jobs.

_______ **17.** The 1950s saw major advances in science, including medical breakthroughs that led to improved treatments for cancer, polio, and

A. Alzheimer's disease.
B. pneumonia.
C. influenza.
D. heart attacks.

_______ **18.** Although most Americans in the 1950s assumed that the country's prosperity provided everyone with a comfortable existence, at least one in five Americans

A. did not have access to medical care.

B. lived below the poverty line.

C. lived in crowded housing projects.

D. struggled against discrimination.

_______ **19.** The federal government's termination policy, launched after World War II, was intended to

A. bring Native Americans into mainstream society.

B. end inner-city poverty by replacing slums with new high-rise buildings.

C. offer Mexican laborers temporary work on American farms.

D. end the dependence of poor Americans on government aid.

_______ **20.** In the 1950s, many Americans stereotyped young people who favored unconventional clothing and hairstyles as

A. members of minority groups.

B. unpatriotic.

C. victims of discrimination.

D. juvenile delinquents.

DIRECTIONS: Essay Answer the following questions on a separate piece of paper.

> "... [It would] reverse the basic direction of our national labor policy, inject the government into private economic affairs on an unprecedented scale, and conflict with important principles of our democratic society. Its provisions would cause more strikes, not fewer."
>
> —President Truman on the Taft-Hartley Act, June 20, 1947

21. Refer to the excerpt above. Explain the Taft-Hartley Act and describe the politics that led to its passage, including labor unrest, the election of 1946, and President Truman's use of the veto.

22. Describe President Eisenhower's domestic agenda, including examples of conservative, liberal, and activist policies.

23. What factors made rock 'n' roll wildly popular in the 1950s, and why did many adults consider this form of music shocking and dangerous?

NAME ______________________ DATE ______________ CLASS ______________

Chapter 14 Test, Form A *cont.*

networks

Postwar America

> "The Indians believed that when the dark clouds of war passed from the skies overhead, their rising tide of expectations, though temporarily stalled, would again reappear. Instead they were threatened by termination. . . . Soaring expectations began to plunge. Termination took on the connotation of extermination for many."
>
> —Benjamin Reifel, a Sioux quoted in *The Earth Shall Weep*

24. Explain the federal government's termination policy and describe how the experience of Native Americans differed from the experiences of other groups in the postwar United States.

NAME ________________ DATE ________ CLASS ________

Chapter 14 Test, Form B

networks

Postwar America

DIRECTIONS: Short Answer Answer each of the following questions on a separate piece of paper.

The Fair Deal Programs and Reforms	
Passed Under the Fair Deal	**Rejected or Blocked by Congress**
Increase in minimum wage to 75¢ an hour	Passage of national health insurance
Increase in Social Security benefits by 75 percent	Provision of subsidies to farmers
National Housing Act to facilitate low-income housing	Establishment of federal aid to schools

1. What did President Truman mean when he described his legislative agenda as "a fair deal"?

2. Which groups were affected by the refusal of Congress to pass all of the Fair Deal programs?

> "[T]ens of millions of Americans are, at this very moment, maimed in body and spirit existing at levels beneath those necessary for human decency. If these people are not starving, they are hungry, and sometimes fat with hunger, for that is what cheap foods do. They are without adequate housing and education and medical care."
>
> —Michael Harrington, *The Other America* (1962)

3. Who were the Americans Michael Harrington describes in the excerpt above?

4. How is this description of millions of poor Americans different from the perception of the United States during the 1950s as the "affluent society"?

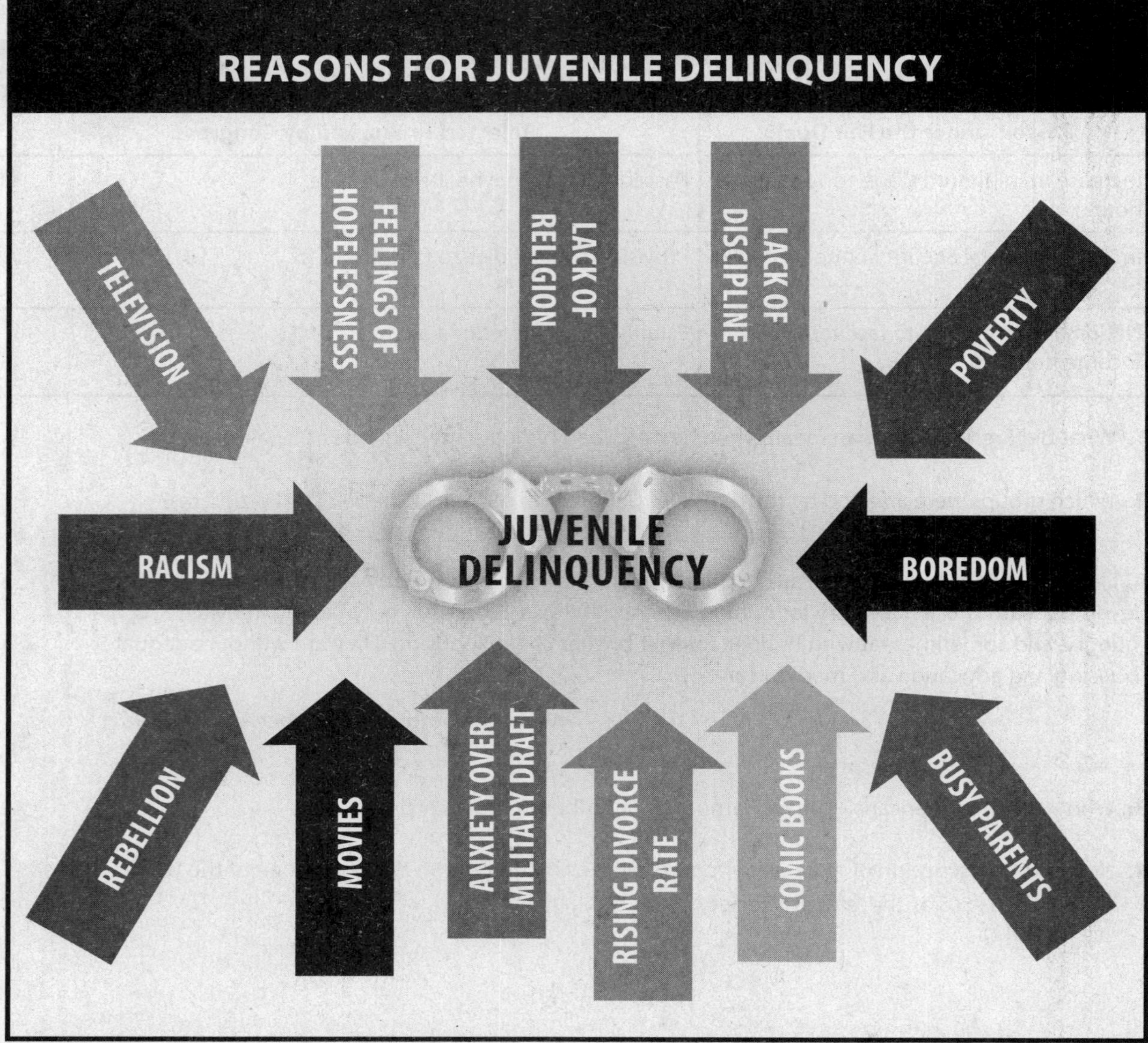

5. What aspect of the problem of juvenile delinquency is illustrated by the graphic above?

6. What does the graphic suggest about how the American public perceived young people in the 1950s?

DIRECTIONS: Essay Answer the following question on a separate piece of paper.

7. Explain how government policies, demographic forces, technological advances, and other factors in the postwar period promoted the unprecedented prosperity of the United States. How did the new prosperity change American society?

NAME ______________________ DATE ______________ CLASS ____________

Lesson Quiz 15-1

networks

The New Frontier and the Great Society

DIRECTIONS: Completion Enter the appropriate word(s) to complete the statement.

1. The Presidential Commission on the Status of Women called for federal action against ______________ discrimination.

2. In decisions such as *Engel* v. *Vitale*, the Supreme Court handed down decisions that reaffirmed the separation of ______________ and state.

3. Although the ______________ Party enjoyed large majorities in both houses of Congress, Kennedy was unable to push through many of his domestic programs.

4. In the *Reynolds* v. *Sims* decision that helped promote the principle of "one person, one vote," the Warren Court required state legislatures to ______________ electoral districts so that all citizens' votes would have equal weight.

5. During the Kennedy administration, Congress agreed with the president and approved a law that raised the ______________.

DIRECTIONS: Multiple Choice Indicate the answer choice that best completes the statement or answers the question.

_____ **6.** The Supreme Court's decision in *Reynolds* v. *Sims* shifted political power throughout the country to

A. rural areas.
B. the South.
C. the suburbs.
D. urban areas.

_____ **7.** In *Gideon* v. *Wainwright*, the Supreme Court ruled that, regardless of the ability to pay, a defendant in a state court had the right to

A. a lawyer.
B. a speedy trial.
C. a telephone call.
D. remain silent.

_____ **8.** Republicans, as well as Southern Democrats, viewed the New Frontier as

A. elitist policies.
B. sound economic policies.
C. too conservative.
D. too expensive.

_____ **9.** Kennedy convinced Congress to invest more funds in

A. defense and space exploration.
B. education.
C. health insurance for the elderly.
D. urban affairs.

_____ **10.** During the space race, Kennedy's goal for America was to be the first to

A. build a space station.
B. land a man on the moon.
C. put a man into orbit.
D. put a man into space.

Lesson Quiz 15-2

networks

The New Frontier and the Great Society

DIRECTIONS: True/False Indicate whether the statement is true or false.

_______ **1.** Kennedy proposed the Alliance for Progress to improve relations between the United States and China.

_______ **2.** The Bay of Pigs action successfully pressured the Soviets into removing their missiles from Cuba.

_______ **3.** With Cold War tensions continuing to rise, the United States and the Soviet Union engaged in a space race—vying for dominance of the heavens to enhance their competitive positions on Earth.

_______ **4.** Khrushchev built a wall through Berlin that blocked movement between the Soviet sector and the rest of the city to keep West Germany from using Berlin as a base from which to flood East Germany.

DIRECTIONS: Multiple Choice Indicate the answer choice that best completes the statement or answers the question.

_______ **5.** On April 17, 1961, armed Cuban exiles landed on the south coast of Cuba at

A. Havana.
B. New Delhi.
C. Santiago de Cuba.
D. the Bay of Pigs.

_______ **6.** President Kennedy pushed for a buildup of conventional troops and weapons that would allow the United States to fight a limited style of warfare with

A. a flexible response.
B. a rigid response.
C. nuclear threats.
D. nuclear weapons.

_______ **7.** To improve relations between the United States and Latin America, President Kennedy proposed a series of cooperative aid projects with Latin American governments called

A. *La Brigada*.
B. the Alliance for Progress.
C. the Bay of Pigs.
D. the Peace Corps.

_______ **8.** Kennedy canceled air support for the Bay of Pigs invasion to

A. avoid going to war with Cuba.
B. give the operation a better chance to succeed.
C. keep the United States's involvement a secret.
D. withdraw his support for the overthrow of Castro's government.

_______ **9.** Which event contributed to Nikita Khrushchev's fall from power in 1964?

A. President Kennedy's assassination
B. the Bay of Pigs invasion
C. the building of the Berlin Wall
D. the Cuban missile crisis

NAME ______________________ DATE ______________ CLASS ____________

Lesson Quiz 15-3

networks

The New Frontier and the Great Society

DIRECTIONS: Completion Enter the appropriate word(s) to complete the statement.

1. President Johnson felt that a wealthy government should try to improve the lives of its citizens and declared a war on ____________________.

2. The Elementary and Secondary ____________________ Act of 1965 granted millions of dollars to public and private schools.

3. The new cabinet agency created during the Johnson administration was the Department of ____________________.

4. Lyndon Johnson's Project ____________________ funded a preschool program for the disadvantaged.

DIRECTIONS: Multiple Choice Indicate the answer choice that best completes the statement or answers the question.

________ 5. What was President Johnson's vision of the more perfect and equitable society the United States could and should become called?

A. the Fair Deal
B. the Great Society
C. the New Deal
D. the New Frontier

________ 6. Which group offered work-study programs to help underprivileged young men and women earn a high school diploma or college degree?

A. Job Corps
B. Neighborhood Youth Corps
C. Peace Corps
D. Upward Bound Corps

________ 7. At Johnson's urging, what agency did Congress set up in 1964 to coordinate programs aimed at improving life for inner city residents?

A. Department of Housing and Urban Development
B. Medicare
C. Office of Economic Opportunity
D. Project Head Start

________ 8. Which Great Society program was a comprehensive health insurance program for all senior citizens?

A. Medicare
B. Model Cities
C. VISTA
D. Upward Bound

________ 9. Johnson's goals for a better America were supported by

A. the failure of business to create enough jobs.
B. the hardships caused by the slumping economy.
C. the prosperity resulting from the strong economy.
D. the success of unions in organizing workers.

NAME ______________ DATE ______________ CLASS ______________

Chapter 15 Test, Form A

networks

The New Frontier and the Great Society

DIRECTIONS: Matching Match each item with the correct statement below.

_____ **1.** suspects must be informed of their right to remain silent before being questioned

_____ **2.** space capsule that carried American astronauts to the moon and back

_____ **3.** congressional reapportionment must follow idea of "one person, one vote"

_____ **4.** courts cannot consider evidence obtained in violation of the U.S. Constitution

_____ **5.** state-mandated Bible reading in school banned

_____ **6.** prohibiting the sale and use of birth control devices violated citizens' constitutional right to privacy

_____ **7.** eliminated the system giving preference to northern European immigrants

_____ **8.** states cannot compose official prayers and require them to be recited in public schools

_____ **9.** protected voters from discriminatory practices

_____ **10.** suspects are entitled to an attorney, regardless of ability to pay

A. *Mapp* v. *Ohio*

B. Voting Rights Act of 1965

C. *Engel* v. *Vitale*

D. *Griswold* v. *Connecticut*

E. Immigration Act of 1965

F. *Escobedo* v. *Illinois*

G. *Abington School District* v. *Schempp*

H. *Gideon* v. *Wainwright*

I. *Reynolds* v. *Sims*

J. *Apollo*

DIRECTIONS: Multiple Choice Indicate the answer choice that best completes the statement or answers the question.

_____ **11.** During the 1960 election campaign, television aired its first

A. political commentary.

B. presidential debate.

C. presidential speech.

D. results of the election.

_____ **12.** The purpose of the Warren Commission was to investigate

A. allegations of a conspiracy in Kennedy's assassination.

B. the relationship between Cuba and the Soviet Union.

C. the result of the Cuban Missile Crisis.

D. who was responsible for the Bay of Pigs.

_____ **13.** Kennedy was unable to pass many of his domestic programs because

A. many Democrats in Congress believed the New Frontier was too expensive.

B. Republicans controlled the most influential committees in Congress.

C. the Democrats held only a small majority in the Senate.

D. the Republicans held a large majority in the House of Representatives.

_____ **14.** In an effort to increase growth and create more jobs, Kennedy advocated

A. deficit spending.

B. price controls.

C. public works programs.

D. raising taxes for the wealthiest Americans.

_____ **15.** The Fourteenth Amendment ensures

A. due process of law.

B. that all defendants be read the Miranda rights.

C. that all defendants get a trial by jury.

D. that all defendants have a lawyer.

_____ **16.** A day camp for children with developmental disabilities, known as Camp Shriver, was the beginning of an effort that later grew into the

A. Great Society.

B. New Frontier.

C. Special Olympics.

D. War on Poverty.

_____ **17.** Who wrote the influential book *The Other America*?

A. Barry Goldwater

B. Earl Warren

C. Eric Sevareid

D. Michael Harrington

Chapter 15 Test, Form A *cont.*

networks

The New Frontier and the Great Society

_______ **18.** Who was the first American to orbit Earth?

A. Alan Shepard
B. Earl Warren
C. John Glenn
D. Neil Armstrong

_______ **19.** In the agreement ending the Cuban missile crisis, Khrushchev promised to remove Soviet missiles from Cuba in exchange for Kennedy's public promise

A. not to invade Cuba.
B. to remove American missiles from Alaska near the Soviet Union.
C. to remove American missiles from China on the Soviet border.
D. to stop testing nuclear weapons in the atmosphere.

_______ **20.** Reapportionment as required by the Warren Court shifted more political power to

A. African Americans.
B. corporations.
C. poor rural farmers.
D. Southern whites.

DIRECTIONS: Essay Answer the following questions on a separate piece of paper.

> "They have used the pretext of anti-communism. . . . The truth is very different. The truth is to be found in the financial interests of the fruit company and the other US monopolies which have invested great amounts of money in Latin America and fear that the example of Guatemala would be followed by other Latin countries. . . . I was elected by a majority of the people of Guatemala, but I have had to fight under difficult conditions. The truth is that the sovereignty of a people cannot be maintained without the material elements to defend it."
>
> —Jacobo Arbenz's resignation speech, 1954

21. Based on the speech by President Arbenz of Guatemala, draw conclusions about the nature of the United States's involvement in Latin America before Kennedy took office, and the response of Latin Americans to this involvement.

Chapter 15 Test, Form A *cont.*

The New Frontier and the Great Society

> "It is clear that this Nation, in concert with all the free nations of this hemisphere, must take an ever closer and more realistic look at the menace of external Communist intervention and domination in Cuba. The American people are not complacent about Iron Curtain tanks and planes less than 90 miles from their shore. But a nation of Cuba's size is less a threat to our survival than it is a base for subverting the survival of other free nations throughout the hemisphere. It is not primarily our interest or our security but theirs which is now, today, in the greater peril. It is for their sake as well as our own that we must show our will."
>
> —President John F. Kennedy, 1961

22. Based on the excerpt from a speech President Kennedy delivered about the Bay of Pigs invasion, what concerned the United States the most about Cuba?

> "Freedom is indivisible, and when one man is enslaved, all are not free. When all are free, then we look—can look forward to that day when this city will be joined as one and this country and this great Continent of Europe in a peaceful and hopeful globe. When that day finally comes, as it will, the people of West Berlin can take sober satisfaction in the fact that they were in the front lines for almost two decades."
>
> —President John F. Kennedy, 1963

23. Why is the city of Berlin not, in President Kennedy's words, "joined as one"? Explain the role of this barrier and assess what it came to symbolize.

24. The 1960 debate between presidential candidates Richard Nixon and John F. Kennedy was the first televised presidential debate. Assess the role that television played in this historic event.

NAME ______________________ DATE ______________ CLASS __________

Chapter 15 Test, Form B

networks

The New Frontier and the Great Society

DIRECTIONS: Short Answer Answer each of the following questions on a separate piece of paper.

"I believe in an America where the separation of the church and state is absolute—where no Catholic prelate would tell the president (should he be a Catholic) how to act."

—President John F. Kennedy

1. In this quotation, Kennedy reacts to what major issue he had to confront?

"For the first time, thanks to the wonders of television, two presidential candidates were coming right into the nation's living rooms to debate. Americans were enthralled: 'You hear each man directly,' observed one. 'There's nothing between you and what he says,' added another. 'You can see which man gets rattled easily.'
The man who seemed to get rattled easily was Nixon. Kennedy, the Democratic nominee, looked healthy, strong, and confident. Nixon, the Republicans' choice, came across as tired and frazzled. . . . As one observer noted, 'Nixon's eyes darted around, perspiration was clearly noticeable on his chin, and with the tight shots . . . these things were more obvious.'"

—adapted from *The Great Debates*

2. Read the passage above describing the televised 1960 presidential debate. John F. Kennedy seemed to "win" the debate. Why?

"That's one small step for a man, one giant leap for mankind."

—Neil Armstrong, July 20, 1969

3. Prior to Armstrong's statement, what was President Kennedy concerned about during the space race with the Soviet Union?

"The walls of the ghettos are not going to topple overnight, nor is it possible to wipe out the heritage of generations of social, economic and educational deprivation by the stroke of a Presidential pen."

—*New York Times*, January 1, 1967

4. What does the writer say about the pace of reform in the United States?

Chapter 15 Test, Form B *cont.*

networks

The New Frontier and the Great Society

> "Only lunatics . . . who themselves want to perish and before they die destroy the world, could do this."
>
> —Soviet Premier Nikita Khrushchev

5. Explain how Khrushchev's statement relates to the international tension associated with the Cuban missile crisis.

Major Decisions of the Warren Court on Due Process	
Mapp v. *Ohio (1961)*	Ruled that unlawfully seized evidence cannot be used in a trial
Gideon v. *Wainwright (1963)*	Established suspects' right to a court-appointed attorney if suspects were unable to afford one
Escobedo v. *Illinois (1964)*	Affirmed right of the accused to an attorney during police questioning
Miranda v. *Arizona (1966)*	Required police to inform suspects of their rights during the arrest process

6. Summarize the result of the Warren Court's decisions on due process. How do you think this affected the legal system in the United States?

DIRECTIONS: Essay Answer the following question on a separate piece of paper.

7. Describe the legacy of Johnson's Great Society. How successful was it? What are some of its lasting effects?

NAME ______________________ DATE ______________ CLASS ____________

Lesson Quiz 16-1

networks

The Civil Rights Movement

DIRECTIONS: Completion Enter the appropriate word(s) to complete the statement.

1. Although the civil rights movement did not lead to large protests until the 1950s, the ____________________ had supported court cases intended to overturn segregation since its founding in 1909.

2. In 1956 a group of 101 Southern members of Congress signed the "Southern ____________," denouncing the Supreme Court's ruling in *Brown* v. *Board of Education* as a "clear abuse of judicial power."

3. African American leaders formed the Montgomery Improvement Association to run the bus boycott and elected a pastor named Dr. Martin Luther ______________, Jr., to lead the new organization.

4. The ____________________ traveled into the South by bus to test compliance with laws outlawing segregation in interstate bus service.

5. When first established, the Southern Christian Leadership Conference set out to end segregation and encourage African Americans to ______________.

DIRECTIONS: Multiple Choice Indicate the answer choice that best completes the statement or answers the question.

______ **6.** Outraged by Rosa Parks's arrest, Jo Ann Robinson, head of a local organization called the Women's Political Council, called on African Americans to

A. boycott Montgomery's buses.
B. elect new city officials.
C. go on strike.
D. stage a sit-in at the courthouse.

______ **7.** CORE successfully integrated many restaurants by using

A. boycotts.
B. protest marches.
C. sit-ins.
D. threats.

______ **8.** The bus boycott in Montgomery lasted for

A. about a year.
B. exactly six months.
C. less than two weeks.
D. nearly nine weeks.

______ **9.** The Supreme Court's ruling in *Brown* v. *Board of Education* ended racial segregation

A. in private clubs.
B. in public schools.
C. on buses.
D. on trains.

NAME ______________________ DATE ______________ CLASS ____________

Lesson Quiz 16-2

networks

The Civil Rights Movement

DIRECTIONS: True/False Indicate whether the statement is true or false.

_______ **1.** Dr. King delivered the powerful speech outlining his dream of freedom and equality for all Americans at the Lincoln Memorial in Memphis, Tennessee, on August 28, 1963.

_______ **2.** The Civil Rights Act of 1964 authorized the attorney general to send federal examiners to register qualified voters, bypassing local officials who often refused to register African Americans.

_______ **3.** In the spring of 1963, Dr. King decided to launch demonstrations in Birmingham, Alabama, knowing they would probably provoke a violent response, because he believed that was the only way to get President Kennedy to actively support civil rights.

_______ **4.** Dr. King's "Letter from Birmingham Jail" was a defense of nonviolent protest.

_______ **5.** The purpose of the Selma March was to campaign for voting rights in the South.

DIRECTIONS: Multiple Choice Indicate the answer choice that best completes the statement or answers the question.

_______ **6.** Which act did President Johnson sign into law on July 2, 1964?

A. Civil Rights Act of 1964
B. Cloture Act of 1964
C. Interstate Travel Act of 1964
D. Voting Rights Act of 1964

_______ **7.** The passage of which law marked a turning point in the civil rights movement?

A. Discrimination Act of 1964
B. Equal Pay Act of 1963
C. Segregation Act of 1965
D. Voting Rights Act of 1965

_______ **8.** In registering African Americans to vote, the Voting Rights Act of 1965 authorized the attorney general to

A. provide literacy tests to newly registered voters.
B. refuse African Americans the right to vote.
C. send federal examiners to register qualified voters.
D. work side-by-side with local officials.

_______ **9.** The Civil Rights Act of 1964 helped protect civil rights, but it did not

A. end discrimination in employment.
B. end segregation in public places.
C. guarantee protection in the workplace.
D. guarantee the right to vote.

NAME ______________________ DATE ______________ CLASS ______________

Lesson Quiz 16-3

networks

The Civil Rights Movement

DIRECTIONS: Completion Enter the appropriate word(s) to complete the statement.

1. After Malcolm X broke with the ______________ of Islam, he continued to criticize the organization and was eventually killed by some of its members.

2. Despite the passage of several civil rights laws in the 1950s and 1960s, ______________—prejudice or discrimination toward people because of their race—was still common in American society.

3. After his pilgrimage to Makkah, ______________ concluded that an integrated society was possible.

4. The "X" in Malcolm X's name stood as a symbol for the family name of his ______________ ancestors who had been enslaved.

5. In the 1950s and 1960s, ______________ trapped many African Americans in inner cities.

DIRECTIONS: Multiple Choice Indicate the answer choice that best completes the statement or answers the question.

_______ **6.** The Kerner Commission blamed the problems of inner cities on

A. overpopulation.
B. poverty.
C. racism.
D. violence.

_______ **7.** The Chicago Movement was an attempt to call attention to the

A. deplorable housing conditions many African American families faced.
B. efforts being made to improve African American neighborhoods.
C. Kerner Commission's recommendation to create two million inner-city jobs.
D. riot during the Democratic National Convention in 1968.

_______ **8.** When the Supreme Court ordered school districts to end school segregation "with all deliberate speed," the wording was vague enough that many districts were able to

A. appeal the *Brown* v. *Board of Education* ruling.
B. keep their schools segregated for many more years.
C. plan a protest march outside the Supreme Court building.
D. use the "Southern Manifesto" to defy the Supreme Court.

_______ **9.** What group called for an end to racial oppression and for control of major institutions in the African American community?

A. Black Muslims
B. Black Panthers
C. CORE
D. SNCC

NAME ______________ DATE ______________ CLASS ______________

Chapter 16 Test, Form A

networks

The Civil Rights Movement

DIRECTIONS: Matching Match each item with the correct statement below.

______ **1.** leader of SNCC who believed in black power		**A.** Dr. Martin Luther King, Jr.
______ **2.** student who was denied admission to her neighborhood school		**B.** Fannie Lou Hamer
______ **3.** arrested for refusing to give up a seat on a bus to a white man		**C.** Thurgood Marshall
______ **4.** became a symbol of the black power movement		**D.** Robert Moses
______ **5.** minister whose vision and nonviolent methods helped the civil rights movement transform American society		**E.** Malcolm X
______ **6.** helped organize the Mississippi Freedom Democratic Party		**F.** Rosa Parks
______ **7.** urged the NAACP to start helping rural Southern African Americans		**G.** Stokely Carmichael
______ **8.** along with Bobby Seale, organized the Black Panthers		**H.** Huey P. Newton
______ **9.** NAACP's chief counsel		**I.** Linda Brown
______ **10.** executive director of the SCLC		**J.** Ella Baker

DIRECTIONS: Multiple Choice Indicate the answer choice that best completes the statement or answers the question.

______ **11.** The "Southern Manifesto" encouraged white Southerners to

A. defy the Supreme Court.

B. embrace desegregation.

C. march against civil rights.

D. obey local law enforcement.

______ **12.** Members of CORE used ______, a form of protest first used by union workers in the 1930s, to desegregate restaurants.

A. bus boycotts

B. lockouts

C. sit-ins

D. freedom marches

_______ **13.** In Little Rock, Arkansas, the governor tried to prevent African American students from entering a white high school by

A. closing the school.

B. deploying the National Guard.

C. hiring the Ku Klux Klan.

D. redrawing the school district.

_______ **14.** One advantage President Johnson had—that Kennedy did not—in getting the Civil Rights Act of 1964 passed was his

A. ability to convince minorities to vote.

B. close relationships with civil rights leaders.

C. intimate knowledge of how Congress worked.

D. willingness to appoint minorities to his cabinet.

_______ **15.** The ruling in *Plessy* v. *Ferguson* in 1896 established

A. the right of African Americans to vote.

B. the right of all Americans to equal protection under the law.

C. the right of all Americans to peaceful protest.

D. the "separate but equal" doctrine.

_______ **16.** Dr. Martin Luther King, Jr., believed the way to end segregation was through

A. economic self-improvement.

B. nonviolent passive resistance.

C. riots and vandalism.

D. separation from white society.

_______ **17.** The Civil Rights Act of 1957, the first since Reconstruction, was intended to

A. end discrimination in hiring.

B. end lynching.

C. protect the right of African Americans to attend desegregated schools.

D. protect the right of African Americans to vote.

_______ **18.** Robert Kennedy tried to help African Americans register to vote by

A. directing the news media to cover the marches in the South.

B. having the Justice Department file lawsuits throughout the South.

C. proposing a voting rights bill to Congress.

D. sending U.S. Marshals to voting booths in the South.

_______ **19.** In 1967 Thurgood Marshall became the first African American to

A. attend an all-white school.

B. be voted into Congress.

C. earn a law degree.

D. serve on the U.S. Supreme Court.

_______ **20.** Dr. King selected Selma, Alabama, for a protest march because

A. African Americans were a majority of the population.

B. most African American residents were not registered to vote.

C. opposition to school desegregation was particularly intense in Selma.

D. violence against Freedom Riders in Selma had been well documented.

DIRECTIONS: Short Answer Answer each of the following questions on a separate piece of paper.

21. The diagram shows two factors that contributed to the new political power for African Americans. Describe how these two events resulted in this new power.

> "One hundred years of delay have passed since President Lincoln freed the slaves, yet their heirs, their grandsons, are not fully free. . . . And this Nation, for all its hopes and all its boasts, will not be fully free until all its citizens are free. . . . Now the time has come for this Nation to fulfill its promise."
>
> —John F. Kennedy

22. What did Kennedy mean when he said African Americans were "not fully free"?

23. Interpret the statement, "justice too long delayed is justice denied" that Dr. King expressed in his "Letter from Birmingham Jail."

NAME ______________________ DATE ______________ CLASS ____________

"We must use the weapon of love. . . . We must realize that so many people are taught to hate us that they are not totally responsible for their hate."

—Martin Luther King, Jr.

24. What does King mean by the "weapon of love"? What do you think King means when he says "people are taught to hate us"?

"The true miracle of the Constitution . . . was not the birth of the Constitution but its life."

—Thurgood Marshall

25. What does Marshall mean when he refers to the Constitution's life as a "miracle"?

Chapter 16 Test, Form B

networks

The Civil Rights Movement

DIRECTIONS: Short Answer Answer each of the following questions on a separate piece of paper.

"This is the significance of black power as a slogan. For once, black people are going to use the words they want to use—not just the words whites want to hear. . . . The need for psychological equality is the reason why SNCC today believes that blacks must organize in the black community. Only black people can . . . create in the community an aroused and continuing black consciousness. . . . Black people must do things for themselves; they must get . . . money they will control and spend themselves; they must conduct tutorial programs themselves so that black children can identify with black people."

—Stokely Carmichael

1. According to this passage, what was Stokely Carmichael trying to motivate African Americans to do?

2. What does Stokely Carmichael's term "psychological equality" mean?

"Now let us say that we are not advocating violence. . . . The only weapon we have in our hands this evening is the weapon of protest. If we were incarcerated behind the iron curtains of a communistic nation—we couldn't do this. If we were trapped in the dungeon of a totalitarian regime—we couldn't do this. But the great glory of American democracy is the right to protest for right!"

—Martin Luther King, Jr., December 5, 1955

Martin Luther King, Jr., "Address to the Montgomery Improvement Association," December 5, 1955, reprinted in The Papers of Martin Luther King, Jr., vol. 3, ed. Clayborne Carson (Berkeley: University of California Press, 1994), 72. Reprinted by arrangement with The Heirs to the Estate of Martin Luther King Jr., c/o Writers House as agent for the proprietor New York, NY. Copyright 1963 Dr. Martin Luther King Jr.; copyright renewed 1991 Coretta Scott King.

3. In what ways is King's statement patriotic? What is he saying about the United States?

"I draw a line in the dust . . . and I say, Segregation now! Segregation tomorrow! Segregation forever!"

—Alabama governor George Wallace

4. In what context were these words stated by Governor Wallace?

networks

Chapter 16 Test, Form B *cont.*

The Civil Rights Movement

Supreme Court Decisions on Civil Rights	
Plessy v. *Ferguson* (1896)	"Separate but equal" doctrine: Segregation was permitted as long as equal facilities were provided for African Americans.
Norris v. *Alabama* (1935)	African Americans should not be excluded from serving on juries.
Morgan v. *Virginia* (1946)	Segregation on interstate buses was unconstitutional.
Sweatt v. *Painter* (1950)	State law schools had to admit qualified African American candidates.
Brown v. *Board of Education* (1954)	Segregation in public schools was unconstitutional and violated the equal protection clause of the Fourteenth Amendment.

5. Compare how two of the Supreme Court decisions in the chart above influence our legal system today.

6. Explain how two Supreme Court rulings almost 60 years apart completely contradict each other, according to the chart above.

DIRECTIONS: Essay Answer the following question on a separate piece of paper.

7. Describe three meanings that the term "black power" held for African Americans during the 1960s.

NAME ______________________ DATE ____________ CLASS ____________

Lesson Quiz 17-1

networks

The Vietnam War

DIRECTIONS: Completion Enter the appropriate word(s) to complete the statement.

1. The ______________ was the belief that if Vietnam fell to communism, so too would the other nations of Southeast Asia.

2. On August 2, 1964, President Johnson announced that North Vietnamese torpedo boats had fired on two American destroyers in the Gulf of ______________.

3. President Johnson feared that directly attacking North Vietnam would bring ______________ into the war.

4. On May 7, 1954, French forces fell to the Vietminh at ______________.

5. North Vietnam sent arms and supplies south by way of a network of jungle paths known as the ______________.

DIRECTIONS: Multiple Choice Indicate the answer choice that best completes the statement or answers the question.

_______ **6.** American officials did not think France should control Vietnam, but they did not want Vietnam to be

A. Communist.
B. part of China.
C. part of Indonesia.
D. Socialist.

_______ **7.** What two events convinced Truman to help France in Vietnam?

A. Japan's surrender in World War II and the fall of China to communism
B. the establishment of a Communist government in Vietnam and the fall of China
C. the establishment of a Communist government in Vietnam and the Korean War
D. the fall of China to communism and the outbreak of the Korean War

_______ **8.** When the French left Vietnam, the United States stepped in to

A. act as peacekeeper along the border between North Vietnam and South Vietnam.
B. make sure free elections were held, as specified by the Geneva Accords.
C. protect the pro-Western government in South Vietnam.
D. try to cause a popular uprising against Ho Chi Minh.

_______ **9.** As the fighting began between the Vietcong and South Vietnamese army, President Eisenhower tried to help South Vietnam by

A. dropping napalm.
B. providing American troops.
C. sending food.
D. sending military advisers.

NAME ______________________ DATE ______________ CLASS ________

Lesson Quiz 17-2

networks

The Vietnam War

DIRECTIONS: True/False Indicate whether the statement is true or false.

_____ **1.** In 1968 the American people were shocked that an enemy supposedly on the verge of defeat—the Vietcong and the North Vietnamese—could launch such a large-scale attack as the Tet Offensive.

_____ **2.** In the election of 1968, Richard Nixon promised to unify the nation and restore Ho Chi Minh as the leader of a united Vietnam.

_____ **3.** A season of violence and protests began after President Johnson announced that he would not run for reelection.

_____ **4.** As the war escalated, the draft call increased, putting college students at risk of being drafted.

_____ **5.** By 1968 the nation seemed to be divided into two camps: the "doves," who wanted to withdraw from Vietnam, and the "hawks," who wanted to stay and fight.

DIRECTIONS: Multiple Choice Indicate the answer choice that best completes the statement or answers the question.

_____ **6.** Which year saw a shocking political announcement, a pair of traumatic assassinations, and finally, a violent political convention in Chicago?

A. 1966
B. 1967
C. 1968
D. 1969

_____ **7.** Who appeared to be on his way to winning the Democratic nomination until he was gunned down by an Arab nationalist?

A. Dr. Martin Luther King, Jr.
B. George Wallace
C. Hubert Humphrey
D. Robert Kennedy

_____ **8.** Nightly news coverage of the Vietnam War on television helped

A. create a credibility gap.
B. raise Johnson's ratings in the polls.
C. support the nation's "hawks."
D. unify Americans behind the war.

_____ **9.** Many college faculty and students against the Vietnam War abandoned their classes and gathered informally to discuss the issues in a new form of protest called a

A. political rally.
B. show trial.
C. sit-in.
D. teach-in.

NAME ______________________ DATE ______________ CLASS ____________

Lesson Quiz 17-3

networks

The Vietnam War

DIRECTIONS: Completion Enter the appropriate word(s) to complete the statement.

1. American cynicism grew with the Vietnam War and the ________________ scandal, making Americans more wary of their leaders.

2. Henry ________________ entered into secret negotiations with North Vietnam's negotiator Le Duc Tho.

3. The invasion of ________________ under President Nixon sparked protests because many Americans viewed it as a widening of the war.

4. Henry Kissinger tried to improve relations with the Soviet Union and China so he could persuade them to cut back on their aid to North Vietnam in a policy called ________________.

DIRECTIONS: Multiple Choice Indicate the answer choice that best completes the statement or answers the question.

______ **5.** Long after troops were home, the war lingered on for the American families whose relatives and friends were classified as missing in action or

A. absent without leave.
B. defectors.
C. draft dodgers.
D. prisoners of war.

______ **6.** What event happened at My Lai that profoundly shocked Americans?

A. American troops invaded Cambodia to destroy Vietcong military bases.
B. Defense Department documents revealed that officials had lied about war decisions.
C. Ohio National Guard soldiers fired on antiwar demonstrators.
D. Unarmed Vietnamese civilians were massacred by U.S. troops.

______ **7.** The Pentagon Papers revealed that

A. American prisoners of war were being tortured in North Vietnamese prisons.
B. American soldiers had massacred Vietnamese civilians at My Lai.
C. many more Americans had died in Vietnam than had been reported.
D. the government had not been honest with the public about Vietnam.

______ **8.** Nixon's Vietnamization plan called for

A. a massive invasion of North Vietnam to finally end the war.
B. a simultaneous withdrawal of troops by North Vietnam and the United States.
C. a withdrawal of American troops from North Vietnam.
D. South Vietnam to assume more of the fighting as American troops withdrew.

NAME ______________________ DATE ____________ CLASS ____________

Chapter 17 Test, Form A

networks

The Vietnam War

DIRECTIONS: Matching Match each item with the correct statement below.

______	**1.** Nixon's special assistant for national security affairs	**A.**	Le Duc Tho
______	**2.** Democratic candidate who was assassinated by an Arab nationalist	**B.**	Dr. Martin Luther King, Jr.
______	**3.** criticized America's involvement in the Vietnam War and the disproportionate number of African American deaths	**C.**	Daniel Ellsberg
______	**4.** won the 1968 presidential election on a campaign to unify the nation and restore law and order	**D.**	Ho Chi Minh
______	**5.** American commander in South Vietnam	**E.**	Richard Nixon
______	**6.** outspoken segregationist who ran as an independent candidate in the 1968 election	**F.**	Robert Kennedy
______	**7.** peace negotiator for the North Vietnamese	**G.**	Ngo Dinh Diem
______	**8.** Communist leader who organized a guerrilla army to fight to reunify Vietnam	**H.**	George Wallace
______	**9.** former Defense Department worker who leaked the Pentagon Papers to the *New York Times*	**I.**	William Westmoreland
______	**10.** pro-Western leader of South Vietnam early in the war who was overthrown in a coup and executed	**J.**	Henry Kissinger

DIRECTIONS: Multiple Choice Indicate the answer choice that best completes the statement or answers the question.

______ **11.** The Vietminh formed initially in Vietnam to

A. create a Communist government.
B. create a pro-Western government.
C. win independence from France.
D. win independence from Japan.

Chapter 17 Test, Form A *cont.*

networks

The Vietnam War

_______ **12.** The Vietcong's power continued to increase in part because of

A. the strong belief in communism.
B. the use of terror by South Vietnam.
C. the Vietnamese opposition to Diem's government.
D. the Vietnamese distrust of the U.S.

_______ **13.** With the Gulf of Tonkin Resolution, Congress, in effect,

A. committed to a limited war only.
B. declared war on North Vietnam.
C. handed its war powers to the president.
D. increased aid to South Vietnam.

_______ **14.** The purpose of Agent Orange was to

A. cut Vietcong supply lines.
B. destroy the Vietcong's ability to hide in jungles.
C. infiltrate the Vietcong military.
D. sabotage Vietcong equipment.

_______ **15.** A main reason President Johnson refused to order a full-scale invasion of North Vietnam was his fear that it would

A. bring China into the war.
B. horrify the American public, ruining him politically.
C. result in the loss of American lives.
D. strengthen the North Vietnamese will to fight.

_______ **16.** In South Vietnam, a monk set himself on fire to protest

A. discrimination against Buddhists.
B. extreme religious ceremonies.
C. the Vietnam War.
D. Western influences in his country.

_______ **17.** The Vietcong used ______________—troops who blended in with the civilian population and used tactics such as ambushes and booby traps.

A. guerrillas
B. the domino theory
C. hawks
D. untrained fighters

_______ **18.** The ____________ called for elections to unite North Vietnam and South Vietnam under a single government.

A. Camp David Accords
B. Geneva Accords
C. Pentagon Papers
D. War Powers Act

_______ **19.** Why was Diem's South Vietnamese government so unpopular?

A. Diem dismantled the strategic hamlets, thus uprooting the peasant population.
B. Diem refused to introduce even limited democratic reforms to help the peasants.
C. Diem discriminated against his country's Buddhist population.
D. Diem was a nationalist, but was not a very capable administrator.

_______ **20.** Who overthrew the Diem government in 1963?

A. a group of Buddhist monks
B. a group of Vietnamese generals
C. the U.S. government
D. the Vietcong

DIRECTIONS: Short Answer Answer each of the following questions on a separate piece of paper.

21. Explain the outcome and significance of the Tet Offensive.

> "We began singing freedom songs and chanting, 'Resist! Resist!' and 'Burn Draft Cards, Not People.'. . . People in the audience were applauding us, shouting encouragement. Then some guys began to come out of the audience with draft cards in hand. They burned them. Alone, in pairs, by threes they came. Each flaming draft card brought renewed cheering and more people out of the crowd. . . . Some of the draft card burners were girls, wives, or girlfriends of male card burners. . . . It lasted this way for about half an hour."
>
> —Martin Jezer, quoted in *The Vietnam War: Opposing Viewpoints*

22. What was the significance of draft cards? Why did the speaker in this passage and his friends want to burn their draft cards?

NAME ______________________ DATE ______________ CLASS ____________

Chapter 17 Test, Form B

networks

The Vietnam War

DIRECTIONS: Short Answer Answer each of the following questions on a separate piece of paper.

> "[T]he conflict in Vietnam is a product of the great shifts and changes triggered by the Second World War. Out of the war, two continent-wide powers emerged—the United States and the Soviet Union. The colonial systems through which the nations of Western Europe had governed more than a third of the people of the world were, one by one, dismantled. . . .
>
> "The bloody encounters in [Vietnam] are thus in a real sense battles and skirmishes in a continuing war to prevent one Communist power after another from violating internationally recognized boundary lines fixing the outer limits of Communist dominion. . . .
>
> "In the long run our hopes for the people of South Vietnam reflect our hopes for people everywhere. What we seek is a world living in peace and freedom."
>
> —Undersecretary of State George W. Ball, 1966

1. Explain the main idea of Ball's speech.

2. In this passage, who does Ball hold directly responsible for Vietnam's bloody conflicts, and why?

> "I have concluded that I should not permit the presidency to become involved in the partisan divisions that are developing in this political year. Accordingly, I shall not seek, and I will not accept, the nomination of my party for another term as your President."
>
> —President Lyndon B. Johnson, March 31, 1968

3. Briefly explain this announcement Johnson made in 1968.

> ". . . Our motives are widely misinterpreted; and the spectacle of Americans inflicting grievous injury on the lives of a poor and helpless people . . . produces reactions among millions of people throughout the world profoundly detrimental to the image we would like them to hold of this country."
>
> —George F. Kennan's Statement to Senator; Senate Foreign Relations Committee Hearing on Vietnam; February 10, 1966; George F. Kennan Papers, Public Policy Papers, Department of Rare Books and Special Collections, Princeton University Library.

4. In what ways does Kennan's statement above reflect the views of the American public on U.S. involvement in the war in Vietnam?

> "You have a row of dominoes set up, you knock over the first one, and what will happen to the last one is the certainty that it will go over very quickly. . . . Asia, after all, has already lost 450 million of its peoples to the Communist dictatorship, and we simply can't afford greater losses."
>
> —President Dwight Eisenhower

5. According to this quote from President Eisenhower, what was the main reason the United States waged war in Vietnam?

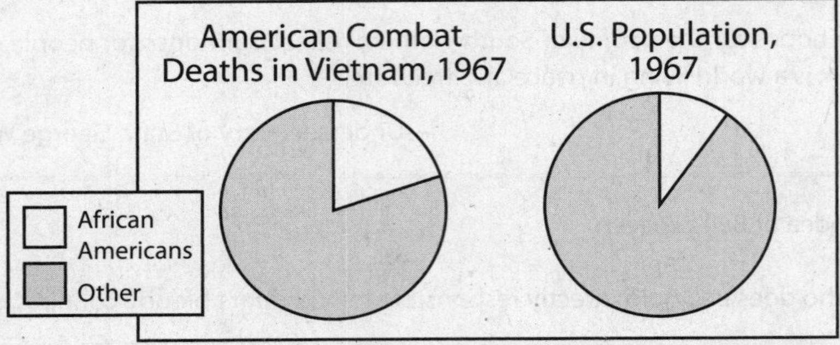

6. What do the circle graphs show about the role of African Americans in the Vietnam War?

Vietnam War's Impact on the United States
Passage of the War Powers Act: required the president to inform Congress of any commitment of troops within 48 hours and to withdraw them within 60 to 90 days unless Congress approved the troop commitment
Increased American cynicism about their government, as many felt they had been misled about the war
Shook the nation's confidence and morale
Led to a spirit of isolationism amongst Americans

7. According to the chart, what did the War Powers Act attempt to resolve?

DIRECTIONS: Essay Answer the following question on a separate piece of paper.

8. Describe the cost of the Vietnam War in military and human terms and the overall impact of the war on the nation.

NAME ______________________ DATE ______________ CLASS ____________

networks

Lesson Quiz 18-1

The Politics of Protest

DIRECTIONS: Completion Enter the appropriate word(s) to complete the statement.

1. Students for a Democratic Society was a prominent organization within what came to be known as the ________________ Left.

2. Tom Hayden was the principal author of the ________________ Statement.

3. In the 1960s young people of the counterculture were commonly called ________________.

4. Originally, the counterculture held up a(n) ________________ ideal of a society that was free, close to nature, and full of love, tolerance, and cooperation.

5. Some members of the counterculture lived together in ________________, group living arrangements in which members shared everything and worked together.

DIRECTIONS: Multiple Choice Indicate the answer choice that best completes the statement or answers the question.

________ **6.** The 1960s youth movement originated with which of the following phenomena?

A. the baby boom
B. the student protest movement
C. the "beat" movement
D. the prosperity of the 1950s

________ **7.** Students for a Democratic Society (SDS) focused most of its energy on

A. protesting the Vietnam War.
B. fighting segregation.
C. questioning American priorities.
D. arguing for free speech.

________ **8.** After a campus-wide strike at the University of California at Berkeley, the Supreme Court upheld the students' rights to

A. desegregated classes and dormitories.
B. protest against university rules.
C. freedom of speech and assembly on campus.
D. be taught by professors rather than graduate students.

________ **9.** Popular folk singers of the 1960s included Joan Baez, Pete Seeger, and especially

A. Jimi Hendrix.
B. Mario Savio.
C. Janis Joplin.
D. Bob Dylan.

NAME ______________________ DATE ______________ CLASS ____________

Lesson Quiz 18-2

networks

The Politics of Protest

DIRECTIONS: True/False Indicate whether the statement is true or false.

_______ **1.** Almost one-third of married women in the United States were part of the paid labor force by 1960.

_______ **2.** After the book *The Feminine Mystique* was published in 1963, many women began reaching out to one another, pouring out their anger and sadness in what came to be known as consciousness-raising sessions.

_______ **3.** The Supreme Court decision in *Roe* v. *Wade* prohibited federally funded schools from discriminating against girls and young women in nearly all aspects of their operations.

_______ **4.** After a decade of debate against increasing significant opposition, the Equal Rights Amendment finally became part of the Constitution in 1982.

DIRECTIONS: Multiple Choice Indicate the answer choice that best completes the statement or answers the question.

_______ **5.** Nearly half of American women were in the workforce in the 1960s, but most worked

A. in high-paying professions.
B. in lower-paying jobs.
C. as doctors and lawyers.
D. in political office.

_______ **6.** For her book *The Feminine Mystique*, Betty Friedan interviewed Smith College graduates and found that most of the women

A. made far less money than men did in comparable jobs.
B. preferred to stay at home and focus on raising families.
C. wanted to work outside the home but could not find satisfying jobs.
D. reported having everything they could want but feeling unfulfilled.

_______ **7.** Which of the following outlawed job discrimination by private employers not only on the basis of race, color, religion, and national origin, but also on the basis of gender?

A. the Equal Rights Amendment
B. Title VII of the 1964 Civil Rights Act
C. the Equal Employment Opportunity Act
D. the Educational Amendments

_______ **8.** In 1966 Betty Friedan and others founded ____________, a new organization that reflected the diverse goals of the modern feminist movement.

A. Women for a Democratic Society
B. the National Women's Party
C. the National Organization for Women
D. the Equal Rights Organization

NAME ______________________ DATE ____________ CLASS ____________

Lesson Quiz 18-3

networks

The Politics of Protest

DIRECTIONS: Matching Match each item with the correct statement below.

_______ **1.** case that successfully challenged school segregation in California

_______ **2.** early anti-discrimination organization

_______ **3.** organization founded to protect the rights of Mexican American military veterans

_______ **4.** ended the exclusion of Mexican Americans from juries in Texas

_______ **5.** founded by Mexican American college students in 1967 in San Antonio, Texas

A. American GI Forum

B. *Hernandez* v. *Texas*

C. League of United Latin American Citizens

D. Mexican American Youth Organization

E. *Mendez* v. *Westminster*

DIRECTIONS: Multiple Choice Indicate the answer choice that best completes the statement or answers the question.

_______ **6.** The wave of emigration from Mexico to the United States that began in 1910 was caused by which of the following?

A. federal repatriation programs
B. the Mexican Revolution
C. the Great Depression
D. the Bracero Program

_______ **7.** The segregated sections of many Southwestern cities in which most Mexican Americans lived were called

A. braceros.
B. Mexican schools.
C. Spanish towns.
D. barrios.

_______ **8.** More than 350,000 Cubans settled in the United States after

A. the 1960s grape boycott.
B. they became citizens in 1917.
C. the 1959 Cuban Revolution.
D. deportation raids in the 1950s.

_______ **9.** César Chávez organized a national boycott of table grapes to demand increased wages for farm workers, better benefits, and

A. job-training programs.
B. an end to discrimination.
C. union recognition.
D. bilingual education.

_______ **10.** Founded in 1969, *La Raza Unida* was a Mexican American

A. political party.
B. immigrant aid organization.
C. protest movement.
D. farmworkers union.

NAME ______________________ DATE ______________ CLASS ____________

Chapter 18 Test, Form A

networks

The Politics of Protest

DIRECTIONS: Matching Match each item with the correct statement below.

______ **1.** author of *The Feminine Mystique* and a founder of the National Organization for Women	**A.** César Chávez
______ **2.** student at the University of California at Berkeley and a leader of the free speech movement	**B.** Phyllis Schlafly
______ **3.** organized a group that fought for the rights of farmworkers, which eventually merged with a group created by César Chávez	**C.** Gloria Steinem
______ **4.** leader in the Mexican American Youth Organization and *La Raza Unida*	**D.** Tom Hayden
______ **5.** outspoken opponent of the Equal Rights Amendment	**E.** Mario Savio
______ **6.** high school student who was banned from competing for her school's swim team	**F.** Betty Friedan
______ **7.** editor of *Ms.* and a leading figure in the women's movement	**G.** Bob Dylan
______ **8.** main author of the Port Huron Statement	**H.** Dolores Huerta
______ **9.** folk singer who was an important voice in the counterculture	**I.** Kathy Striebel
______ **10.** United Farm Workers leader who held a hunger strike in 1968 to support farmworkers	**J.** José Angel Gutiérrez

DIRECTIONS: Multiple Choice Indicate the answer choice that best completes the statement or answers the question.

______ **11.** Issued in 1962, the Port Huron Statement expressed the views of the

A. United Farm Workers.
B. free speech movement.
C. National Organization for Women.
D. Students for a Democratic Society.

______ **12.** Students involved in the free speech movement at the University of California at Berkeley demonstrated by

A. holding college administrators as hostages.
B. rioting on campus grounds.
C. organizing large music festivals.
D. holding sit-ins and stopping classes.

Chapter 18 Test, Form A *cont.*

The Politics of Protest

_______ **13.** Although the counterculture of the 1960s did not achieve its utopian ideals, it had a lasting influence on

A. fashion and music in the United States.

B. practices and rules at large universities.

C. living arrangements in the United States.

D. middle-class, white-collar values.

_______ **14.** Which of the following developments helped revitalize the women's movement in the early 1960s?

A. adoption of the woman suffrage amendment

B. the postwar baby boom of the 1950s

C. creation of the President's Commission on the Status of Women

D. the debate over the ratification of the Equal Rights Amendment

_______ **15.** The Equal Pay Act of 1963 outlawed

A. hiring discrimination on the basis of gender.

B. paying farmworkers less than the minimum wage.

C. the exclusion of Mexican Americans from some professions.

D. paying men more than women for the same job.

_______ **16.** The Equal Rights Amendment failed to become part of the Constitution because

A. not enough states ratified the amendment by the deadline.

B. Congress did not pass the amendment.

C. the American public voted against ratification.

D. opposition by conservative groups blocked passage.

_______ **17.** For much of the twentieth century, ethnic Mexicans in California and the U.S. Southwest were segregated into barrios and also faced

A. laws banning bilingualism.

B. employment discrimination.

C. expanding opportunities.

D. illegal immigration.

_______ **18.** Beginning in the 1950s, large numbers of Puerto Ricans and immigrants from _______________ arrived in the United States.

A. Venezuela

B. Panama

C. Spain

D. Cuba

Chapter 18 Test, Form A *cont.*

networks

The Politics of Protest

_______ **19.** To push for better wages and working conditions for farmworkers, César Chávez organized a successful

A. march on Washington.

B. sit-down strike.

C. advertising and publicity campaign.

D. national boycott on grapes.

_______ **20.** Latino organizations formed in the 1960s included the United Farm Workers, the Mexican American Youth Organization, and

A. the Bracero program.

B. the League of United Latin American Citizens.

C. *La Raza Unida*.

D. Students for a Democratic Society.

DIRECTIONS: Essay Answer the following questions on a separate piece of paper.

"Come mothers and fathers
Throughout the land
And don't criticize
What you can't understand
Your sons and your daughters
Are beyond your command
Your old road is
Rapidly agin'.
Please get out of the new one
If you can't lend your hand
For the times they are a-changin'."

—Bob Dylan, from "*The Times They Are A-Changin'*"
The Times they Are a-Changin', by Bob Dylan.
Copyright © 1963; renewed 1996 Special Rider Music.

21. Explain how music and fashion expressed the ideals of the 1960s counterculture and describe their effect on mainstream American culture. How do the lyrics above reflect the changing values of the time?

Chapter 18 Test, Form A *cont.*

The Politics of Protest

"The truth is that all our problems stem from the same sex-based myths. We may appear before you as white radicals or the middle-aged middle class or black soul sisters, but we are all sisters in fighting against these outdated myths. Like racial myths, they have been reflected in our laws."

—Gloria Steinem, address in support of the ERA, May 1970

"This Amendment will absolutely and positively make women subject to the draft. . . . Foxholes are bad enough for men, but they certainly are *not* the place for women—and we should reject any proposal that would put them there in the name of 'equal rights.'"

—Phyllis Schlafly, from the *Phyllis Schlafly Report*, February 1972

22. Describe the arguments for and against passage of the Equal Rights Amendment, including the arguments expressed in the excerpts above.

23. Describe the conditions that led Latino Americans to organize a civil rights movement in the postwar period and identify key campaigns to improve conditions for Latino Americans.

NAME ______________________ DATE ______________ CLASS ____________

Chapter 18 Test, Form B

networks

The Politics of Protest

DIRECTIONS: Short Answer Answer each of the following questions on a separate piece of paper.

> "There's a time when the operation of the machine becomes so odious, makes you so sick at heart, that you . . . can't even tacitly take part. And you've got to put your bodies upon the gears and upon the wheels . . . you've got to make it stop. And you've got to indicate to the people who run it, to the people who own it, that unless you're free the machine will be prevented from working at all."
>
> —Mario Savio, University of California at Berkeley student and free speech movement leader

1. In the excerpt above, what does Mario Savio use the analogy of a "machine" to describe?

2. Describe the strategies used by members of the free speech movement to challenge the status quo that Savio criticizes in the excerpt.

Important Women's Rights Milestones		
Equal Pay Act	1963	Outlawed paying men more than women for the same job, in most cases
Title VII of the Civil Rights Act of 1964	1964	Outlawed job discrimination not only on the basis of race, color, religion, and national origin, but also on the basis of gender
Title IX of the Educational Amendments	1972	Prohibited federally funded schools from discriminating against women in admissions, athletics, and other areas

3. In what areas did the legislation listed in the chart above expand and protect women's rights in the United States?

4. Based on your reading, was the legislation listed in the chart above effective in ending gender discrimination?

Chapter 18 Test, Form B *cont.*

The Politics of Protest

Civil Rights for Latinos	
United Farm Workers	***La Raza Unida***
Fought for: • Increased wages • Better benefits • Union recognition	• Mobilized Mexican American voters • Called for job-training programs • Promoted greater access to financial institutions

5. Describe the goals of the United Farm Workers and *La Raza Unida,* as illustrated in the chart.

6. Based on the information in the chart, in what ways were the United Farm Workers and *La Raza Unida* different?

DIRECTIONS: Essay Answer the following question on a separate piece of paper.

7. Describe the similarities among and differences between the social movements that began in the 1960s. In what ways did these movements shape American society and political culture?

NAME ______________________ DATE ______________ CLASS __________

Lesson Quiz 19-1

networks

Politics and Economics

DIRECTIONS: Completion Enter the appropriate word(s) to complete the statement.

1. ________________ bills, an important element of President Nixon's New Federalism, granted federal funds to state and local agencies.

2. President Nixon's policy of turning the responsibility for South Vietnam's defense over to the South Vietnamese military was known as ________________.

3. President Nixon's policy of ________________ profoundly eased tensions between the Soviet Union and the United States.

4. In May 1972, President Nixon and the Soviets signed the first ________________ Treaty, also known as SALT I, a plan to limit nuclear arms.

DIRECTIONS: Multiple Choice Indicate the answer choice that best completes the statement or answers the question.

________ **5.** In 1969 President Richard Nixon announced that the United States would now expect its allies to take care of their own defense, a policy known as

A. détente.
B. the Nixon Doctrine.
C. Vietnamization.
D. the New Federalism.

________ **6.** President Nixon dismantled a number of federal programs and gave more control to state and local governments, a policy he called

A. the New Federalism.
B. détente.
C. States' Rights.
D. the Nixon Doctrine.

________ **7.** Which of the following was one purpose of President Nixon's trip to China?

A. confronting the Chinese government about its human rights violations
B. negotiating an arms limitation treaty with the Chinese government
C. encouraging the Soviets to pursue diplomacy more actively
D. negotiating an alliance with China against the Soviet Union

________ **8.** Shortly after the public learned of U.S. negotiations with China, the Soviet Union proposed an American-Soviet high-level diplomatic meeting, or

A. détente.
B. revenue sharing.
C. summit.
D. limitation treaty.

________ **9.** President Nixon once expressed the hope that a "competent cabinet" of advisers could run the country, which would allow him to focus his energies on

A. writing his memoirs.
B. negotiating treaties.
C. empowering the states.
D. foreign affairs.

NAME ______________________ DATE ____________ CLASS ____________

Lesson Quiz 19-2

networks

Politics and Economics

DIRECTIONS: Matching Match each item with the correct statement below.

_____ **1.** after Watergate, could be appointed to investigate and prosecute wrongdoing by high government officials

_____ **2.** member of President Nixon's inner circle who leveled accusations against the president

_____ **3.** limited campaign contributions and established an independent agency to administer stricter election laws

_____ **4.** took Nixon to court to make him give up the Watergate tapes and was eventually fired at the president's request

_____ **5.** President Nixon's Democratic opponent in the 1972 presidential election

A. John Dean

B. Federal Campaign Act Amendments

C. George McGovern

D. independent counsel

E. Archibald Cox

DIRECTIONS: Multiple Choice Indicate the answer choice that best completes the statement or answers the question.

_____ **6.** In June 1973, John Dean testified that the Watergate break-in had been ordered by

A. former Attorney General John Mitchell.

B. President Nixon.

C. Alexander Butterfield.

D. Vice President Spiro Agnew.

_____ **7.** President Nixon argued that recordings of White House conversations should remain confidential to protect national security, a principle known as

A. self-incrimination. **C.** cover-up.

B. independent counsel. **D.** executive privilege.

_____ **8.** Vice President Spiro Agnew was forced to resign in disgrace when investigators discovered that he had

A. destroyed evidence. **C.** spied on the Democrats.

B. accepted bribes. **D.** lied to Congress.

_____ **9.** The House Judiciary Committee voted to impeach President Nixon, or

A. force him to resign.

B. send him to prison.

C. charge him with misconduct.

D. investigate his actions.

NAME ______________________ DATE ____________ CLASS ____________

Lesson Quiz 19-3

networks

Politics and Economics

DIRECTIONS: Matching Match each item with the correct statement below.

_____ **1.** combination of rising prices and economic stagnation

_____ **2.** historic peace treaty between Israel and Egypt, brokered by President Carter

_____ **3.** name for Iran's monarch

_____ **4.** rise in the cost of goods

_____ **5.** Iranian monarch supported by the United States

A. shah

B. inflation

C. Camp David Accords

D. stagflation

E. Ayatollah Khomeini

DIRECTIONS: Multiple Choice Indicate the answer choice that best completes the statement or answers the question.

_____ **6.** American manufacturing was in decline by the 1970s, in large part because

A. taxes on U.S. industries were prohibitively high.

B. prices on imported oil began to rise dramatically.

C. U.S. manufacturing plants were old and inefficient.

D. the manufacturing industry had been deregulated.

_____ **7.** In 1973 the Organization of Petroleum Exporting Countries announced that its members would impose a(n) ________________ of petroleum to countries that supported Israel.

A. inflation　　**C.** embargo

B. deregulation　　**D.** restriction

_____ **8.** In August 1975, President Gerald Ford met with leaders of NATO and the Warsaw Pact to sign the

A. Helsinki Accords.　　**C.** WIN plan.

B. Camp David Accords.　　**D.** Nixon pardon.

_____ **9.** President Jimmy Carter felt that the most serious problem related to the U.S. economy was the nation's dependence on

A. coal.　　**C.** the federal government.

B. foreign oil.　　**D.** the defense industry.

_____ **10.** After inflation surged in 1978, President Carter responded by reducing the money supply and

A. cutting taxes.

B. increasing government spending.

C. increasing taxes.

D. raising interest rates.

NAME ______________________ DATE ____________ CLASS ____________

Lesson Quiz 19-4 networks

Politics and Economics

DIRECTIONS: Completion Enter the appropriate word(s) to complete the statement.

1. Critics of the affirmative action programs that emerged in the 1970s viewed them as a form of "______________ discrimination."

2. Unlike other groups demanding more assimilation into mainstream society, many ______________ wanted greater independence from it.

3. The disability rights movement began with the ______________ living movement at the University of California at Berkeley.

4. The ______________ Act of 1973 prohibited discrimination against people with disabilities by any federally funded program.

DIRECTIONS: Multiple Choice Indicate the answer choice that best completes the statement or answers the question.

______ **5.** In the 1970s, civil rights leaders began to focus on securing for African Americans access to good jobs and

A. integrated neighborhoods.
B. adequate schools.
C. voting rights.
D. suburban homes.

______ **6.** Although the Supreme Court had ordered an end to segregated public schools in 1954, many schools remained segregated in the early 1970s because

A. neighborhoods were still segregated and children went to neighborhood schools.
B. many school districts ignored the *Brown* v. *Board of Education* decision.
C. most African American children attended private schools rather than public schools.
D. Congress passed laws supporting the separation of races in public schools.

______ **7.** In its 1978 *University of California Regents* v. *Bakke* decision, the Supreme Court ruled that

A. universities could not use "fixed quotas" to maintain a diverse student body.
B. the University of California had to admit Bakke to its medical program.
C. universities could not use race as part of their admissions criteria.
D. the University of California had not violated Bakke's civil rights.

______ **8.** The Indian Civil Rights Act of 1968 recognized the legitimacy of local reservation law and guaranteed reservation residents the protections of

A. affirmative action.
B. the Bureau of Indian Affairs.
C. the Bill of Rights.
D. the National Guard.

NAME ______________________ DATE ____________ CLASS ____________

Lesson Quiz 19-5

networks

Politics and Economics

DIRECTIONS: True/False Indicate whether the statement is true or false.

_______ **1.** During the 1960s and 1970s, a growing number of Americans began to examine how their highly industrialized society was affecting the environment, and many were alarmed at what they discovered.

_______ **2.** Citizen involvement in local environmental groups and long-standing organizations such as the Sierra Club, the Audubon Society, and the Wilderness Society declined after the first Earth Day.

_______ **3.** In 1970 Congress passed and President Richard Nixon signed a new antipollution law that created the Environmental Protection Agency.

_______ **4.** Opponents of nuclear energy warned of the risks it posed, in particular the potentially devastating consequences of an accidental release of radiation into the air.

DIRECTIONS: Multiple Choice Indicate the answer choice that best completes the statement or answers the question.

_______ **5.** Rachel Carson's *Silent Spring*, one of the most controversial and influential books of the 1960s, assailed the increasing use of

A. pesticides.
B. fossil fuels.
C. nuclear energy.
D. toxic wastes.

_______ **6.** The Environmental Defense Fund was established by a group of scientists to finance a series of legal actions in the late 1960s and early 1970s to halt

A. automobile safety violations.
B. DDT spraying.
C. the Environmental Protection Agency.
D. nuclear power.

_______ **7.** Many observers point to April 1970 and the celebration of _______________ as the beginning of the environmental movement.

A. the banning of DDT
B. Earth Day
C. Love Canal
D. the Endangered Species Act

_______ **8.** Which of the following established emissions standards for factories and automobiles?

A. National Traffic and Motor Vehicles Act
B. Environmental Protection Act
C. Clean Air Act
D. Clean Water Act

NAME ______________________ DATE ______________ CLASS ___________

Chapter 19 Test, Form A

networks

Politics and Economics

DIRECTIONS: Matching Match each item with the correct statement below.

______ **1.** first African American woman to serve in Congress	**A.** Love Canal
______ **2.** author who sounded the alarm on the effect of pesticides on birds, fish, and other creatures	**B.** Camp David Accords
______ **3.** civil rights leader who founded Operation PUSH (People United to Save Humanity)	**C.** Bob Woodward
______ **4.** historic peace treaty between Israel and Egypt, brokered by President Carter	**D.** Wounded Knee
______ **5.** stated that no person with a disability can be discriminated against by an entity receiving federal funding	**E.** Shirley Chisholm
______ **6.** cartel that placed an embargo on petroleum to the United States	**F.** OPEC
______ **7.** special prosecutor who took Nixon to court to give up the Watergate tapes and was eventually fired by Nixon's order	**G.** Rachel Carson
______ **8.** seized and occupied for 70 days by Native American activists	**H.** Jesse Jackson
______ **9.** housing development in New York state evacuated because of toxic waste	**I.** Rehabilitation Act of 1973
______ **10.** *Washington Post* reporter who helped break the Watergate story	**J.** Archibald Cox

DIRECTIONS: Multiple Choice Indicate the answer choice that best completes the statement or answers the question.

______ **11.** President Richard Nixon and his national security adviser, Henry Kissinger, both believed that ______________ would lead to establishing positive relations with the United States's Cold War enemies.

A. increased manufacture of strategic arms

B. prosecuting militant antiwar protesters

C. negotiation with Communists

D. abandoning the war in Vietnam

Chapter 19 Test, Form A *cont.*

networks

Politics and Economics

_______ **12.** Détente began when President Nixon

A. set out to improve relations with China's communist government.

B. attended an American-Soviet summit.

C. signed the first Strategic Arms Limitation Treaty.

D. announced his policy of New Federalism.

_______ **13.** The House Judiciary Committee voted to impeach President Nixon in the summer of 1974, just days after the president

A. blocked release of the Watergate tapes.

B. turned over the Watergate tapes.

C. fired the special prosecutor investigating Watergate.

D. ordered the Watergate break-in.

_______ **14.** The Watergate crisis led to new laws intended to limit the power of the executive branch, including the Ethics in Government Act, the FBI Domestic Security Investigation Guidelines Act, and the

A. Special Prosecutor Act.

B. Executive Privilege Guidelines.

C. Federal Campaign Act Amendments.

D. SALT I treaty.

_______ **15.** The economic condition called "stagflation" had its beginnings in the early 1970s, when

A. prices for consumer goods began to fall.

B. the increasing cost of goods took a toll on the economy.

C. millions of workers lost their jobs.

D. manufacturing declined while prices were rising.

_______ **16.** The crisis in Iran that undermined Jimmy Carter's presidency began in November 1979, when

A. the Shah, a monarch supported by the United States, was forced to flee the country.

B. militants stormed the American embassy in Tehran and took 52 Americans hostage.

C. religious leader Ayatollah Khomeini declared an Islamic republic in Iran.

D. Carter helped broker a historic peace treaty known as the Camp David Accords.

_______ **17.** Affirmative action, an approach to civil rights that emerged in the 1970s, called for companies and institutions to

A. establish and meet quotas in hiring African Americans.

B. develop and provide diversity training for all employees.

C. actively recruit African American employees and students.

D. hire candidates without regard to race, gender, or national origin.

Chapter 19 Test, Form A *cont.*

Politics and Economics

______ **18.** Which of the following statements accurately describes conditions faced by Native Americans in 1970?

A. Life expectancy for Native Americans was two years above the national average.
B. Average family income for Native Americans and African Americans was about the same.
C. Nearly 90 percent of all Native Americans lived on reservations.
D. The unemployment rate for Native Americans was much higher than the national average.

______ **19.** In the early 1970s, long-standing environmental organizations grew rapidly in membership and political influence, and environmental activists formed new groups such as

A. the *Silent Spring*.
B. the Environmental Protection Agency.
C. People United to Save Humanity.
D. the Natural Resources Defense Council.

______ **20.** The Environmental Protection Agency sets and enforces pollution standards, promotes research, and

A. coordinates antipollution activities with state and local governments.
B. organizes citizens in grassroots movements.
C. identifies endangered species and sets procedures for protecting them.
D. uses DDT to protect crops from insects.

DIRECTIONS: Essay Answer the following questions on a separate piece of paper.

> "We must understand that détente is not a love fest. It is an understanding between nations that have opposite purposes, but which share common interests, including the avoidance of a nuclear war. Such an understanding can work—that is, restrain aggression and deter war—only as long as the potential aggressor is made to recognize that neither aggression nor war will be profitable."
>
> —Richard Nixon, quoted in *The Limits of Power*

21. Explain the policy of détente as it is described by President Nixon in the excerpt above. In what ways was détente successful?

Chapter 19 Test, Form A *cont.*

networks

Politics and Economics

"Watergate was probably a good thing for the country; it was a good, sobering lesson. Accountability to the law applies to everyone. The problem with kings and prime ministers and presidents is that they think that they are above it . . . that they have some special rights, and privileges, and status. And a process that says: No. We have our laws and believe them, and they apply to everyone, is a very good thing."

—Bob Woodward, quoted in *Nixon: An Oral History of His Presidency*

22. Do you agree with Bob Woodward that the Watergate scandal was "a good thing" for the United States? Why or why not?

23. Explain how the United States economy in the 1970s was different from the economy of the 1950s and 1960s.

"When we would go to white schools, we'd see these lovely classrooms with a small number of children in each class. The teachers were permanent. We'd see wonderful materials. When we'd go to our schools, we'd see overcrowded classrooms, children sitting out in the corridors. And so then we decided that where there were a large number of white students, that's where the care went. That's where the books went. That's where the money went."

—Ruth Baston of the NAACP, 1965, quoted in *Freedom Bound*

24. Explain the problem described by Ruth Baston in the excerpt above, and explain whether or not the problem was solved by busing.

25. Describe the origins of the environmental movement in the United States during the 1960s and early 1970s.

NAME _______________ DATE _______________ CLASS _______________

Chapter 19 Test, Form B

networks

Politics and Economics

DIRECTIONS: Short Answer Answer each of the following questions on a separate piece of paper.

> "I reject the patronizing idea that government in Washington, D.C., is inevitably more wise and more efficient than government at the state or local level. The idea that a bureaucratic elite in Washington knows what's best for people . . . is really a contention that people cannot govern themselves."
>
> —Richard Nixon

1. Explain what President Richard Nixon hoped to accomplish through the New Federalism program.

2. In what way were the actual results of the New Federalism different from what President Nixon intended?

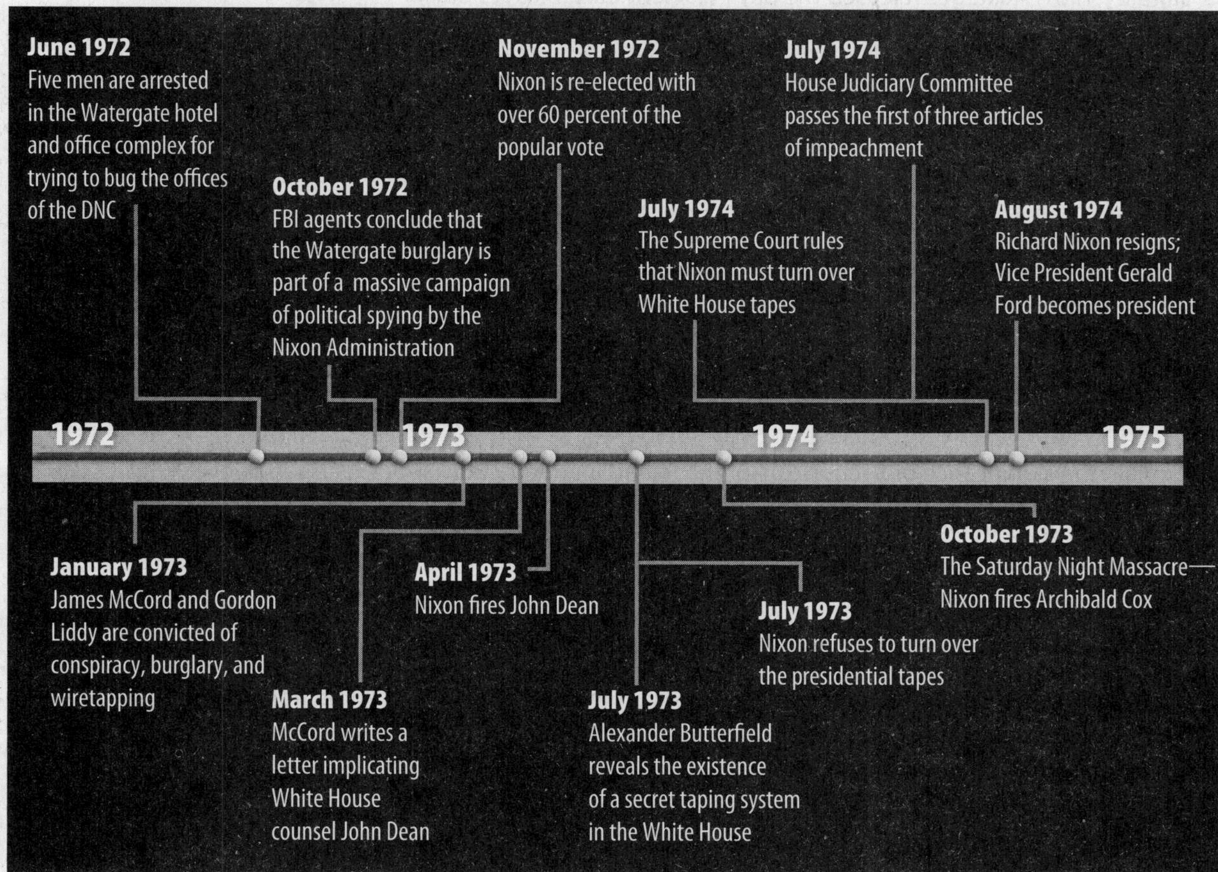

June 1972
Five men are arrested in the Watergate hotel and office complex for trying to bug the offices of the DNC
November 1972
Nixon is re-elected with over 60 percent of the popular vote
July 1974
House Judiciary Committee passes the first of three articles of impeachment
October 1972
FBI agents conclude that the Watergate burglary is part of a massive campaign of political spying by the Nixon Administration
July 1974
The Supreme Court rules that Nixon must turn over White House tapes
August 1974
Richard Nixon resigns; Vice President Gerald Ford becomes president
1972
1973
1974
1975
January 1973
James McCord and Gordon Liddy are convicted of conspiracy, burglary, and wiretapping
April 1973
Nixon fires John Dean
October 1973
The Saturday Night Massacre—Nixon fires Archibald Cox
July 1973
Nixon refuses to turn over the presidential tapes
March 1973
McCord writes a letter implicating White House counsel John Dean
July 1973
Alexander Butterfield reveals the existence of a secret taping system in the White House

3. Based on the time line above, at what point did the Watergate break-in begin to turn into the scandal that ended Richard Nixon's presidency?

4. Explain how events in the summer of 1974 led President Nixon to resign from office.

Chapter 19 Test, Form B *cont.*

Politics and Economics

Triumph and Failure in the Middle East, 1978–1981

- September 1978: President Carter brokers Camp David Accords between Israel and Egypt.
- January 1979: The Shah flees Iran. An Islamic Republic is declared, led by Ayatollah Khomeini.
- March 1979: Israel and Egypt sign peace treaty.
- November 1979: Revolutionaries storm the American embassy in Tehran and take 52 Americans hostage.
- April 1980: President Carter approves a rescue attempt. The rescue mission fails.
- November 1980: President Carter loses the 1980 election.
- January 1981: Hostages released the day President Carter leaves office.

5. Explain the significance of the Camp David Accords, as listed in the outline of events above.

6. Based on the outline of events, what effect did the Iranian hostage crisis have on Jimmy Carter's presidency?

> "[N]o otherwise qualified individual with a disability . . . shall . . . be excluded from participation in, be denied the benefits of, or be subjected to discrimination under any program or service or activity receiving Federal financial assistance . . ."
>
> —Section 504 of the Rehabilitation Act of 1973

7. Explain the significance of Section 504 of the Rehabilitation Act of 1973, excerpted above.

8. What actions by the federal government and by persons with disabilities were required before the provisions of the Rehabilitation Act took effect?

DIRECTIONS: Essay Answer the following question on a separate piece of paper.

9. Describe the new and ongoing international, economic, social, and environmental problems faced by the United States during the period from 1968 to 1980. How did the U.S. government and American citizens attempt to solve these problems?

NAME ______________________ DATE ______________ CLASS ___________

Lesson Quiz 20-1

networks

The Resurgence of Conservatism

DIRECTIONS: Matching Match each item with the correct statement below.

_____ **1.** movement founded by Jerry Falwell that backed conservative candidates and issues

_____ **2.** worked to spread conservative ideas to a wider audience by founding the magazine *National Review*

_____ **3.** Southern and Western regions of the United States

_____ **4.** conservative Republican nominee for president in 1964

_____ **5.** Protestant minister who built a national following

A. Sunbelt

B. Billy Graham

C. Moral Majority

D. William F. Buckley

E. Barry Goldwater

DIRECTIONS: Multiple Choice Indicate the answer choice that best completes the statement or answers the question.

_____ **6.** Although liberals tend to favor government intervention in the economy, they are generally suspicious of attempts to use the government to regulate

A. higher education.
B. social behavior.
C. the states.
D. private businesses.

_____ **7.** Which of the following developments was necessary for conservatives to build a coalition that could elect a president?

A. Westerners began shifting their votes to the Republican Party.
B. Liberals began moving to the suburbs in large numbers.
C. Southerners began shifting their votes to the Republican Party.
D. Conservatives began moving to the Northeast in large numbers.

_____ **8.** For many Americans, the conservative idea that the government had become too big meant simply that

A. taxes were too high.
B. social programs were too generous.
C. regulations were too restrictive.
D. too many people were disadvantaged.

_____ **9.** The largest religious group within the social conservative movement that formed by the late 1970s was

A. Catholics.
B. conservative Jews.
C. evangelical Protestants.
D. Mormons.

NAME ______________________________ DATE ______________ CLASS ____________

Lesson Quiz 20-2

networks

The Resurgence of Conservatism

DIRECTIONS: True/False Indicate whether the statement is true or false.

_______ **1.** The economic expansion the nation experienced during Reagan's first term as president made him very popular, contributing to his reelection in 1984.

_______ **2.** Believers in supply-side economics supported higher taxes, allowing businesses and investors to use extra capital on new investments.

_______ **3.** President Reagan believed cutting taxes and building up the military were more important than balancing the budget.

_______ **4.** President Reagan believed the United States should oppose guerrilla groups fighting to overthrow Communist or pro-Soviet governments, an approach that came to be known as the Reagan Doctrine.

_______ **5.** The Intermediate Range Nuclear Forces Treaty signed by President Reagan and Soviet leader Mikhail Gorbachev in 1987 marked the beginning of the end of the Cold War.

DIRECTIONS: Multiple Choice Indicate the answer choice that best completes the statement or answers the question.

_______ **6.** Reagan's first act as president was to sign an executive order eliminating price controls on oil and gasoline, a step towards

A. "trickle-down economics."
B. deficit spending.
C. cutting spending.
D. deregulation.

_______ **7.** President Reagan encouraged the Federal Reserve to raise interest rates and asked Congress to pass a massive tax cut, in what critics called

A. monetarist theory.
B. Reaganomics.
C. supply-side economics.
D. stagflation.

_______ **8.** The tax cut President Reagan won from Congress would increase the budget deficit, so Reagan proposed _______________ to keep the deficit under control.

A. decreasing interest rates
B. cutting social programs
C. issuing government bonds
D. increasing taxes

_______ **9.** During his presidency, Reagan launched the largest peacetime buildup of

A. the U.S. military.
B. government spending.
C. the budget surplus.
D. U.S. oil reserves.

NAME ______________________ DATE ______________ CLASS __________

Lesson Quiz 20-3

networks

The Resurgence of Conservatism

DIRECTIONS: Completion Enter the appropriate word(s) to complete the statement.

1. The portion of the nation's wealth earned by the ______________ five percent of Americans began to rise in the late 1980s.

2. In 1975 entrepreneur Ted Turner launched the television station ______________.

3. ______________, a disease that weakens the immune system and lowers resistance to illnesses, became an epidemic during the 1980s.

4. During the 1980s, ______________ citizens became vocal in the political arena, especially about issues such as Social Security and Medicare.

DIRECTIONS: Multiple Choice Indicate the answer choice that best completes the statement or answers the question.

________ **5.** The rapid economic growth of the 1980s and the cultural emphasis on accumulating wealth was partly caused by

A. baby boomers entering the workforce.

B. revolutionary approaches to retailing.

C. new energy in social activism.

D. advances in media technology.

________ **6.** The strong economic growth of the 1980s mostly benefited

A. young urban professionals.

B. middle- and upper-class Americans.

C. entrepreneurs in retailing.

D. Americans at all economic levels.

________ **7.** Which of the following statements about discount retailers is accurate?

A. They have lower profits than traditional retailers.

B. They sell large quantities of goods at low prices.

C. Their sales fell from the mid-1960s to 1985.

D. Their presence was limited to a few large cities.

________ **8.** Which of the following entertainment technologies changed television viewing habits as well as the movie industry in the 1980s?

A. the World Wide Web

B. digital video recorders

C. personal computers

D. videocassette recorders

NAME ______________________ DATE ______________ CLASS __________

Lesson Quiz 20-4

networks

The Resurgence of Conservatism

DIRECTIONS: Matching Match each item with the correct statement below.

_____ **1.** term used by presidential candidate Jesse Jackson for a broad group of minorities and the poor

_____ **2.** "openness," allowing more freedom of religion and speech in the Soviet Union

_____ **3.** paid by businesses and investors when they sell stocks or real estate for a profit

_____ **4.** "restructuring," allowing some private enterprise and profit making in the Soviet Union

_____ **5.** laying off workers and managers to increase a company's efficiency

A. perestroika

B. rainbow coalition

C. capital gains tax

D. glasnost

E. downsizing

DIRECTIONS: Multiple Choice Indicate the answer choice that best completes the statement or answers the question.

_____ **6.** In late December 1991, Mikhail Gorbachev announced the end of

A. perestroika and glasnost.
B. Operation Desert Storm.
C. the Soviet Union.
D. the Berlin Wall.

_____ **7.** In May 1989, students and workers held demonstrations calling for democracy in

A. China.
B. Germany.
C. Panama.
D. Iraq.

_____ **8.** Who sent his army to invade oil-rich Kuwait in August 1990?

A. Manuel Noriega
B. Saddam Hussein
C. Boris Yeltsin
D. Mikhail Gorbachev

_____ **9.** The recession that began in 1990 was caused in part by the end of the Cold War, because the United States

A. relied on deficit spending to build up the military to face new challenges.
B. began reducing its armed forces and canceling orders for military equipment.
C. provided economic support to help rebuild Russia and Eastern Europe.
D. deregulated savings-and-loan institutions, many of which collapsed.

NAME ______________________ DATE ______________ CLASS ______________

Chapter 20 Test, Form A

networks

The Resurgence of Conservatism

DIRECTIONS: Matching Match each item with the correct statement below.

_______ **1.** idea that high taxes weaken the economy by taking money away from investors

_______ **2.** chief figure in the Iran-Contra scandal who admitted to covering up illegal actions

_______ **3.** first African American to make a serious run for a presidential nomination

_______ **4.** conservative movement founded by evangelical minister Jerry Falwell

_______ **5.** restructuring plan instituted by Mikhail Gorbachev in the late 1980s to save the Soviet economy

_______ **6.** island nation invaded by the United States in 1983

_______ **7.** location of pro-democracy demonstrations violently crushed by the Chinese government in 1989

_______ **8.** policy of supporting guerrilla groups fighting Communist or pro-Soviet governments

_______ **9.** first woman on the Supreme Court, appointed by President Reagan

_______ **10.** a plan, nicknamed "Star Wars," to develop weapons that could destroy incoming missiles

A. Tiananmen Square

B. Strategic Defense Initiative

C. perestroika

D. Jesse Jackson

E. Oliver North

F. Sandra Day O'Connor

G. supply-side economics

H. Moral Majority

I. Grenada

J. Reagan Doctrine

DIRECTIONS: Multiple Choice Indicate the answer choice that best completes the statement or answers the question.

_______ **11.** While liberals generally believe the government should help disadvantaged Americans through social programs, many conservatives believe social problems can be solved through

A. limiting the power of big business.

B. government welfare programs.

C. limiting the power of the wealthy.

D. religious faith and private efforts.

Chapter 20 Test, Form A *cont.*

networks

The Resurgence of Conservatism

_____ **12.** Members of the new conservative coalition that had come together by the late 1970s were united by a common belief that

A. American society had lost its way.

B. the United States was stronger than ever before.

C. American society was moving in a positive direction.

D. increased government spending was needed.

_____ **13.** In an approach to economic policy that came to be called "Reaganomics," President Ronald Reagan sought to keep interest rates high while

A. cutting spending to reduce the budget deficit.

B. increasing the amount of money in circulation.

C. asking Congress to pass a huge tax cut.

D. borrowing heavily to build up the military.

_____ **14.** President Reagan encouraged and promoted deregulation because he believed

A. excessive government regulations hurt the economy.

B. the government must regulate key industries to maintain economic stability.

C. removing government regulations would increase the prices of goods and services.

D. free trade required effective regulation of major industries.

_____ **15.** President Reagan began a massive buildup of the U.S. military, in part because he believed

A. with a stronger military, the United States could defeat the Soviets in a nuclear war.

B. massive Soviet defense spending would cause the Communist system to collapse.

C. massive defense spending would stimulate economic growth in the United States.

D. an arms race with the Soviets would reduce the likelihood of nuclear war.

_____ **16.** The American economy grew rapidly in the 1980s for several reasons, including lower taxes that spurred investment and spending, new technology that created new business opportunities, and

A. new efforts to solve social problems.

B. sharp cuts in government spending.

C. new methods of retailing that lowered prices.

D. increased income for the wealthiest Americans.

Chapter 20 Test, Form A *cont.*

networks

The Resurgence of Conservatism

______ **17.** As cable television spread across the country in the late 1970s and 1980s, many of the new networks that appeared specialized in one type of broadcasting or

A. focused on specific audiences.
B. sold low-cost programs via satellite.
C. broadcast music videos.
D. promoted specific businesses.

______ **18.** The collapse of the Soviet Union's economy that began in the late 1980s was caused by

A. President Reagan's policies of "trickle-down" economics.
B. revolutions in Eastern Europe and the destruction of the Berlin Wall.
C. Boris Yeltsin's outlawing of the Communist Party in Russia.
D. inefficient central planning and huge expenditures in the arms race.

______ **19.** In January 1991, the United Nations went to war in the Persian Gulf for what reason?

A. Iraq had invaded Saudi Arabia.
B. Saudi Arabia had invaded Kuwait.
C. Iraq had invaded Kuwait.
D. Kuwait had threatened Saudi Arabia.

______ **20.** The central message of H. Ross Perot's 1992 presidential campaign was the need to

A. increase government regulation.
B. end deficit spending.
C. increase taxes on wealthy Americans.
D. cut taxes for the middle class.

DIRECTIONS: Essay Answer the following questions on a separate piece of paper.

> "The answer is that all those young men went on their spree of looting because they had been given permission to do so. They had been given permission to do so by all the papers and magazines, movies and documentaries—all the outlets for the purveying of enlightened liberal attitude and progressive liberal policy—which had for years and years been proclaiming that race and poverty were sufficient excuses for lawlessness. . . ."
>
> —Midge Decter, *Commentary*, September 1977

21. Explain how conservative responses to political, economic, and social problems in the late 1970s, such as the violence that hit New York City following a blackout in July 1977, helped bring together a new conservative coalition.

NAME ______________________ DATE ______________ CLASS ____________

Chapter 20 Test, Form A *cont.*

networks

The Resurgence of Conservatism

". . . [T]he plan that we have had and that we are following is a plan that is based on growth in the economy. . . . Our tax cut, we think, was very instrumental in bringing about this economic recovery. . . . So, we believe that as we continue to reduce the level of government spending . . . and, at the same time, as the growth in the economy increases the revenues the government gets, without raising taxes, those two lines will meet. . . . The deficit is the result of excessive government spending."

—Ronald Reagan, presidential debate, October 7, 1984

22. Describe Ronald Reagan's economic policies and their effect on social programs.

23. Explain how the entertainment industry was transformed during the 1980s. What caused the industry to change?

24. Describe the domestic challenges George H.W. Bush faced as president and explain the actions President Bush took in response to those challenges.

NAME ______________________ DATE ______________ CLASS ____________

Chapter 20 Test, Form B

networks

The Resurgence of Conservatism

DIRECTIONS: Short Answer Answer each of the following questions on a separate piece of paper.

Population Growth, 1950–1980

State	1950 Population	1980 Population	Percent Growth
Arizona*	749,587	2,718,215	262%
California*	10,586,223	23,667,902	124%
Colorado	1,325,089	2,889,964	118%
Florida*	2,771,305	9,746,324	252%
Georgia*	3,444,578	5,463,105	59%
Idaho	588,637	943,935	60%
Louisiana*	2,683,516	4,205,900	57%
Nevada*	160,083	800,493	400%
New Mexico*	681,187	1,333,241	96%
Oregon	1,521,341	2,633,105	73%
Texas*	7,711,194	14,229,191	85%
Utah	688,862	1,461,037	112%
Virginia*	3,318,680	5,346,818	61%
Washington	2,378,963	4,132,156	74%
Wyoming	290,176	469,557	62%

* Indicates a Sunbelt state
Table shows only states having 50% or more population growth between 1950 and 1980.

1. What does the table above suggest about population growth in the Sunbelt during the years between World War II and 1980?
2. How did the growth illustrated by the table affect the conservative resurgence of 1980 to 1992?

The Resurgence of Conservatism

> "Lifeguarding provides one of the best vantage points in the world to learn about people. During my career at the park, I saved seventy-seven people. . . . Not many thanked me, much less gave me a reward, and being a little money-hungry, I'd done a little daydreaming about this. They felt insulted. . . . I got to recognize that people hate to be saved."
>
> —Ronald Reagan, from *Where's the Rest of Me?*
>
> "In this present crisis, government is not the solution to our problem. Government is the problem."
>
> —Ronald Reagan, from the first Inaugural Address

3. What do the excerpts above reveal about President Reagan's political views and guiding philosophy?

Economic Growth of the 1980s

1967–1986	End of 1980s	By mid-1990s
Top 5 percent of Americans earned approximately 15–17 percent of nation's total income.	Top 5 percent of Americans earned approximately 20 percent of nation's total income.	Top 5 percent of Americans earned more than 21 percent of nation's total income.

4. According to the table above, to what extent did the wealthiest Americans benefit from economic growth in the 1980s?

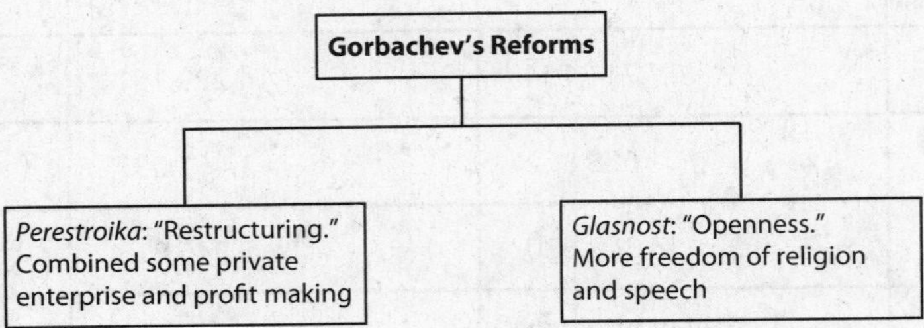

5. Based on your reading, what was the main reason Soviet leader Mikhail Gorbachev instituted perestroika in the late 1980s?

6. Explain how Gorbachev's glasnost policy contributed to the collapse of the Soviet Union.

DIRECTIONS: Essay Answer the following question on a separate piece of paper.

7. Explain how the resurgence of conservatism changed American politics, society, and its economy during the 1980s. In what ways can the impact of the new conservatism be seen in the United States today?

NAME ______________________________ DATE ______________ CLASS ____________

Lesson Quiz 21-1

networks

A Time of Change

DIRECTIONS: True/False Indicate whether the statement is true or false.

_______ **1.** Clinton's health care reform plan died without ever coming to a vote in Congress.

_______ **2.** President Clinton opposed new gun-control laws.

_______ **3.** President Clinton convinced Congress to grant China permanent normal trade relation status.

_______ **4.** Clinton's AmeriCorps program put students to work improving low-income housing, teaching children to read, and cleaning up the environment.

_______ **5.** In 1995 the federal government was shut down after President Clinton was impeached.

DIRECTIONS: Multiple Choice Indicate the answer choice that best completes the statement or answers the question.

_______ **6.** A problem Clinton faced in trying to reduce the federal deficit was that it was not easy to cut funding for ____________________ because so many people relied on them.

A. entitlement programs
B. public works programs
C. schools
D. military operations

_______ **7.** Opposition to Clinton's health care plan came from many groups, including small business owners who believed that the plan

A. might not help many Americans.
B. was too complicated to use.
C. would be too expensive for them.
D. would not be passed by Congress.

_______ **8.** Choose the statement below that most accurately describes Clinton's impeachment.

A. Clinton was impeached on charges of perjury and obstruction of justice.
B. Clinton was not charged with perjury but was charged with obstruction of justice.
C. Congress had enough support to remove Clinton from office.
D. Gingrich was the special investigator charged with investigating the Clinton scandal.

_______ **9.** Despite strong opposition from many Republicans and the National Rifle Association, the Democrats in Congress passed a gun-control law known as the

A. Brady Bill.
B. Contract with America.
C. Firearms Act.
D. HOPE Bill.

NAME ______________________ DATE ______________ CLASS ____________

Lesson Quiz 21-2

networks

A Time of Change

DIRECTIONS: Matching Match each item with the correct statement below.

_______ **1.** allowed people fleeing communism to enter the United States as refugees

_______ **2.** punished employers who hired illegal immigrants

_______ **3.** has one of the highest populations of foreign-born residents

_______ **4.** result of immigration policy that favored the children, spouses, and parents of U.S. citizens

_______ **5.** place from which many legal immigrants came

A. migration chains

B. Immigration Reform and Control Act

C. India

D. Illinois

E. McCarran-Walter Act

DIRECTIONS: Multiple Choice Indicate the answer choice that best completes the statement or answers the question.

_______ **6.** The Reagan administration's amnesty program of 1986 was intended to solve the problem of

A. high unemployment.

B. the Haitian crisis.

C. unauthorized immigration.

D. violent crime.

_______ **7.** American public opinion split over whether unauthorized immigrants should be allowed to

A. claim they were refugees if they were not fleeing Communist countries.

B. send their children to public schools.

C. use migration chains to settle in the United States.

D. vote on immigration policies.

_______ **8.** The USA PATRIOT Act of 2001 put immigration under the control of

A. individual state governments.

B. the Department of Defense.

C. the Department of Homeland Security.

D. the Minutemen Civil Defense Corps.

_______ **9.** Which of the following was a result of the Immigration Act of 1965?

A. Amnesty was offered to all undocumented immigrants.

B. Anyone who wanted to immigrate to the United States could do so.

C. Immigration from non-European countries soared.

D. U.S. citizens no longer helped their relatives to immigrate.

NAME ________________ DATE ________________ CLASS ________________

Lesson Quiz 21-3

A Time of Change

DIRECTIONS: Completion Enter the appropriate word(s) to complete the statement.

1. A(n) ________________ serves as a place for people to share stories and photos on the Internet.

2. In the 1970s, the federal government began deregulating the ________________ industry, leading to the rise of competing phone companies.

3. In 1977 Stephen Wozniak and Steve Jobs introduced the Apple II, the first practical and affordable ________________ for personal use.

4. By 2007 over one billion people worldwide were regularly using the ________________.

5. Several nations agreed to phase out the production of CFCs after seeing evidence of a hole in the ________________ layer above Antarctica.

DIRECTIONS: Multiple Choice Indicate the answer choice that best completes the statement or answers the question.

________ **6.** As Steve Jobs and Stephen Wozniak were creating Apple, Bill Gates cofounded Microsoft to design PC

A. blogs.
B. hardware.
C. software.
D. Web sites.

________ **7.** The Telecommunications Act passed in 1996 changed the telecommunications industry by

A. allowing cable companies to offer telephone service.
B. allowing workers to telecommute from their homes.
C. creating cell phones.
D. deregulating personal computers.

________ **8.** What had its roots in a computer networking system established by an agency of the U.S. Defense Department?

A. ENIAC
B. integrated circuits
C. the Internet
D. the Windows operating system

________ **9.** The goal of the Kyoto Protocol was to

A. bring peace to troubled areas in the former Yugoslavia.
B. open free trade among member nations.
C. reduce carbon dioxide emissions worldwide.
D. stop nuclear proliferation.

NAME ______________________ DATE ______________ CLASS __________

Chapter 21 Test, Form A

networks

A Time of Change

DIRECTIONS: Matching Match each item with the correct statement below.

_______ **1.** software that enabled Internet users to click links to jump from Web site to Web site

_______ **2.** IBM's first compact computer

_______ **3.** policy of the Serbs to brutally expel Bosnian Muslims from the region

_______ **4.** wireless digital technology made it possible to miniaturize these devices

_______ **5.** charge of lying under oath included in Clinton impeachment articles

_______ **6.** programs that pardoned undocumented immigrants, allowing them to stay in the United States

_______ **7.** early computer operating system developed for the PC

_______ **8.** environmental threat that could lead to droughts

_______ **9.** chemical used in air conditioners and refrigerators that could potentially deplete the Earth's protective atmosphere

_______ **10.** program of proposed changes that helped Republicans win the majority in both houses of Congress in 1994

A. amnesty

B. global warming

C. Personal Computer

D. cell phones

E. ethnic cleansing

F. Contract with America

G. Web browser

H. chlorofluorocarbon

I. MS-DOS

J. perjury

DIRECTIONS: Multiple Choice Indicate the answer choice that best completes the statement or answers the question.

_______ **11.** A problem Clinton faced in trying to reduce the federal deficit was

A. entitlement programs.

B. public works programs.

C. schools.

D. the military.

Chapter 21 Test, Form A *cont.*

A Time of Change

_______ **12.** In the period after NAFTA passed,

A. American workers shifted to less-skilled industrial jobs.

B. American workers shifted to more-skilled jobs or to the service industry.

C. unemployment rose in the United States.

D. wages fell in the United States.

_______ **13.** Those who opposed the United States joining the World Trade Organization worried that

A. a lack of copyright protection would destroy the American entertainment industry.

B. no new markets would be opened to American products.

C. the United States would be banned from APEC.

D. the United States would have to accept rulings in trade disputes that might hurt the economy.

_______ **14.** The Dayton Accords was an agreement intended to bring peace to

A. Afghanistan.

B. Bosnia.

C. Haiti.

D. Kosovo.

_______ **15.** The process by which the world is becoming increasingly interconnected is called

A. democratization.

B. free trade.

C. globalization.

D. internationalism.

_______ **16.** President Clinton did not submit the Kyoto Protocol to the Senate for ratification because

A. developing nations trying to industrialize would be hurt by the treaty.

B. few nations were going to comply with it.

C. he knew that most senators were opposed to it.

D. the United States did not want to cut carbon dioxide emissions.

_______ **17.** Which act granted a pardon to undocumented immigrants already living in the United States?

A. Immigration Act of 1965

B. Immigration Reform and Control Act of 1986

C. McCarran-Walter Act of 1952

D. Refugee Act of 1980

_______ **18.** The Illegal Immigration Reform and Immigrant Responsibility Act of 1996

A. called for building a fence between Mexico and the United States.
B. made it harder to deport undocumented aliens.
C. made several changes to U.S. immigration law.
D. reduced the penalties for smuggling people into the United States.

_______ **19.** China became an important factor in world trade because

A. Communist ideology prevented any trade with the West.
B. increased trade would keep it isolated from the world community.
C. it had suppressed trade protests in Tiananmen Square.
D. its huge population offered a potential market for American goods.

_______ **20.** President Clinton spent much of his time during the second term on

A. foreign policy matters.
B. health care reform.
C. increasing federal deficits.
D. passing tax cuts.

DIRECTIONS: Short Answer Answer each of the following questions on a separate piece of paper.

21. Why was President Clinton impeached, and what was the outcome?

22. What do many experts believe causes global warming, and why is this issue controversial?

23. Describe how Clinton's tax policies led to a federal budget surplus.

> "Just as we sought to eliminate discrimination in our land through the Civil Rights Act, today we seek by phasing out the national origins quota system to eliminate discrimination in immigration to this nation composed of the descendants of immigrants."
>
> —U.S. Representative Philip Burton

24. Think about immigration policies before and after the Immigration Act of 1965. Then read the quote from Philip Burton. Do you think the current policies have achieved the goal of eliminating discrimination? Why or why not?

NAME ______________________ DATE ______________ CLASS ____________

Chapter 21 Test, Form B

networks

A Time of Change

DIRECTIONS: Short Answer Answer each of the following questions on a separate piece of paper.

> "The world is getting warmer, and by the end of the 21st century could warm by another 6 degrees Celsius [10.8 degrees Fahrenheit]. . . . And climate scientists at the heart of the research are now convinced that human action is to blame for some or most of this warming. . . .
>
> "Everywhere climatologists look—at tree-ring patterns, fossil successions in rock strata, ocean-floor corings . . . they see evidence of dramatic shifts from cold to hot to cold again. . . . None of these ancient shifts can be blamed on humans. . . . There is still room for argument about the precise role of the sun or other natural cycles in the contribution to global warming. . . ."
>
> —from *The Guardian* (London), November 15, 2000

1. Read the above passage. Summarize the two contrasting perspectives that climate scientists have about global warming.

> "The real debate is not . . . whether to engage China but what are the terms of that engagement and whose values are to be represented. . . . America's working families understand the cruelty of a world economy regulated in favor of the corporations. . . . Over two-thirds oppose bringing China into the WTO without further progress on human rights and religious freedom. . . . Incorporating enforceable workers' rights, human rights and environmental protections in every U.S. trade and investment agreement is the right way; admitting a repressive China into the WTO is the wrong way."
>
> —John Sweeney, President AFL-CIO

2. Based on the above quote, why did unions oppose normalizing trade relations with China?

> "Broadband access, along with the content and services it might enable, has the potential to transform the Internet—both what it offers and how it is used. For example, a two-way high speed connection could be used for interactive applications such as online classrooms, showrooms, or health clinics, where teacher and student (or customer and salesperson, doctor and patient) can see and hear each other through their computers. An 'always on' connection could be used to monitor home security, home automation, or even patient health remotely through the Web."
>
> —Congressional Research Service, 2006

3. Based on the above analysis, what are some areas of the economy that broadband Internet access has enhanced?

NAME ______________________ DATE ____________ CLASS ____________

Chapter 21 Test, Form B *cont.*

networks

A Time of Change

Rise and Fall of the "Dot-com" Economy
1969: Defense Department's Advanced Research Project linked government agencies, scientists, and defense contractors by electronic mail.
1985: National Science Foundation funded supercomputer centers across the United States, paving the way for growth of the Internet, a global information system operating commercially rather than through the government.
1990s: Web browser use grew through the last half of the 1990s, expanding by 300 percent in a three-year time frame.
1990s: "Dot-com" companies developed and made enormous profits throughout the 1990s based on the technological promises they represented.
2000: Stocks in "dot-com" companies helped fuel the prosperity of the 1990s but crashed in 2000 because there were no tangible profits.

4. The technology behind the Internet and e-mail dates back as far as 1969. Compare the early Internet and e-mail usage with the services available today.

North American Free Trade Agreement (NAFTA)	
Advantages	**Disadvantages**
• Exports from the United States to Canada rose. • Rising employment in Mexico reduced the flow of undocumented immigrants into the United States. • Unemployment in the United States decreased as workers shifted to more skilled jobs. • Small businesses increased their trade with Canada and Mexico.	• Mexico purchased fewer goods from the United States. • Mexico exported more to the United States than it imported. • American industrial jobs moved to Mexico where labor costs were lower.

5. What does the chart indicate is a disadvantage of NAFTA in terms of employment?

DIRECTIONS: Essay Answer the following question on a separate piece of paper.

6. Describe how immigration policies in the late 1980s and 1990s have attempted to address the issue of illegal immigration.

NAME ______________________________ DATE ______________ CLASS ____________

Lesson Quiz 22-1

networks

America's Challenges for a New Century

DIRECTIONS: True/False Indicate whether the statement is true or false.

______ **1.** The 2000 election was one of the closest in American history; Bush won the popular vote.

______ **2.** The U.S. Supreme Court ruled that the vote recount in Florida for the 2000 presidential election violated the Constitution's equal protection clause.

______ **3.** The attack on September 11, 2001, killed nearly 3,000 people.

______ **4.** The al-Qaeda organization was initially founded to fight the Soviet Union in Iraq.

DIRECTIONS: Multiple Choice Indicate the answer choice that best completes the statement or answers the question.

______ **5.** Why did the United States attack Afghanistan and defeat its Taliban government?

A. Afghanistan was part of Bush's "axis of evil" and was considered dangerous.
B. The Taliban supported and sheltered Osama bin Laden and al-Qaeda.
C. The Taliban tried to develop weapons of mass destruction.
D. The United States wanted to stop the civil war between the Taliban and the Northern Alliance.

______ **6.** To protect Americans from further attacks by terrorists, a new cabinet agency, the ______________, was established.

A. USA PATRIOT Act
B. Department of Justice
C. National Security Agency
D. Department of Homeland Security

______ **7.** The USA PATRIOT Act is an antiterrorist bill that allows the government to

A. analyze information collected by the FBI and the CIA.
B. wiretap suspects, seize voicemail, and track Internet communications.
C. create new government agencies within the Department of Homeland Security.
D. freeze the financial assets of any group or individual suspected of terrorism.

______ **8.** The 2000 presidential election was determined by the contested results of

A. California.
B. Colorado.
C. Iowa.
D. Florida.

NAME ______________________ DATE ______________ CLASS ____________

Lesson Quiz 22-2

networks

America's Challenges for a New Century

DIRECTIONS: Completion Enter the appropriate word(s) to complete the statement.

1. The United States invaded Iraq because it was believed that Saddam Hussein possessed weapons of ______________.

2. Less than a month after the attacks of September 11, 2001, the United States invaded ______________, the country that had sheltered Osama bin Laden and other al-Qaeda members.

3. In 2005 the Iraqi people were able to participate in the country's first free ______________.

4. The Islamic fundamentalist group called the ______________ controlled Afghanistan at the time of the terrorist attacks on the World Trade Center and Pentagon.

5. A UN resolution set a deadline for Iraq to take several actions including declaring its weapons of mass destruction and readmitting ______________.

DIRECTIONS: Multiple Choice Indicate the answer choice that best completes the statement or answers the question.

_______ 6. Iraqi insurgents have used several tactics to fight coalition forces, including

A. developing weapons of mass destruction.
B. freezing financial assets inside Iraq.
C. participating in Iraq's first national elections.
D. sniper attacks and bombings.

_______ 7. Which nation allowed the United States to attack Iraq from its territory in 2003?

A. Kuwait
B. Iran
C. Saudi Arabia
D. Turkey

_______ 8. The leader of Iraq who was tried and executed for ordering mass executions was

A. Hamid Karzai.
B. Khalid Shaikh Mohammed.
C. Osama bin Laden.
D. Saddam Hussein.

_______ 9. The United States sent military aid to the Northern Alliance in Afghanistan because

A. al-Qaeda was an ally of the Northern Alliance.
B. the Afghan people were enemies of the United States.
C. the Northern Alliance had sheltered Osama bin Laden.
D. the Northern Alliance was fighting against the Taliban.

NAME ______________________ DATE ______________ CLASS __________

Lesson Quiz 22-3

networks

America's Challenges for a New Century

DIRECTIONS: Completion Enter the appropriate word(s) to complete the statement.

1. During the administration of George W. Bush, the ________________ Agency began wiretapping some domestic telephone calls to overseas locations.

2. In 2005 ________________ became the Chief Justice of the Supreme Court.

3. The George W. Bush administration maintained that the detainees held at Guantanamo Bay were not covered by the Geneva Conventions because they were ________________, not suspects charged with a crime.

4. Due to the economic recession, by 2009 the ________________ rate was up to 7.2 percent.

5. George W. Bush convinced Congress to enact a program that allows people over age 65 to sign up for insurance to help cover the cost of ________________.

DIRECTIONS: Multiple Choice Indicate the answer choice that best completes the statement or answers the question.

_______ **6.** In the case of *Hamdan* v. *Rumsfeld*, the Supreme Court ruled that the military tribunals at Guantanamo Bay violated the

A. FEMA rules.
B. Geneva Conventions.
C. National Security Act.
D. USA PATRIOT Act.

_______ **7.** In the 2006 midterm elections, it became clear that voters were unhappy with the president and the Republican Congress when

A. Democrats won a majority in both the House and the Senate.
B. voters refused to show up at the polls.
C. Republicans lost their majority in the House but not the Senate.
D. Republicans lost their majority in the Senate but not the House.

_______ **8.** Criticism of the government's response to Hurricane Katrina led to

A. a mandatory evacuation of New Orleans.
B. government-sponsored destruction of all devastated areas.
C. removal of all National Guard troops from Louisiana.
D. the dismissal of the head of FEMA.

_______ **9.** An economic recession was sparked in 2007 when many people with low incomes or poor credit began ________________ and housing prices began to fall.

A. selling their homes for more than they were worth
B. abandoning their homes in large numbers
C. taking out second mortgages to pay their bills
D. defaulting on their mortgage payments

NAME ______________________ DATE ______________ CLASS ____________

Lesson Quiz 22-4

networks

America's Challenges for a New Century

DIRECTIONS: True/False Indicate whether the statement is true or false.

_______ **1.** John McCain selected Condoleezza Rice to be his running mate in the 2008 presidential campaign.

_______ **2.** President Bush pushed Congress to approve a $700 billion bailout of financial institutions.

_______ **3.** In 2008 the Republicans nominated Vietnam veteran Mitt Romney as their candidate for president.

_______ **4.** In 2008 Barack Obama became the first African American to run for president.

_______ **5.** Hillary Clinton was Barack Obama's running mate in the 2008 presidential election.

DIRECTIONS: Multiple Choice Indicate the answer choice that best completes the statement or answers the question.

_______ **6.** One of President Obama's priorities while in office was to expand and reform the

A. Constitution.

B. tax code.

C. economy.

D. health care system.

_______ **7.** In February 2009, Obama signed the American Recovery and Reinvestment Act, which aimed to

A. stimulate the economy through tax cuts and federal funding.

B. provide funds to clean up the BP oil spill.

C. reduce the deficit through tax increases and budget cuts.

D. reform health care and energy policy.

_______ **8.** The 2010 midterm elections resulted in

A. Democrats losing control of the House and Senate.

B. Democrats retaining control of the House but not the Senate.

C. Republicans regaining control of the House and Senate.

D. Republicans regaining control of the House but not the Senate.

_______ **9.** In one of the first tests of the Obama administration, a massive oil spill in 2010 caused major environmental damage in the

A. Atlantic Ocean.

B. Arctic Ocean.

C. Gulf of Mexico.

D. Pacific Ocean.

NAME ______________________ DATE ______________ CLASS __________

Chapter 22 Test, Form A

networks

America's Challenges for a New Century

DIRECTIONS: Matching Match each item with the correct statement below.

_______ **1.** regime that held power in Afghanistan and sheltered Osama bin Laden

_______ **2.** the first Jewish American vice-presidential candidate for a major political party

_______ **3.** the state that determined the winner of the 2000 presidential election

_______ **4.** John Kerry's running mate in the 2004 presidential election

_______ **5.** secretary of defense who resigned in 2006

_______ **6.** led to the spread of Western ideas in the Middle East

_______ **7.** elected president of Afghanistan in the country's first democratic election

_______ **8.** nation accused of sponsoring terrorism

_______ **9.** dictator overthrown by United States-led forces in 2003

_______ **10.** Chief Justice appointed by George W. Bush

A. Joseph Lieberman

B. oil industry

C. Florida

D. Saddam Hussein

E. John Edwards

F. Donald Rumsfeld

G. Iran

H. John Roberts

I. Hamid Karzai

J. Taliban

DIRECTIONS: Multiple Choice Indicate the answer choice that best completes the statement or answers the question.

_______ **11.** The Bush administration claimed that procedures regarding the treatment of prisoners specified in the Geneva Conventions did not apply to terrorists because

A. the Geneva Conventions did not apply to prisoners held on military bases.

B. they were not charged with a crime.

C. they were not part of any nation's armed forces.

D. their actions outweighed their right to human treatment.

_______ **12.** Why did Al Gore challenge the Florida state law that set a deadline to certify election results?

A. He thought the law was wrong and needed to be changed.

B. He wanted a machine recount instead of a hand recount.

C. Not all of the hand recounts could be completed by the deadline.

D. The U.S. Supreme Court ordered him to challenge the deadline.

_______ **13.** Americans responded quickly to the attacks on September 11, 2001, by

A. donating food, money, and supplies.

B. holding demonstrations against their government.

C. ordering cruise missiles to be fired at terrorist camps in Sudan.

D. writing stories in the foreign press to gain sympathy.

_______ **14.** A UN resolution set a deadline for Iraq to take several actions including

A. giving weapons inspectors more time to find evidence of a weapons program.

B. readmitting weapons inspectors and declaring its weapons of mass destruction.

C. surrendering Osama bin Laden to the United States.

D. surrendering Saddam Hussein to be tried for crimes against humanity.

_______ **15.** In the 2000 presidential campaign, both Al Gore and George W. Bush promised to

A. cut taxes and improve public education.

B. defend the country against terrorist attacks.

C. improve public education and lower the cost of health care for everyone.

D. pass legislation to protect the environment.

_______ **16.** Hurricane Katrina caused large amounts of damage to New Orleans because

A. the city was flooded from an earlier storm.

B. the city's residents had all been evacuated.

C. the storm hit during high tide.

D. rising waters breached the levees that protected the city.

_______ **17.** The "axis of evil" was comprised of

A. Iraq, Afghanistan, and Syria.

B. Iran, Iraq, and North Korea.

C. North Korea, Syria, and Russia.

D. Russia, Iran, and Saudi Arabia.

_______ **18.** In 2003 ______________ took command of peacekeeping efforts in Afghanistan.

A. NATO

B. the United States

C. Iraq

D. the UN

_______ **19.** The Department of Homeland Security was created to coordinate efforts to

A. fight terrorism.
B. wiretap suspected terrorists.
C. clean up after environmental disasters.
D. fight recessions.

_______ **20.** Which nation allowed the United States to attack Iraq from its territory in 2003?

A. Iran
B. Kuwait
C. Saudi Arabia
D. Turkey

DIRECTIONS: Essay Answer the following questions on a separate piece of paper.

21. How did United States foreign policy change after September 11, 2001?

22. How did George W. Bush win the presidential election of 2000?

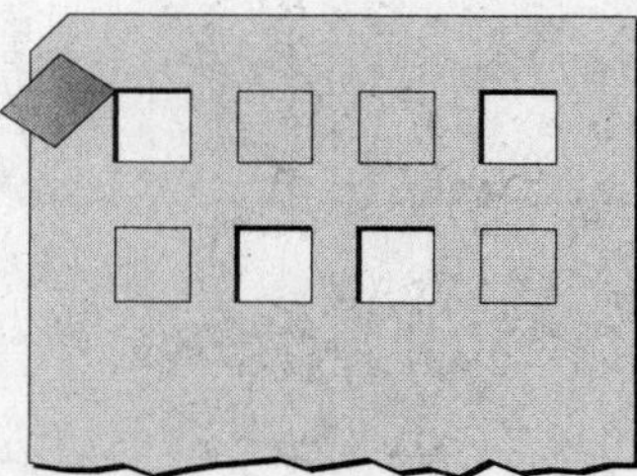

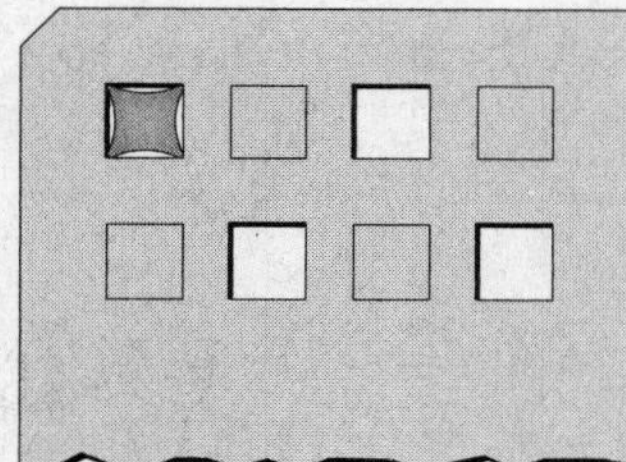

23. Study the illustration of the ballots to help you answer the following question: What effect did chads have on the outcome of the 2000 presidential election?

"What can those who allege that this is a war against terrorism say? What terrorism are they speaking about at a time when the Islamic nation has been slaughtered for tens of years without hearing their voices and without seeing any action by them?

"But when the victim starts to take revenge for those innocent children in Palestine, Iraq, southern Sudan, Somalia, Kashmir and the Philippines, the rulers' ulema (Islamic leaders) and the hypocrites come to defend the clear blasphemy. It suffices me to seek God's help against them."

—Osama bin Laden, 2001

24. Based on the above excerpt, why does Osama bin Laden call on Muslims to kill Americans?

NAME ____________________ DATE ____________ CLASS ____________

Chapter 22 Test, Form B

networks

America's Challenges for a New Century

DIRECTIONS: Short Answer Answer each of the following questions on a separate piece of paper.

". . . [T]his war will be a war like none other our nation has faced. . . . [The enemy is] committed to deny people the opportunity to live as they choose."

—Secretary of Defense Donald Rumsfeld, letter to the *New York Times*

1. Summarize Rumsfeld's message to the *New York Times* and the American people concerning the war on terrorism.

2. Why does Rumsfeld think this war will be different from others the United States has fought in the past?

"A tragedy like this could have torn our country apart. But instead it has united us and we have become a family."

—Reverend Billy Graham, in reference to the attacks on September 11, 2001

3. How did the attacks on September 11, 2001, unite the nation as a family? What did Graham mean by this statement?

"We are all Americans!"

—A French journalist writing after the attacks on September 11, 2001

4. What did the journalist mean by this statement?

"From this day forward, any nation that continues to harbor or support terrorism will be regarded by the United States as a hostile regime."

—President George W. Bush, address to Congress, September 20, 2001

5. Which nation might Bush have considered a hostile regime when he made this statement and what were the repercussions?

Chapter 22 Test, Form B *cont.*

America's Challenges for a New Century

USA PATRIOT Act, October 2001	
Features of the Law	**Criticisms of the Law**
• Permits secret searches to avoid alerting suspects • Grants nationwide search warrants for any jurisdiction • Allows wiretapping of suspects • Law enforcement can track all forms of communication, such as voice mail	• Violates the Fourth Amendment protection against unreasonable search and seizure

6. Which features of the USA PATRIOT Act have civil libertarians protested against?

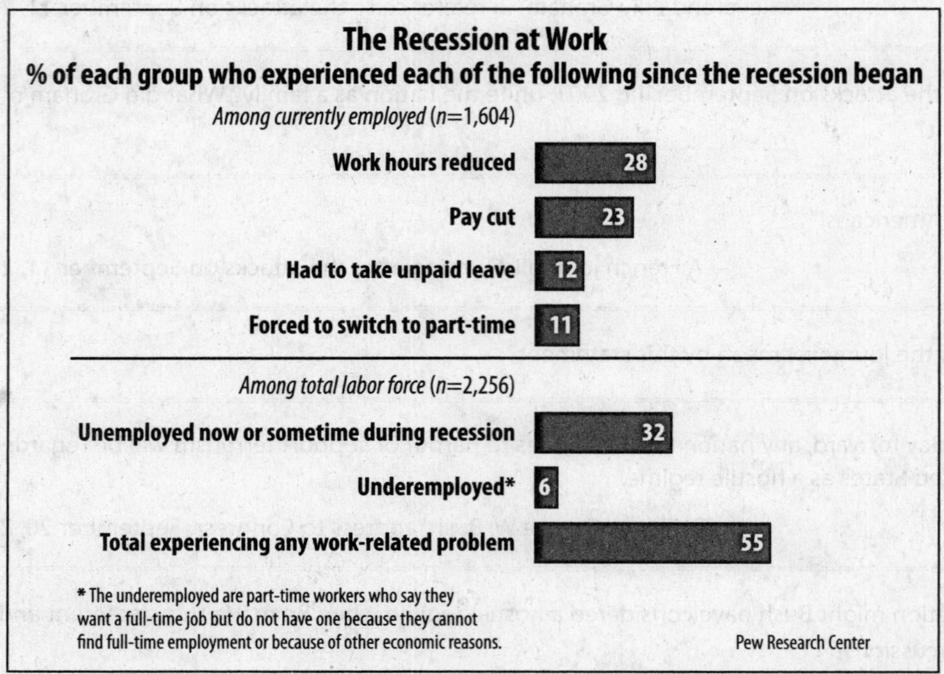

7. Based on information in the chart, describe how the American workforce was affected by the recession.

DIRECTIONS: Essay Answer the following question on a separate piece of paper.

8. What role did oil play in spawning terrorism?

CHAPTER 1

LESSON QUIZ 1-1

Completion

1. Vespucci
2. France
3. Great Awakening
4. Renaissance
5. colonies

Multiple Choice

6. d 7. a 8. d 9. c

LESSON QUIZ 1-2

Matching

1. e 2. c 3. a 4. b 5. d

Multiple Choice

6. c 7. d 8. a 9. b 10. a

LESSON QUIZ 1-3

Modified True/False

1. True
2. True
3. False—The rise of Southern industry LAGGED against the spread of cotton plantations across the South.
4. False—Missouri's application for statehood stirred up the issue of whether slavery SHOULD EXPAND WESTWARD.

Multiple Choice

5. c 6. a 7. b 8. c 9. b

LESSON QUIZ 1-4

Matching

1. e 2. c 3. d 4. a 5. b

Multiple Choice

6. b 7. a 8. d 9. a 10. b

LESSON QUIZ 1-5

Completion

1. vote
2. amnesty
3. Emancipation
4. Thirteenth

Multiple Choice

5. c 6. d 7. a 8. c 9. d

CHAPTER 1 TEST, FORM A

Matching

1. f 2. d 3. j 4. i 5. b
6. c 7. g 8. h 9. a 10. e

Multiple Choice

11. b 12. a 13. a 14. a 15. a
16. c 17. c 18. b 19. c 20. d

Short Answer

21. Hamilton's argument is based on the concept of enumerated and implied powers. Enumerated powers are specifically granted to the federal government in the Constitution. To exercise such powers, the Constitution gave the government authority to make laws that were "necessary and proper" for doing so. Implied powers were not included in the Constitution, but were needed to carry out the powers that were. Hamilton argued that the power to establish a national bank was implied by the government's power to regulate commerce and raise funds through taxation. Because the bank would help the government do its job and was not explicitly ruled out in the Constitution, it was constitutional.

22. In *Marbury* v. *Madison*, the Supreme Court decided that part of a law, the Judiciary Act of 1789, was unconstitutional and thus invalid. In his opinion, Chief Justice Marshall declared that it was the duty of the Supreme Court to determine if laws created by the government were constitutional. If a law violated the Constitution, the court had the authority to invalidate that law. This was the first time the Supreme Court asserted the power of judicial review, or the power to determine the constitutionality of laws. *Marbury* v. *Madison* firmly established this important power of the court and the judiciary branch.

23. In addition to enduring a lifetime of bondage, enslaved persons had few legal rights. State slave codes forbade enslaved men and women from owning property or leaving a slaveholder's premises without permission. They could not possess firearms or testify in court against a white person. Laws banned them from learning to read and write. Society viewed enslaved persons as property and treated them that way. Some enslaved people quietly staged work slowdowns. Others broke tools or set fire to houses or barns. Still others risked physical

punishments in order to run away. Some turned to more violent means of rebellion, such as killing their slaveholders or plotting armed uprisings.

24. Dred Scott was an enslaved man whose Missouri slaveholder had taken him to live in free territory before returning to Missouri. Assisted by abolitionists, Scott sued to end his slavery, arguing that the time he had spent in free territory meant he was free. The Supreme Court ruled against Scott, claiming that the founders of the nation had not intended for African Americans to be citizens. Instead of removing the issue of slavery in the territories from politics, this decision itself became a political issue and further intensified the sectional conflict. The Court had said that the federal government could not prohibit slavery in the territories.

25. The North's victory in the Civil War saved the Union and strengthened the power of the federal government over the states. It also transformed American society by finally ending the enslavement of millions of African Americans. At the same time, it left the South socially and economically devastated.

CHAPTER 1 TEST, FORM B

Short Answer

1. The very sight of the Spanish soldiers terrified the Aztecs.

2. The Spanish conquest of the Aztec was mainly driven by greed. They wanted to seize all the gold and treasure possessed by the Aztec.

3. The Constitution established a system of checks and balances. This gives each branch of the federal government the ability to limit the power of the other branches.

4. The new governmental system divided power between the federal government and the state governments. The Constitution also divided the federal government into three separate branches.

5. The number of bales of cotton produced in the South increased dramatically between 1792 and 1860. In 1792 only six thousand bales were produced, while in 1860 the number had grown to four million.

6. By 1860 Southern cotton accounted for nearly two-thirds of the total export trade of the United States. Cotton was grown in a wide belt stretching from inland South Carolina west into Texas. The spread of cotton plantations boosted the Southern economy, and this greatly increased the demand for enslaved labor.

7. The South only had small financial institutions, while most of the wealth and currency resided in the North. In addition, Southerners bore a lot of debt on their farms. They were not in a good position to finance a war effort.

8. Because most Southern planters were in debt and southern banks were small and had few cash reserves, they could not buy many bonds. The South also had difficulty raising money by taxing trade and by taxing its own people because many Southerners resented the taxes and refused to pay. The Confederacy printed paper money, which caused rapid inflation.

CHAPTER 2

LESSON QUIZ 2-1

Completion

1. Virginia City
2. boomtowns
3. longhorn
4. the federal government
5. prospectors

Multiple Choice

6. b **7.** d **8.** c **9.** b **10.** a

LESSON QUIZ 2-2

Matching

1. e **2.** a **3.** c **4.** b **5.** d

Multiple Choice

6. b **7.** b **8.** c **9.** d **10.** c

LESSON QUIZ 2-3

Modified True/False

1. False—The Dawes Act DID NOT SUCCEED in achieving its goals of assimilating Native Americans into American society as landowners and citizens.

2. False—After losing many of his people in a series of battles, Chief Joseph and the remaining Nez Perce under him were exiled to OKLAHOMA in 1877.
3. True
4. True

Multiple Choice

5. a 6. a 7. d 8. d

CHAPTER 2 TEST, FORM A

Matching

1. b 2. c 3. h 4. a 5. f
6. d 7. e 8. j 9. i 10. g

Multiple Choice

11. a 12. a 13. b 14. a 15. b
16. c 17. c 18. c 19. c 20. a

Short Answer

21. The Dakota Sioux had agreed to live on a small reservation in Minnesota in exchange for annuities, or regular payments, from the United States government. The payments were small, however, and much of the money never reached them. As a result, some of the Dakota were starving. When local traders refused to give them food on credit, the Dakota then slaughtered hundreds of settlers in the area.

22. The number of labor hours required to produce 100 bushels of wheat dropped drastically between 1830 and 1890. Many inventions during this time period (such as mechanical reapers and threshing machines) revolutionized agriculture and allowed farmers to become more productive and reduced their number of labor hours. In reducing the need for farm labor, these technological developments forced many workers to leave farming to find jobs in urban factories, enabling large cities to develop. In addition, the surplus of food produced on farms created more demand for factory-produced goods, which led to the Industrial Revolution

23. The Native American population dropped as the number of railroad track miles increased. One possible reason for this is that as railroad tracks were built, buffalo were killed. As the number of buffalo declined, the Native American population, which relied on buffalo as a food source, also declined. In addition, cattle ranching and gold and silver mining contributed to the growth of white settlements, towns, and cities, forever changing the Western frontier and permanently altering the Native American way of life.

24. Custer viewed Native Americans as savages, who were wilder than beasts. This view caused him to make a disastrous attack on Native American warriors in 1876. Native Americans have been considered as subhuman throughout the history of the United States and have experienced massacres, deadly forced marches, and oppressive government policies that removed Native Americans from their lands and forced them onto reservations with poor natural resources. Since the arrival of Europeans in North America, the Native American population has declined dramatically.

CHAPTER 2 TEST, FORM B

Short Answer

1. The discovery of gold was the main reason many people migrated west at this time. People also moved west to raise cattle on the Plains and to grow crops on farms throughout the Plains.

2. Railroads made it easier to transport goods from the East to settlers and provided settlers a fast, reliable method of shipping goods to Eastern markets.

3. In the late 1870s, bonanza farms would have allowed farmers to prosper. In the late 1880s, however, Western farmlands were hit by a drought and farmers suffered.

4. The soldiers acted recklessly by cutting timber and killing buffalo; often the soldiers did not eat the buffalo that was slain, thus acting selfishly and childlike.

5. Custer viewed Native Americans as savages, who were wilder than beasts. This view may have contributed to his disastrous attack on Native American warriors in 1876.

6. Since there was little to no wood available on the Great Plains, most people could not build wooden cabins.

7. The settlers had to be independent and self-reliant as they were isolated and endured many hardships, including those such as the three-day blizzard referenced here.

Essay

8. The construction of railroads provided easy access to the Great Plains. Railroad companies sold land along the rail lines at low prices and provided credit to prospective settlers. With the completion of the Transcontinental Railroad, the country was finally united from sea to shining sea. The convenient and efficient transport enabled people and goods to travel coast to coast more cheaply and paved the way for the Industrial Revolution and for the United States to become a global economic power.

CHAPTER 3

LESSON QUIZ 3-1

Modified True/False

1. True
2. False—The United States POSSESSED the natural resources upon which industrialization in the 1800s depended, including water, timber, coal, iron, and copper.
3. False—ALEXANDER GRAHAM BELL stood as a symbol of the emerging age of technology with his invention of the telephone.
4. True
5. True

Multiple Choice

6. d **7.** a **8.** b **9.** a

LESSON QUIZ 3-2

Matching

1. d **2.** a **3.** e **4.** b **5.** c

Multiple Choice

6. c **7.** a **8.** c **9.** c **10.** a

LESSON QUIZ 3-3

Matching

1. e **2.** b **3.** a **4.** c **5.** d

Multiple Choice

6. b **7.** a **8.** b **9.** d **10.** a

LESSON QUIZ 3-4

Modified True/False

1. False—As industrialism brought more machines into the workplace, jobs became SIMPLER and required FEWER skills.
2. True
3. False—In the late 1800s, large trade unions generally PROSPERED, but industrial unions FAILED.
4. False—In the late 1800s, workers' buying power generally INCREASED.
5. True

Multiple Choice

6. b **7.** c **8.** a **9.** c

CHAPTER 3 TEST, FORM A

Matching

1. e **2.** f **3.** c **4.** h **5.** a
6. g **7.** d **8.** b **9.** j **10.** i

Multiple Choice

11. b **12.** a **13.** c **14.** c **15.** b
16. d **17.** c **18.** d **19.** a **20.** d

Short Answer

21. A corporation is an organization owned by many people but treated by law as though it were a single person. It can own property, pay taxes, and make contracts. The people who own the corporation are called stockholders, because they own shares of ownership called stock. Issuing stock allows a corporation to raise large amounts of money for big projects, while spreading out the risk.

22. The economic strategy is known as vertical integration. Andrew Carnegie developed this system to grow his Carnegie Steel Company. By employing vertical integration in his business plan, Carnegie sought to cut out the middleman and control every aspect of steel production from owning his own iron and coal mines and railroads to selling his product directly to the user. Because of the cost savings and efficiencies associated with owning the raw materials of steel production, Carnegie was able to undersell his competitors and dominate the steel industry during the Industrial Revolution.

23. Socialists such as Debs argued that the basic force shaping capitalist society was the class struggle between workers and owners. The workers in the mills, factories, mines, and railways struggled to earn a living while being paid low wages in often dangerous conditions. Union leaders led strikes against hugely profitable industries that were meant to improve working conditions for laborers, while more radical Socialists began to call for the end of capitalism rather than its reform.

CHAPTER 3 TEST, FORM B

Short Answer

1. Abundant natural resources
2. Edison and his team of workers were so excited that they could not sleep. They did not want to step away from the lamp as long as it was burning.
3. Carnegie believes that those who hoard great sums of money until they die are doing a disservice to society by being selfish with their wealth. The money that was hoarded, Carnegie states, would have been better used to do work that benefits the community.
4. Workers wanted nothing less than an eight-hour workday and more money than they received the year before.
5. The government's main action was usually calling out troops to restore order.

Essay

6. By linking the nation, railroads helped increase the size of markets, providing greater opportunities for many industries and individuals. Huge consumers themselves, the railroads also stimulated the economy by spending extraordinary amounts of money on steel, coal, timber, and other needs. Captains of industry, or railroad barons such as Jay Gould and James J. Hill, connected the country like never before and led the transition of the United States from a predominantly rural, agrarian society to an urban, industrial nation.

CHAPTER 4

LESSON QUIZ 4-1

Matching

1. b 2. c 3. e 4. a 5. d

Multiple Choice

6. b 7. a 8. b 9. d 10. c

LESSON QUIZ 4-2

True/False

1. True
2. False
3. True
4. False
5. True

Multiple Choice

6. a 7. c 8. d 9. c 10. b

LESSON QUIZ 4-3

Completion

1. individualism
2. realists
3. ragtime
4. settlement house
5. Salvation Army

Multiple Choice

6. c 7. b 8. d 9. b 10. a

LESSON QUIZ 4-4

Matching

1. b 2. e 3. c 4. a 5. d

Multiple Choice

6. c 7. a 8. d 9. c 10. b

LESSON QUIZ 4-5

Completion

1. sharecroppers
2. Plessy
3. Jim Crow
4. Washington
5. W.E.B. Du Bois

Multiple Choice

6. d 7. b 8. a 9. d

CHAPTER 4 TEST, FORM A

Matching

1. c **2.** f **3.** j **4.** a **5.** i
6. h **7.** d **8.** g **9.** b **10.** e

Multiple Choice

11. c **12.** a **13.** d **14.** b **15.** a
16. b **17.** b **18.** c **19.** c **20.** a

Short Answer

21. Crime, violence, disease, and pollution posed threats to city dwellers. The rapid growth of cities made these problems worse. Pickpockets, swindlers, and thieves thrived in urban living conditions. Alcohol contributed to violent crime both inside and outside the home. Improper sewage disposal contaminated drinking water and triggered epidemics of typhoid fever and cholera. Pollution resulted from the smoke, soot, and ash from coal and wood fires.

22. Hull House was a famous settlement house, or community center, in Chicago. Opened by Jane Addams and other reformers in 1889, it became an example for other settlement houses around the country and for the settlement house movement. In settlement houses around the country, reformers lived in poor, largely immigrant communities and provided a wide range of services. For example, Hull House fulfilled the purposes set out in its charter by offering daycare, kindergartens, libraries, an art gallery, an employment agency, a meeting place for unions, and other services to many poor immigrant families in Chicago.

23. Many poor European farmers came simply because the United States had plenty of jobs available and few immigration restrictions. Some Europeans moved to avoid forced military service. Others, especially Jews living in Poland and Russia, fled to avoid religious persecution. By the late 1800s, most European countries had made it easier to move to the United States. They had repealed laws that kept people from leaving. At the same time, moving to the United States offered a chance to break away from the European class system and move to where newcomers had a chance to climb the social ladder.

24. "Deflation" is an increase in the value of money and a decrease in the general level of prices. Deflation hit farmers especially hard. Most farmers had to borrow money for seeds and other supplies to plant their crops. Because money was in short supply, interest rates began to rise, which increased the amount farmers owed. For those who wanted to expand their farms, rising interest rates also made mortgages more expensive. The falling prices of the period of deflation meant that farmers sold their crops for less. Nonetheless, they still had to make the same mortgage payments to the bank.

25. Booker T. Washington proposed that African Americans concentrate on achieving economic goals rather than legal or political ones. In his famous speech known as the Atlanta Compromise, he urged fellow African Americans to postpone the fight for civil rights and instead concentrate on preparing themselves educationally and vocationally for full equality. W.E.B. Du Bois challenged Washington's ideas. He pointed out that white Southerners continued to strip African Americans of their civil rights, in spite of the progress they were making in educational and vocational training. Du Bois argued that African Americans could regain that lost ground and achieve full equality only by demanding their rights. Du Bois was particularly concerned with protecting and exercising voting rights.

CHAPTER 4 TEST, FORM B

Short Answer

1. Millions of immigrants came to the United States in the late 1800s. The largest numbers by far came from Germany and Ireland, but many immigrated from eastern and southern European nations, such as Italy and Poland, as well as from Asia. Immigrants tended to settle in cities; states with large cities, such as New York and Illinois, became home to the highest numbers of immigrants.

2. Immigrants from China settled primarily in western states such as California. Nationwide, immigration from China was a very small fraction of overall immigration totals. In California, however, China accounted for as much as a quarter of all immigration during this period.

3. The theory of Social Darwinism held that human society "evolved" and progressed when people competed against one another, with only the fittest surviving. In the statement, Sumner argues against providing any kind of economic assistance to people. He believes that if people compete and fail, it is their own fault—although he does allow that "misfortune" may play some role.

4. The doctrine of laissez-faire holds that government should not interfere with business in any way at all. Sumner's argument against providing help to people reflects the laissez-faire argument against policies that targeted economic inequality. Both were seen as misguided efforts to protect the weak and undeserving, efforts that hindered the economic progress of the strong.

5. New technology enabled farmers to produce more crops, but that caused prices to fall. High tariffs made it difficult for them to sell their crops overseas, high interest rates increased their debt, and high railroad rates made shipping crops within the United States unaffordable. Farmers felt they were being victimized by faraway entities such as the banks and the railroads.

6. Farmers who considered themselves to be "losing ground" did a number of things in the late 1800s. They supported political organizations such as the Grange and the Farmers' Alliance. Economically they formed cooperatives to drive prices up and negotiate shipping rates, and they supported unlimited silver coinage and the establishment of subtreasuries.

Essay

7. American cities grew dramatically in the late 1800s. Between 1870 and 1900, the urban population of the United States tripled from around 10 million to over 30 million. A wave of immigrants was one cause for this growth; millions of immigrants from eastern and southern Europe and from Asia settled in ethnic neighborhoods of New York, Chicago, San Francisco, and other cities. Americans also moved from rural areas to cities in search of economic opportunity and the excitement of urban life. Growing cities faced many new problems, including crowding and congestion, pollution, poverty and crime, and political corruption. Urban Americans met these challenges in a variety of ways. New building and transportation technology helped to ease crowding and reduce pollution. Social reformers worked to help working class communities and campaigned for laws and programs to relieve poverty. Urban political machines were often corrupt, but provided vital services in poor communities.

CHAPTER 5

LESSON QUIZ 5-1

Matching

1. b **2.** c **3.** a **4.** e **5.** d

Multiple Choice

6. b **7.** d **8.** c **9.** b

LESSON QUIZ 5-2

Completion

1. yellow journalists
2. jingoism
3. independent
4. Rough Riders
5. Puerto Rico

Multiple Choice

6. c **7.** d **8.** b **9.** a **10.** a

LESSON QUIZ 5-3

True/False

1. False
2. True
3. True
4. True
5. False

Multiple Choice

6. b **7.** a **8.** d **9.** c

CHAPTER 5 TEST, FORM A

Matching

1. j **2.** g **3.** b **4.** e **5.** a
6. h **7.** d **8.** c **9.** i **10.** f

Multiple Choice

11. b **12.** d **13.** c **14.** c **15.** c
16. b **17.** a **18.** d **19.** b **20.** b

Short Answer

21. Economic and military competition from other nations, as well as a growing feeling of cultural superiority, led the shift in American opinion toward imperialism. Several European nations were expanding their power overseas, forming colonies and protectorates to protect their new markets and investments in other nations. In the United States, the Western frontier was filling up, and many Americans concluded that the nation had to develop new overseas markets to keep its economy strong. Influential author Alfred T. Mahan argued that the United States needed to build a large navy to protect its merchant ships and to defend its right to trade with other countries. To support the navy, the United States had to acquire territory for overseas bases. At the same time, many Americans began to believe in Anglo-Saxonism—the idea that English-speaking nations had superior character, ideas, and systems of government, and were destined to dominate the planet.

22. The United States went to war with Spain for several reasons. Cuba had rebelled against Spain, and Americans both sympathized with Cuban rebels and wished to protect U.S. investments in Cuba. Support for the rebels was fueled by sensationalized stories of Spanish atrocities in leading American newspapers. Finally, the mysterious explosion of the U.S. battleship *Maine* was widely blamed on Spain. The resolution emphasizes "abhorrent conditions" that "have shocked the moral sense of the people of the United States" and the destruction of the *Maine*, suggesting that yellow journalism and reaction to the ship's destruction were major forces leading the drive to war. The resolution also declares that it is "the duty of the United States" to demand Spain leave Cuba but does not mention growing U.S. power and influence in Latin America.

23. Many supporters of annexation based their arguments on the economic and military benefits of taking the Philippines. They would provide the United States with a Pacific naval base and a large market for American goods. Other arguments were based on the idea that the United States had a duty to help "less civilized" people by governing them. For example, Senator Beveridge argued that Filipinos were not capable of governing themselves. Many opponents of annexation felt such arguments contradicted American principles. In addition, they argued that the economic and military costs of annexation would far outweigh the benefits. Bryan argues that the United States could have a friendly port and trade with the Philippines without the burden of governing a foreign people.

24. Theodore Roosevelt believed in a strong global military presence. He insisted that displaying American power to the world would make nations think twice about fighting, thus promoting global peace. He often expressed this belief with a West African saying, "Speak softly and carry a big stick." The voyage of the Great White Fleet was one application of this policy, showcasing the nation's mighty fleet to the world. Another example was the use of the United States military to aid the revolt in Panama.

25. Although Wilson opposed imperialism, he recognized the influence the United States could have on foreign nations. After revolution overtook Mexico in 1911, Victoriano Huerta seized power and presumably had his predecessor, Francisco Madero, murdered. Wilson viewed Huerta as a brutal dictator. When the Mexican government refused to apologize for arresting American sailors who had entered a restricted area, Wilson sent troops into Mexico. Anti-American riots ensued, and Pancho Villa, a guerrilla, burned the town of Columbus, New Mexico.

CHAPTER 5 TEST, FORM B

Short Answer

1. During this period, the Western frontier was becoming more settled. Also, American agriculture and industry produced more goods than Americans could consume. The United States needed to invest in other countries in order to develop foreign markets for its goods and keep its economy growing.

2. The need to develop foreign markets for U.S. goods was one factor that led the United States to assert itself as a world power. As the nation's overseas investments increased, the United States used forceful diplomacy and even military interventions to protect those investments. The need to protect U.S. investments was a factor in the Spanish-American War, for example.

3. The Platt Amendment was submitted by U.S. Senator Orville Platt after the Spanish-American War. As a condition of independence, President McKinley required Cuba to include the Platt Amendment in its new constitution.

4. Cuba could not make any treaty with another nation that would weaken its independence or allow another foreign power to gain territory in Cuba. Also, Cuba had to allow the United States to buy or lease naval stations in Cuba. Cuba's debts had to be kept low to prevent foreign countries from landing troops to enforce payment. Finally, the United States would have the right to intervene to protect Cuban independence and keep order.

5. The actions listed in the chart are primarily focused on U.S. economic interests. Opening Japanese markets, the Open Door policy in China, support for trade with Latin America, support for Cuban rebels, and other actions served to create and expand foreign markets for American goods and increase U.S. access to raw materials.

6. The United States asserted its power and influence more forcefully in Latin America than it did in the Pacific. For example, the United States supported an Open Door trade policy in China, while it used the Pan-American Conference and the Roosevelt Corollary to limit the influence of other powers in Latin America.

Essay

7. Between 1872 and 1917, the United States began to assert itself as a world power and to seek to influence other nations. In many cases, the United States sought to create markets for U.S. goods in other nations. Examples include the first Pan-American Conference in 1889 and the Open Door policy in China beginning in 1899. The United States also attempted to limit the influence of European powers over other nations, especially in Latin America and in the Pacific. At the end of the Spanish-American War, for example, the Platt Amendment tied the newly independent Cuba to the United States while attempting to seal the nation off from European influence. During this period, the United States became an imperial power as a result of its interactions with other nations. The United States acquired territories in the Pacific and in Latin America, including Hawaii, the Philippines, and Puerto Rico. Also, actions such as the construction of the Panama Canal and policies such as the Roosevelt Corollary established the United States as a dominant power in the Americas.

CHAPTER 6

LESSON QUIZ 6-1

Completion

1. women
2. science
3. compensation
4. direct
5. expert

Multiple Choice

6. c **7.** c **8.** d **9.** d **10.** c

LESSON QUIZ 6-2

True/False

1. True
2. False
3. True
4. True
5. True

Multiple Choice

6. c **7.** c **8.** c **9.** a **10.** d

LESSON QUIZ 6-3

Modified True/False

1. True
2. False—Woodrow Wilson entered politics as a firm PROGRESSIVE.
3. False—The most conspicuous limit to progressivism came in its failure to address RACIAL, ETHNIC, AND RELIGIOUS reform issues.
4. False—Woodrow Wilson wanted the Federal Trade Commission to WORK TOWARD LIMITING BUSINESS ACTIVITIES THAT UNFAIRLY LIMITED COMPETITION.
5. True

Multiple Choice

6. a **7.** a **8.** d **9.** c

CHAPTER 6 TEST, FORM A

Matching

1. h	**2.** e	**3.** j	**4.** f	**5.** i
6. a	**7.** g	**8.** b	**9.** d	**10.** c

Multiple Choice

11. b	**12.** b	**13.** b	**14.** a	**15.** a
16. c	**17.** b	**18.** b	**19.** a	**20.** c

Short Answer

21. In an era before modern pharmaceuticals had been developed, many companies patented and marketed potions they claimed would cure a variety of ills. Many patent medicines contained unknown ingredients. Consumers had no way to know what they were taking, nor received any assurance the potions worked as claimed. Journalists reported on these potentially dangerous practices, which enraged consumers. In 1906 the Pure Food and Drug Act was passed, prohibiting the manufacture, sale, or shipment of impure or falsely labeled food and drugs.

22. Roosevelt and Taft were very different kinds of men. Roosevelt was a dynamic person who loved the spotlight and the rough-and-tumble world of politics. He had grand ideas and schemes, but left the details of administering them to others. Taft was in many ways the opposite. He was a skillful administrator and judge. He disliked political maneuvering and preferred to avoid conflict with others. Unlike Roosevelt, who acted quickly and decisively on issues, Taft responded slowly, approaching problems from a legalistic point of view.

23. In the council-manager form of government, the voters elect a city council. The city council elects a mayor and hires a city manager and establishes city policies. The city manager appoints the heads of city departments who carry out the city's policies. In this system, the voters elect the people directly in charge of government, but the people operating city services and departments are trained professionals hired to be objective and do their job efficiently.

24. Roosevelt accepted the economic power of the trusts as a fact of life and proposed a more powerful federal government and a strong executive to regulate them. Wilson criticized Roosevelt's program as one that supported "regulated monopoly." Monopolies, Wilson believed, were evils to be destroyed, not regulated. Wilson argued that Roosevelt's approach gave the federal government too much power in the economy and did nothing to restore competition.

CHAPTER 6 TEST, FORM B

Short Answer

1. Muckrakers wrote articles and books that publicized societal problems and corruption. Often these writings brought about changes, as in the case of Upton Sinclair's *The Jungle*.

2. Theodore Roosevelt's Bull Moose Party

3. That the employer was breaking the law regulating how late children could work

4. The author is referencing the horrific practice of lynching, when white mobs murdered African Americans in the most brutal ways imaginable.

5. The table shows that progressive reformers were interested in making changes in several different areas and sought solutions to problems in government, business, and society.

Essay

6. Progressivism was not a tightly organized political movement. Progressives often disagreed with one another, although they generally believed that industrialism and urbanization had created many social problems. Progressives belonged to both major political parties and usually were urban, educated, middle-class Americans. Some progressives saw corruption and inefficiency in government. They focused on making government more efficient by applying principles of scientific management to it. Other progressives wanted to make elected officials more responsive to the concerns of voters. They pushed for reforms such as direct primaries and direct election of senators. Other groups saw the unequal status of women and focused on gaining women the right to vote. Some progressives wanted to solve problems such as crime, illiteracy, drunkenness, and threats to health and safety. They pushed for social welfare reform, such as child labor laws, health and safety codes, and prohibition.

CHAPTER 7

LESSON QUIZ 7-1

Completion

1. Prussia
2. Balkans
3. U-boats
4. Allied Powers
5. *Lusitania*

Multiple Choice

6. b 7. b 8. a 9. a

LESSON QUIZ 7-2

Modified True/False

1. False—To help prevent strikes from disrupting the war effort, the government established the NATIONAL WAR LABOR BOARD in April 1918.
2. False—The War Industries Board worked TO COORDINATE THE PRODUCTION OF WAR MATERIALS.
3. False—A new government agency, the Committee on Public Information, had the task of "SELLING" THE WAR TO THE AMERICAN PEOPLE.
4. True

Multiple Choice

5. c 6. c 7. b 8. d

LESSON QUIZ 7-3

Completion

1. poison
2. Fourteen
3. airplanes
4. Congress
5. Germany

Multiple Choice

6. c 7. a 8. a 9. a 10. c

LESSON QUIZ 7-4

True/False

1. False
2. True
3. True
4. True
5. False

Multiple Choice

6. d 7. d 8. a 9. d

CHAPTER 7 TEST, FORM A

Matching

1. d 2. f 3. a 4. j 5. b
6. i 7. g 8. e 9. h 10. c

Multiple Choice

11. c 12. d 13. a 14. b 15. c
16. b 17. b 18. c 19. a 20. a

Short Answer

21. In the first five points, President Wilson proposed to eliminate the general causes of war through free trade, disarmament, freedom of the seas, impartial adjustment of colonial claims, and open diplomacy instead of secret agreements. The next eight points addressed the right of self-determination. They also required the Central Powers to evacuate all of the countries invaded during the war. The fourteenth point called for the creation of the League of Nations. The League's member nations would help preserve peace and prevent future wars by pledging to respect and protect each other's territory and political independence.

22. The purpose of the War Industries Board was to organize industry to increase efficiency and maximize production. It set priorities, told manufacturers what they could and could not make, controlled the flow of raw materials, ordered the construction of new factories, and occasionally, with the president's approval, set prices. The purpose of the National War Labor Board was to maintain cooperation between industry management and labor unions. It attempted to mediate labor disputes that might otherwise lead to strikes. It frequently pressured industry to grant concessions to workers in exchange for the agreement of labor leaders not to disrupt war production with strikes and other disturbances.

23. When the war ended, government agencies removed their controls on the economy. This released pent-up demand. People raced to buy goods that had been rationed, while businesses rapidly raised prices they had been forced to keep low during the war. The result was rapid

inflation. Workers wanted to raise their wages to keep up with inflation. On the other hand, companies wanted to hold down wages because inflation was also driving up their operating costs. These competing desires helped spark the wave of strikes.

24. It suggests that a representative of the Military Intelligence Service would worry that someone speaking out against the war would discredit America's participation in it.

25. Wilson believed that it was his constitutional duty to protect the welfare of the United States. Events such as the discovery of the Zimmermann telegram and unrestricted submarine warfare by the Germans strengthened his resolve.

CHAPTER 7 TEST, FORM B

Short Answer

1. The sloops or patrol boats were positioned to the front, back, and sides of the convoy in order to better detect and defend the cargo transports against enemy vessels, such as German U-boats.

2. Debs thought that the Espionage Law went against America's principles as a free, open, and democratic society and that it should be peacefully opposed.

3. The industrialists and factory owners lead a luxurious lifestyle, drinking champagne and having banquets. Meanwhile, the workers barely have enough food to survive and only desire a bit of leisure time to enjoy life.

4. To prepare for war, the U.S. government needed to do several things. It needed to organize the economy, set up a workforce, and build up the military. However, none of these could have been accomplished without the support of the public. Public support was the key to everything else.

5. The telegram instructed the German ambassador in Mexico to propose that Mexico ally itself with Germany in the event of war between Germany and the United States. In return, Mexico would regain its "lost territory in Texas, New Mexico, and Arizona."

Essay

6. To try to cut off supplies going to Britain, the Germans announced in 1915 that their U-boats would sink without warning any ship found in the waters around Great Britain. This announcement outraged the United States because it violated an international treaty requiring military vessels to reveal their intentions to merchant ships and provide for the safety of the people aboard before sinking the ships. In implementing their policy, the Germans sank the British passenger liner *Lusitania* in the war zone, killing 1,200, including 128 Americans. In 1917 British intelligence intercepted a telegram from Arthur Zimmermann, a German official. It proposed to offer the Mexican government its "lost territory in Texas, New Mexico, and Arizona" if Mexico sided with Germany in the event the United States entered the war. After Germany resumed unrestricted submarine warfare in February 1917, the United States moved to declare war.

CHAPTER 8

LESSON QUIZ 8-1

True/False

1. True
2. False
3. True
4. False
5. False

Multiple Choice

6. a **7.** d **8.** c **9.** a

LESSON QUIZ 8-2

Completion

1. installment
2. radio programs
3. Advertisers
4. assembly line
5. farmers

Multiple Choice

6. b **7.** a **8.** a **9.** a **10.** c

LESSON QUIZ 8-3

Completion

1. quota
2. flappers
3. Eighteenth Amendment
4. the Ku Klux Klan

Multiple Choice

5. c **6.** a **7.** c **8.** b **9.** c

LESSON QUIZ 8-4

True/False

1. True
2. False
3. True
4. False

Multiple Choice

5. d **6.** d **7.** a **8.** a **9.** a

LESSON QUIZ 8-5

Matching

1. b **2.** d **3.** c **4.** e **5.** a

Multiple Choice

6. c **7.** d **8.** d **9.** c **10.** b

CHAPTER 8 TEST, FORM A

Matching

1. f **2.** e **3.** b **4.** c **5.** h
6. j **7.** d **8.** i **9.** g **10.** a

Multiple Choice

11. d **12.** b **13.** b **14.** b **15.** c
16. a **17.** b **18.** a **19.** d **20.** d

Short Answer

21. Technological advances enabled farmers to produce more, but higher yields without a corresponding increase in demand meant that they received lower prices. The cost of the improved technology to farmers, meanwhile, continued to increase. Many factors contributed to the "quiet depression" in American agriculture. During the war, the government had urged farmers to produce more to meet the great need for food supplies in Europe. Many farmers borrowed heavily to buy new land (at inflated prices) and new machinery in order to raise more crops. After the war, however, European farm output rose, and the debt-ridden countries of Europe had little to spend on American farm products anyway. Then Congress passed a tariff law in 1922 that provoked a reaction in foreign markets against American agricultural products. Farmers in the United States could no longer sell as much of their output overseas, and prices tumbled.

22. Supporters of supply-side economics, such as Secretary of the Treasury Mellon, believed that high taxes reduced the money available for private investment and prevented business expansion. Mellon argued that high tax rates actually reduced the amount of tax money the government collected. If taxes were lower, businesses and consumers would spend and invest their extra money, causing the economy to grow. As the economy grew, Americans would earn more money, and the government would actually collect more taxes at a lower rate than it would if it kept rates high.

23. In the 1920s, Americans persisted in blatantly ignoring Prohibition laws. People flocked to secret bars called speakeasies where they could buy alcohol. Organized crime specialized in supplying and often running these speakeasies, which popped up all over the country. The great demand for liquor meant that huge profits could be made. Because making and selling liquor were illegal, legitimate businesses could not fill the need. As a result, supplying the demand for liquor became a billion-dollar industry for gangsters.

24. Although not the typical American woman, the young, unconventional "flapper" personified women's quest for personal freedom in the 1920s. While flappers pursued social freedoms, other women sought financial independence by entering the workforce. Many single and working-class women worked simply because they needed the wages for themselves or for their families, but for some young, single women, work was a way to break away from parental authority and establish a personal identity. Work also provided the wages that allowed women to participate in the consumer culture. Many women who attended college in the 1920s found support for their emerging sense of independence. Women's colleges, in particular, encouraged their students to pursue careers and to challenge traditional ideas about the nature of women and their role in society.

25. Henry Ford adopted the assembly line, which enormously increased manufacturing efficiency. Ford's system divided operations into simple tasks that unskilled workers could do, and it cut unnecessary motion to a minimum. In 1914 he installed the first moving assembly line, which enabled workers to build a car in a fraction of the time required only one year before. These mass production methods lowered the cost per car, which lowered prices for consumers. As lower prices increased sales volume, prices could be reduced even more, leading to affordable cars for the majority of Americans.

CHAPTER 8 TEST, FORM B

Short Answer

1. The economic prosperity of the 1920s allowed many Americans more time for entertainment. Increased attendance at events related to sports and entertainment made it more profitable to build bigger and better theaters.

2. Commercial radio began its rise as a national phenomenon in 1920 with coverage of the presidential election. Amateur listeners are less fortunate because they typically do not listen to more than six radio stations.

3. The 1920s was a time of many inventions and innovations that made life easier for people and gave them more leisure time.

4. The Scopes jury was composed mostly of rural Tennesseans, who were more likely to be religious fundamentalists who would uphold the traditional interpretation of Creation over evolution.

5. Vanzetti describes the atmosphere of hysteria at the time and cites Americans' fears of his anarchist political principles, slackers or "draft dodgers" and foreigners in general as reasons for his conviction.

6. In 1922 Congress passed the Fordney-McCumber Act, which actually made the situation worse for farmers. By raising tariffs on foreign goods, it provoked a backlash against American agricultural products, which lowered income for farmers even more.

7. Cars revolutionized American life. The auto industry created jobs in related industries, such as rubber, plate glass, nickel, and petroleum. Cars eased the isolation of rural life, putting towns within reach of many farmers and the countryside a mere ride away for city dwellers. Cars also enabled people to live farther away from work. An entirely new kind of consumer and worker, the auto commuter, appeared. Commuters lived in growing suburban communities and drove to work in the city.

CHAPTER 9

LESSON QUIZ 9-1

Matching

1. b **2.** e **3.** a **4.** c **5.** d

Multiple Choice

6. a **7.** c **8.** b **9.** d **10.** b

LESSON QUIZ 9-2

Modified True/False

1. False—The Depression WORSENED steadily during President Hoover's administration.
2. True
3. True
4. True
5. False—"Okies" were usually farmers who LOST their land and TRAVELED to California TO LOOK FOR WORK.

Multiple Choice

6. a **7.** d **8.** d **9.** c

LESSON QUIZ 9-3

Completion

1. Reserve
2. economy
3. Relief and Construction
4. Bonus Army

Multiple Choice

5. d **6.** b **7.** b **8.** c **9.** a

CHAPTER 9 TEST, FORM A

Matching

1. i **2.** e **3.** j **4.** g **5.** d

6. b **7.** a **8.** f **9.** c **10.** h

Multiple Choice

11. a **12.** d **13.** a **14.** a **15.** b
16. d **17.** c **18.** c **19.** a **20.** b

Short Answer

21. When buying stock on margin, investors made only a small cash down payment—as low as 10 percent of the price. For example, with a $1,000 down payment, an investor could buy $10,000 worth of stock. The other $9,000 would come as a loan from a stockbroker. If the stock price then rose to $12,000, the investor could sell the stock, pay off the loan, and make a quick $2,000 profit on the $1,000 investment. However, if the stock price dropped, the broker could demand that the investor repay the loan at once. This created problems for the investor. For example, if the stock price dropped and the investor sold it for $8,000, he or she would still have to come up with $1,000 to pay off the $9,000 loan. Not only would the initial $1,000 investment be lost, but with this additional $1,000, the investor's total loss would be $2,000. Worse still, the investor might not be able to repay the loan at all.

22. Marx lost a lot of money in the stock market crash. His broker had told him that he would not face any real risk when he allowed the broker to invest his money in the stock market. Many people were caught up in speculating on rising stock prices during the 1920s. Eventually the stock prices adjusted down to reflect real economic value and many people lost a great deal of money. Based on the excerpt, Marx felt he had made a mistake when he accepted his broker's assurance that there was no risk and nothing could go wrong. Instead of carefully picking stocks based on the companies' performances, he allowed himself to get drawn into very expensive speculation.

23. Most economists agree that overproduction was a key cause of the Depression. Increasingly efficient machinery greatly sped up the production of factory and farm goods. Most Americans, however, did not earn enough to buy the flood of goods they helped produce. As consumers bought more goods on the installment plan, the debt incurred forced some to reduce their other purchases. As sales slowed, manufacturers cut production and laid off employees. Jobless workers had to cut back purchases even more, causing business activity to spiral downward. A second cause was the loss of export sales. American banks were making loans to speculators instead of to foreign companies. This, along with the Hawley-Smoot Tariff that dampened foreign sales in the United States, caused foreign countries to buy fewer American products. A third cause was mistakes by the Federal Reserve. Instead of raising interest rates to curb excessive speculation, it kept rates low. This action encouraged banks to make risky loans and encouraged businesses to borrow more money to expand production, adding to the problem of overproduction.

24. Many farmers lost their land as a result of the Depression and of the drought that turned the Great Plains into a "Dust Bowl." Often, these farmers migrated to California with their families in search of work and a new start. Because many of the destitute farmers came from Oklahoma, they were known as "Okies." In California, the migrants took whatever work they could find harvesting other farmers' crops. Because there were far more migrants than there was work, they were paid very little. Migrants lived in roadside camps or paid growers exorbitant rents to live in shacks. They remained impoverished.

Essay

25. In the 1930s, many Americans preferred popular entertainment that let them escape the worries of the Depression. More than 60 million people went to the movies every week and the most popular movies included comedies, musicals—vehicles for child stars such as Shirley Temple—and cartoons. Radio provided entertainment in the home. Comedians such as Jack Benny, George Burns, and Gracie Allen were popular, as were adventure serials and daytime dramas nicknamed "soap operas." While movies and radio programs provided entertainment and distraction, literature and art often tried to portray the reality of life. Writers such as John Steinbeck used the homeless and unemployed as their subjects. Photographers such as Dorothea Lange and Margaret Bourke-White showed how the Great Depression affected average Americans. New styles of literature and art also flourished, including the stream-of-consciousness novels of William Faulkner and the paintings of the regionalist school.

CHAPTER 9 TEST, FORM B

Short Answer

1. The stock market crash severely weakened the banks. Banks had loaned a great deal of money to speculators and had invested in the market as well. That money was now lost. The crash was a key factor in causing banks to begin closing.

2. Some banks closed immediately after the crash, but the graph indicates that bank closings did not become a crisis right away. When the first banks closed, depositors at other banks became frightened their banks would also close and they would lose their savings. Many depositors panicked and withdrew their money, causing bank runs. By 1932 around 10 percent of the nation's banks had closed; even more closed in 1933.

3. One might notice empty buildings and idle factories. Also the streets might not be so crowded with trucks.

4. During the Depression, soup kitchens and bread lines that stretched for blocks were common sights in many American cities. Also, newly homeless people set up shantytowns they called Hoovervilles.

5. Hoover believed in a limited role for government. He did not support federal intervention in the economy or federal involvement in public relief. Hoover believed the American system of "rugged individualism" would keep the economy moving. If relief programs were needed, he believed state and city governments, along with charities and religious groups, should be responsible for them.

6. President Hoover's response to the Depression was limited by his belief in the limited role of government. He increased funding for public works, but refused to massively increase government spending—which would have been necessary to spur economic recovery. Hoover also believed government should not step in to help individuals. When Congress passed the Emergency Relief and Construction Act in 1932, Hoover signed it only reluctantly. By then, it was too late to stem the Depression.

7. Many farmers heavily mortgaged their land to pay for seed, feed, and equipment. When the farmers were unable to repay these loans, their creditors moved to seize their lands through foreclosure.

8. During World War I, prices for agricultural products were high and farmers expanded production. After the war, prices sank so low farmers began losing money. By destroying their crops, farmers hoped to cause a drop in supply that might raise prices.

Essay

9. The economy of the 1920s was characterized by overproduction, uneven income distribution, high tariffs that suppressed export sales, low interest rates, and a long bull market. Americans were encouraged to borrow heavily to purchase consumer goods and speculate in the stock market. The stock market crash wiped out around $30 billion of wealth, leaving many Americans unable to repay their debts to banks and to stockbrokers. Under the pressure of the crash and of bank runs by nervous depositors, banks began to close. Unable to sell excess goods, businesses began to cut back production and close. Also, agricultural overproduction led to a collapse in prices. These economic changes had a dramatic effect on the lives of American citizens. Business cutbacks and failures left more than 12 million workers unemployed. When banks closed, depositors lost their savings. Indebted Americans lost their homes to foreclosures; farmers, also unable to pay their mortgages, lost their land. Bread lines, soup kitchens, and shantytowns known as Hoovervilles became common sights throughout the United States. The Depression was a powerful example of the real impact economic changes have on ordinary people.

CHAPTER 10

LESSON QUIZ 10-1

Completion

1. optimism
2. much
3. work
4. Relief

Multiple Choice

5. c **6.** c **7.** b **8.** a

LESSON QUIZ 10-2

Matching

1. d **2.** e **3.** c **4.** a **5.** b

Multiple Choice

6. d **7.** a **8.** b **9.** c

LESSON QUIZ 10-3

True/False

1. True
2. True
3. False
4. False
5. True

Multiple Choice

6. b **7.** b **8.** d **9.** c

CHAPTER 10 TEST, FORM A

Matching

1. h **2.** i **3.** f **4.** g **5.** e

6. c **7.** a **8.** b **9.** d **10.** j

Multiple Choice

11. b **12.** d **13.** c **14.** a **15.** c

16. b **17.** d **18.** a **19.** b **20.** d

Short Answer

21. President Roosevelt projected an energy and optimism that gave Americans hope despite the tough economic times. His serenity and confidence amazed many people, and his talks to the nation—such as his "fireside chats"—helped reassure them. Roosevelt's confidence that he could make things better contrasted sharply with Hoover's apparent failure to do anything effective. In his campaign for president, Roosevelt revealed the approach he would take as president: "Above all, try something." He repeats this call to "action, and action now" in the excerpt from his inaugural address. Once in office, Roosevelt implemented his campaign promise with a flurry of bills to Congress during the first "Hundred Days." Unlike the public impression of Hoover, Roosevelt was taking "action now."

22. Also known as the Wagner Act, the National Labor Relations Act guaranteed workers the right to organize unions without interference from employers and to bargain collectively. The law set up the National Labor Relations Board, which organized factory elections by secret ballot to determine whether workers wanted a union. The NLRB then certified the successful unions. The new law also set up a process whereby dissatisfied union members could take their complaints to binding arbitration, in which a neutral party would listen to both sides and decide the issues. The NLRB was authorized to investigate the actions of employers and could issue "cease and desist" orders against unfair practices.

23. The Social Security program was meant to work much as insurance worked. Workers would pay "premiums" in the form of a tax and receive benefits. The core of Social Security was the monthly retirement benefit, which people could collect when they stopped working at age 65. The plan also included unemployment insurance, providing temporary income to unemployed workers looking for new jobs. In addition, the law also provided modest welfare payments to other needy people, including those with disabilities and poor families with young dependent children, as Secretary Perkins explains in the excerpt. Social Security initially left out many of the neediest members of society—farm and domestic workers, many of whom were African American workers.

24. The New Deal had only limited success in ending the Depression. Unemployment remained high, and economic recovery was not complete until after World War II. Even so, the New Deal gave many Americans a stronger sense of security and stability. The New Deal tended to operate so that it balanced competing economic interests. Business leaders, farmers, workers, consumers, home owners, and others now looked to government to protect their interests. This "broker" role in mediating among competing interests has continued under the administrations of both parties ever since. Also, the New Deal programs created a "safety net" that protected people against economic disaster. After the Roosevelt years, the American people felt that the government had a duty to maintain this safety net, even though it required a larger, more expensive federal government.

CHAPTER 10 TEST, FORM B

Short Answer

1. The Federal Deposit Insurance Corporation guaranteed bank deposits up to $2,500. The Securities and Exchange Commission regulated the stock market to avoid dishonest practices. These were especially crucial as safeguards following the stock market crash of 1929. Both agencies were designed to prevent future financial problems from becoming national catastrophes.

2. The relief programs such as FERA and the CCC were designed to create jobs so people would have money coming in. Recovery programs such as the AAA and NRA helped agriculture and industry reestablish themselves and restart production and stabilize prices. Employed people with steady salaries were better able to buy the food and goods produced by the agricultural and industrial sectors.

3. The acts protected laborers and created insurance programs for the unemployed, elderly, disabled, and children. The acts also promoted new jobs, strengthened the economy, and brought electricity to rural areas.

4. The Second New Deal programs were in part a response to the shortcomings of the First New Deal. Second New Deal programs were generally bolder and more controversial than the earlier programs. The Social Security Act and the Wagner Act, for example, fundamentally changed the relationship between Americans and their government.

5. The Supreme Court is not pulling its weight because it is not adhering to its constitutional responsibility of acting as a judicial body. Instead, it has turned into a policy-making body.

6. Roosevelt's plan was to increase the size of the court by as many as six justices, giving him the power to appoint justices who would support New Deal policies. The court-packing plan, as it came to be known, was a mistake because it created the impression that the president was trying to undermine the Court's independence.

Essay

7. In 1932 the country was deep in the Depression. Millions of Americans were unemployed, and many had lost their homes. Disappointed with President Herbert Hoover's apparent failure to address their economic problems, voters were drawn to Franklin Roosevelt's promise that he would take bold and decisive action. As a result, Roosevelt won the 1932 election. Once in office, President Roosevelt launched the New Deal, a series of bold actions to address the Depression. The Emergency Banking Relief Act, the Securities Act of 1933, the Glass-Steagall Banking Act, the Agricultural Adjustment Act, the Civilian Conservation Corps, the Federal Emergency Relief Administration, the Public Works Administration, and many other laws, programs, and agencies were quickly enacted and created. The Works Progress Administration, the National Labor Relations Act, and the Social Security Act followed later in Roosevelt's term. The New Deal did not end the Depression, and some programs, such as the National Recovery Administration, failed entirely. However, Roosevelt's efforts to address the real problems many Americans faced won him the loyalty of groups, including women, African Americans, and laborers. The New Deal coalition represented a major political realignment from the Republican Party to the Democratic Party, and it reelected Roosevelt by a landslide in 1936.

CHAPTER 11

LESSON QUIZ 11-1

True/False

1. False
2. True
3. True
4. True
5. False

Multiple Choice

6. c **7.** b **8.** c **9.** a **10.** d

LESSON QUIZ 11-2

Completion

1. Nye
2. Neutrality
3. internationalism
4. Lend-Lease
5. Atlantic Charter

Multiple Choice

6. c **7.** a **8.** b **9.** d

LESSON QUIZ 11-3

Matching

1. d **2.** c **3.** b **4.** e **5.** a

Multiple Choice

6. c **7.** a **8.** b **9.** d **10.** d

CHAPTER 11 TEST, FORM A

Matching

1. d **2.** e **3.** f **4.** a **5.** i
6. b **7.** j **8.** h **9.** g **10.** c

Multiple Choice

11. a **12.** d **13.** b **14.** c **15.** b
16. d **17.** a **18.** a **19.** c **20.** b

Essay

21. Fascism was a type of aggressive nationalism. Fascists believed the nation was more important than the individual. They argued that a strong government led by a dictator was needed to impose order on society. Fascism stood for the protection of private property and the middle class, and was also strongly anti-communist and anti-union. Fascists also believed a nation became great by expanding its territory and building up its military. In the political and economic chaos that plagued Europe after World War I, these beliefs were appealing to many people. Benito Mussolini and, later, Adolf Hitler were able to exploit fear of communism and social and economic anxiety to seize power and establish dictatorships in Italy and Germany. Military leaders in Japan followed a similar course of action. As the new dictatorships seized new territory by military force, they triggered World War II.

22. In *Mein Kampf*, Hitler called for the unification of all Germans under one government. He claimed that certain Germans, particularly blond, blue-eyed Germans, were descendants of a "master race" called Aryans. He argued that these Germans needed more living space and called for Germany to expand east into Poland and Russia. According to Hitler, the Slavic people of Eastern Europe belonged to an inferior race, which Germans should enslave. He believed Jews were responsible for many of the world's problems. In particular he blamed them for Germany's defeat in World War I. Hitler's hatred of Jews resonated with many German people. Germany had a long history of anti-Jewish prejudice and Germans felt a sense of injury after World War I—both of which historians believe were factors that helped make the Holocaust possible.

23. Roosevelt's vision was for a world in which people in other countries had the same freedoms American citizens enjoyed under the U.S. Constitution. He believed these rights should be universal to all people. It was a vision of a world without fascism or dictatorships and without the aggression and militaristic expansion of Germany, Japan, and Italy. To achieve this goal, Roosevelt believed the Axis powers—and the ideology they represented—had to be defeated. He wanted the United States to expand its role in the war and to do more to help Britain, a nation fighting to defend democracy against fascism.

24. During the early years of Nazi rule, many Jews were reluctant to leave Germany. They were well integrated into German society, considered themselves to be German citizens, and did not want to give up the lives they had built there. Many believed conditions would improve. When conditions instead worsened—and especially in the aftermath of *Kristallnacht*—large numbers of Jews did try to emigrate. However, they encountered numerous and often insurmountable obstacles. German law forbade Jews from taking more than about four dollars out of Germany. American immigration laws would not allow anyone to immigrate to the United States if they were "likely to become a public charge." Immigration officials assumed this applied to German Jews, who had to leave their money behind. Unemployment and anti-Semitic attitudes also made the idea of increasing immigration quotas unpopular with Americans. In 1939 the SS *St. Louis* was sent back to Europe from the United States with 930 Jewish refugees aboard, most of whom perished in the Holocaust.

CHAPTER 11 TEST, FORM B

Short Answer

1. Britain and France agreed to Hitler's demand for the Sudetenland at the 1938 Munich Conference. Before that, European nations failed to take action when Germany began rearming in 1935—a direct violation of the Treaty of Versailles.

2. By not enforcing the Treaty of Versailles, European nations allowed Hitler to build up Germany's military might between 1935 and 1938. The decision at the Munich Conference to allow Hitler to seize the Sudetenland permitted Germany to invade and divide Czechoslovakia. By the time Britain and France announced they would defend Poland, Germany's military was too powerful for them to defeat.

3. Hitler's appointment as chancellor of Germany in 1933 and the beginning of the Spanish Civil War in 1936 were most likely factors. Isolationists wanted to prevent the United States from becoming involved in the conflicts developing in Europe.

4. In the "destroyers-for-bases" deal, the United States gave Britain greatly needed destroyers in exchange for the right to build bases in British-held territories. By making the deal, Roosevelt was able to aid Britain in its war with Germany without technically violating the Neutrality Acts.

5. Answers will vary but may include: freedom of speech and expression—Nazis persecuted anyone who opposed them or spoke out against them; freedom of worship—they persecuted people of Jewish faith; freedom from want—they took the possessions of prisoners and starved them in concentration camps; freedom from fear—they used weapons to aggressively attack other countries.

6. Roosevelt proposes protecting the freedom from fear by reducing the world's supply of weapons so that no nation will be able to commit an act of aggression against others.

7. They were thirsty and had not been given any water to drink.

8. Prisoners in concentration camps were worked until they died from exhaustion, disease, or malnutrition. They faced horrible living conditions in cramped quarters with little food or water. Those who were too weak or too young to work were killed in extermination camps.

Essay

9. For much of the 1930s, European and American leaders failed to respond aggressively to the threats posed by the Nazis. Americans, discouraged by the rise of fascism and dictatorships in Europe, passed neutrality laws to prevent U.S. involvement in foreign conflicts. Europeans, eager to avoid a repeat of the bloodshed of World War I, were willing to negotiate with Hitler in hopes he would be willing to accept peace if Germany gained more territory. Neutrality and appeasement enabled Germany to build military strength and win early victories. In addition, the international response to the Holocaust was limited at best. Nations were unwilling to raise immigration quotas or to welcome refugees fleeing the Nazis. President Roosevelt and British Prime Minister Churchill, however, recognized the seriousness of the threat posed by the Nazis and their allies. Roosevelt managed to provide help for Britain and France even while maintaining American neutrality. He and Churchill developed the Atlantic Charter, which gave nations a foundation for opposing the Axis powers. Roosevelt ultimately was able to convince most Americans that support for Britain in the war against Germany and its allies was necessary.

CHAPTER 12

LESSON QUIZ 12-1

Matching

1. b **2.** e **3.** a **4.** c **5.** d

Multiple Choice

6. b **7.** a **8.** c **9.** c **10.** a

LESSON QUIZ 12-2

Completion

1. Bataan
2. Doolittle
3. New Guinea
4. Midway

Multiple Choice

5. d **6.** c **7.** b **8.** a

LESSON QUIZ 12-3

True/False

1. True
2. False
3. True
4. True
5. False

Multiple Choice

6. d 7. a 8. c 9. b

LESSON QUIZ 12-4

Completion

1. Manhattan
2. George Patton
3. napalm
4. Nagasaki

Multiple Choice

5. a 6. b 7. c 8. d 9. c

CHAPTER 12 TEST, FORM A

Matching

1. j 2. g 3. d 4. h 5. c
6. b 7. a 8. e 9. i 10. f

Multiple Choice

11. c 12. b 13. b 14. c 15. a
16. d 17. a 18. d 19. c 20. a

Essay

21. During World War II President Roosevelt issued Executive Order 9906 and other legislation, which allowed the military to relocate many people of Japanese, German, and Italian descent from places designated as military areas. A Japanese American man refused to relocate and was found guilty for violating Civilian Exclusion Order No. 34. He petitioned the Supreme Court to review the decision. In the case *Korematsu* v. *United States*, the Supreme Court ruled that while exclusion based on race was unconstitutional, during times of "emergency and peril" the government is sometimes justified in suspending citizens' civil rights. In other words, the Court ruled that suspending the civil rights of some people is sometimes justified to protect the public as a whole.

22. Executive Order 8802 made it illegal for defense industry employers to discriminate in hiring based on "race, creed, color, or national origin." This expanded job opportunities for African Americans and brought many new workers into the workforce. It also expanded the workforce pool for the defense industry. The order was necessary because the defense industry needed more workers to support the war effort, but employers were still reluctant to hire African Americans.

23. Hitler fortified the coast along the English Channel because he knew the Allies would eventually invade France. However, the Germans did not know for sure exactly when or where Allied forces would choose to land. They believed the Allies would land in Pas-de-Calais, which was closest to Britain. The Allies used this assumption to their advantage by placing dummy equipment across the coast from Calais while planning to land along the Normandy coast instead. In addition to German fortifications, the Allies also had to deal with weather conditions and tides. Their timing had to be perfect—the invasion had to begin at night to hide the ships crossing the English Channel. The ships had to arrive at low tide to see obstacles on the beach, and the low tide had to be at dawn so gunners could see their targets. Most importantly, the weather had to be good. The Allies chose the time of the invasion with all these things in mind.

CHAPTER 12 TEST, FORM B

Short Answer

1. Mass production was critical in modern warfare because the country that could move troops and supplies most quickly usually won the battle. The mobilization of the U.S. economy gave the Allies an enormous advantage because the United States could rapidly produce jeeps, trucks, and cargo ships, while Germany often moved supplies using pack animals.

2. President Roosevelt's creation of the National Defense Advisory Committee, the decision to offer cost-plus contracts, and Congress's authorization of the Reconstruction Finance Corporation helped shift U.S. industry to wartime production quickly. The automobile industry was well suited to manufacturing trucks, jeeps, tanks, and other critical materials. Mass production allowed Liberty Ships to be manufactured in only 41 days.

3. In 1942 Toyosaburo Korematsu refused to leave San Leandro, California, which had been designated as a "military area." He was convicted of violating an executive order that barred people of Japanese descent from such areas and forced them to relocate to internment camps. The Court upheld the conviction and said the suspension of Japanese American citizens' civil rights was justified by the emergency of war with Japan.

4. Justice Roberts stated that the executive order Korematsu was convicted of violating unjustly imprisoned people "solely because of [their] ancestry" without even considering that most or all Japanese Americans were loyal citizens. For this reason, Roberts argued that the order was unconstitutional.

5. The war was devastating for the Axis powers. Germany and Japan, nations that fought until the end of the war, suffered more than 7 million military and civilian casualties. The United States and Great Britain lost far fewer soldiers and civilians. The Soviet Union, however, lost over 17 million people, far more than any other nation.

6. The Holocaust caused the deaths of millions of civilians. In addition, military actions such as the Japanese occupation of Manchuria, the German bombing of London during the Battle of Britain, the Allied bombing of Germany, the American firebombing of Tokyo, and the use of atomic bombs resulted in numerous civilian casualties. The German invasion of the Soviet Union contributed to the vast number of Soviet civilian deaths.

Essay

7. During World War II, the Axis powers—Germany, Italy, and Japan—were led by militaristic dictators bent on establishing empires through aggressive expansion and conquest. Their regimes were antidemocratic, putting the nation above the individual and putting supreme power in the hands of a single leader. Adolph Hitler's Nazi Reich was also profoundly racist and sought to destroy all the Jews of Europe. In fighting the Axis powers, the United States, Great Britain, and most of their allies shared a commitment to democracy. President Roosevelt and Prime Minister Churchill believed they were fighting for the preservation of democratic values and for a world free of military aggression. The exception among the Allies was the Soviet Union, which Joseph Stalin led as a dictator. The war affected American political values in strikingly different ways. During the war, the rights of women and African Americans were expanded, while basic rights were stripped from citizens of Japanese descent. Also, the United States succeeded in defending the world against militaristic aggression only by greatly expanding its own military might. The firebombing of Tokyo and the use of atomic bombs at Hiroshima and Nagasaki further tested American values.

CHAPTER 13

LESSON QUIZ 13-1

Matching

1. b **2.** d **3.** a **4.** e **5.** c

Multiple Choice

6. a **7.** d **8.** c **9.** b

LESSON QUIZ 13-2

True/False

1. False
2. True
3. True
4. False

Multiple Choice

5. c **6.** c **7.** a **8.** d

LESSON QUIZ 13-3

Completion

1. perjury
2. Joseph McCarthy
3. McCarran
4. Rosenberg

Multiple Choice

5. c **6.** d **7.** c **8.** a

LESSON QUIZ 13-4

Matching

1. e **2.** a **3.** b **4.** c **5.** d

Multiple Choice

6. b **7.** c **8.** a **9.** d

CHAPTER 13 TEST, FORM A

Matching

1. f **2.** j **3.** c **4.** b **5.** i
6. a **7.** e **8.** h **9.** g **10.** d

Multiple Choice

11. a **12.** b **13.** c **14.** c **15.** b
16. d **17.** a **18.** d **19.** b **20.** a

Essay

21. As the war ended, Soviet leaders became concerned about security, a point about which Kennan was correct. Germany had invaded Russia twice in less than 30 years. They wanted

to keep Germany weak and make sure that the countries between Germany and the Soviet Union were under Soviet control. The Soviet leaders also believed that communism would eventually replace capitalism, and that they should encourage communism in other nations. They accepted Lenin's theory that capitalism causes wars and would try to destroy communism, another point Kennan emphasized. American leaders, on the other hand, believed that the Depression had caused World War II by helping Hitler rise to power and forcing Japan to expand to get resources. American leaders believed that economic growth was the key to world peace, and that increasing world trade would promote growth. For these reasons, they wanted to promote democracy, believing that it would lead to stability and prosperity. This goal conflicted with the goals of the Soviets, but Kennan's assertion that the Soviets were determined to destroy the American way of life appears to be inaccurate.

22. Eisenhower believed that the United States could not contain communism by fighting a series of small wars. Instead, these wars had to be prevented by threatening the use of nuclear weapons if a Communist state tried to seize territory by force. This policy came to be called "massive retaliation." "Brinkmanship" was the willingness to go to war to force the other side to back down. As Dulles explains in the excerpt, the strategic use of these concepts involved taking strong, if risky, action, such as threatening nuclear war, in the hope of avoiding an actual war. Eisenhower used these two concepts in international confrontations. In Korea, for example, he quietly let the Chinese know that the United States might use nuclear weapons. In 1954 he again hinted to the Chinese that the United States would use nuclear weapons, this time to prevent an invasion of Taiwan. The willingness to go to the brink of nuclear war seemed to work, leading to an armistice in Korea and China's backing down from its position on Taiwan.

23. McCarthy came to prominence when he made the assertion in the excerpt. He never produced the list he claimed to have, but his accusations brought him notoriety and political clout. Three years later, McCarthy became chairman of the Senate subcommittee on investigations. He used the power of his committee to force government officials to testify about alleged Communist influences. He turned the investigation into a witch hunt, insinuating disloyalty based on flimsy evidence and irrational fears. He blackened reputations with vague and unfounded charges. His theatrics and sensational accusations drew the attention of the press, which put him in the headlines and quoted him widely. Relishing the spotlight, he became bolder. When he questioned witnesses, McCarthy would badger them and then refuse to accept their answers. His tactics left a cloud of suspicion that McCarthy and others interpreted as guilt. In addition, people were afraid to challenge him for fear of becoming targets themselves.

24. The Cold War caused the American public to become concerned about Communist subversion of society and the threat of nuclear war. Popular culture during this period reflected and commented on these concerns. During the 1950s, themes of nuclear war and Communist infiltration appeared in films, plays, television, the titles of dance tunes, and popular fiction. Some writers, such as Arthur Miller, criticized McCarthyism. Suspenseful films and television shows such as *I Was a Communist for the FBI* entertained viewers with tales of espionage. Songs such as "Atomic Boogie" were heard on the radio. Some writers sought to warn the public about the dangers of atomic weapons. Philip Wylie published *Tomorrow!* in 1954. This novel described the effects of nuclear war on an American city. Wylie hoped the novel would educate the public about the horrors of atomic war. Nonfiction works such as John Hersey's *Hiroshima* described the real consequences of a nuclear attack.

CHAPTER 13 TEST, FORM B

Short Answer

1. The Yalta Conference was a meeting between U.S. President Franklin Roosevelt, British Prime Minister Winston Churchill, and Soviet leader Joseph Stalin in February 1945. World War II was not yet over, but it was clear at that point that the Allies would win and the three leaders began to plan for the postwar world. Among the issues they addressed were a dispute over who governed Poland, the issuing of the Declaration of Liberated Europe, and the question of what to do with Germany after the war.

2. Although issues were resolved and decisions made at Yalta, several issues, such as deciding how the government of Poland would be formed, contributed to hostility between the West and the Communist Soviet Union, which fueled the Cold War.

3. In the excerpt, Marshall is describing the European Recovery Program, also known as the Marshall Plan. Under the plan, the United States provided aid for European nations to rebuild their economies, pumping billions of dollars in supplies, machinery, and food into Western Europe.

4. Soviet leaders believed the Marshall Plan was designed solely to strengthen other nations' resistance to Communist expansion during Europe's postwar recovery and rebuilding phase. Aid was offered to the Soviet Union and its satellite nations under the plan, but the Soviets rejected it.

5. NATO was a mutual defense alliance formed in response to the Soviet blockade of West Berlin. The members of NATO—initially the United States, Canada, Britain, France, Italy, Belgium, Denmark, Portugal, the Netherlands, Norway, Luxembourg, and Iceland—agreed to come to the aid of any member who was attacked. This was the first time the United States committed itself to maintaining peace in Europe.

6. The establishment of the People's Republic of China in 1949 shocked Americans who did not expect to see one of the world's largest countries—one whose government had received U.S. support—fall to the Communists. The launching of *Sputnik* in 1957 also shocked Americans, who believed they were ahead of the Soviets in developing military technology.

Essay

7. During the Cold War period, U.S. foreign policy was driven by tensions with the Soviet Union. The Soviets engineered the rise of Communist, pro-Soviet governments in Poland, Romania, Bulgaria, Hungary, and Czechoslovakia after World War II, a move that was seen as evidence of aggressive expansionism. Beginning in 1946, major components of U.S. foreign policy such as containment, the Truman Doctrine, the formation of NATO, massive retaliation, and the Eisenhower doctrine focused on containing communism and responding to actual or perceived Soviet aggression. Tensions with the Soviets also led to a major military buildup and an expansion of the U.S. nuclear arsenal. American society was affected by the Cold War as well. Revelations of Soviet spying provoked a Red Scare, which subjected individuals in and out of government to sometimes unwarranted anti-Communist scrutiny. The most dramatic example was the rise of Senator Joseph McCarthy, who smeared many Americans with unsupported accusations of subversion. The Cold War also had a profound impact on other nations. The United States and the Soviet Union competed in the area of economic aid, further dividing Western and Eastern Europe. More dramatically, Soviet-backed North Korea and U.S.-backed South Korea went to war, and U.S. covert operations in countries such as Iran and Guatemala overthrew pro-Communist governments.

CHAPTER 14

LESSON QUIZ 14-1

Completion

1. GI Bill
2. Taft-Hartley
3. Dixiecrat
4. controls

Multiple Choice

5. c **6.** d **7.** a **8.** b

LESSON QUIZ 14-2

Matching

1. b **2.** c **3.** a **4.** e **5.** d

Multiple Choice

6. c **7.** b **8.** a **9.** b **10.** c

LESSON QUIZ 14-3

True/False

1. True
2. False
3. False
4. True
5. True

Multiple Choice

6. c **7.** a **8.** b **9.** d

CHAPTER 14 TEST, FORM A

Matching

1. f	**2.** i	**3.** h	**4.** d	**5.** j
6. e	**7.** c	**8.** a	**9.** g	**10.** b

Multiple Choice

11. b	**12.** c	**13.** d	**14.** a	**15.** b
16. a	**17.** d	**18.** b	**19.** a	**20.** d

Essay

21. The Taft-Hartley Act, passed by Congress over President Truman's veto in 1947, restricted organized labor by outlawing closed shops, allowing states to outlaw union shops, and barring some actions by unions. The act grew out of the labor unrest of the early postwar years. After World War II, a demand for goods led to rising prices, which in turn led workers in the automobile, steel, electrical, and mining industries to demand better pay. Truman took forceful action to resolve disputes and end strikes. At one point, he responded to a strike by miners by seizing the mines and pressuring owners to agree to union demands. In 1946 Republicans won control of Congress for the first time since 1930 by appealing to public anxiety over labor unrest. The new Congress quickly passed the Taft-Hartley Act, which Truman vetoed. In the statement excerpted above, he argued that the act was a mistake that interfered with the economy and with the rights of laborers. However, Congress overrode Truman's veto, and the act became law.

22. Much of Eisenhower's agenda was based in economic conservatism. Under the guidance of business leaders in his cabinet, Eisenhower ended government price and rent controls, vetoed a school construction bill, and slashed government aid to public housing. To accompany these cuts, he supported some modest tax reductions. In addition, he abolished the Reconstruction Finance Corporation and drastically cut funding for the Tennessee Valley Authority. Eisenhower's agenda was not entirely focused on cutting spending and limiting the federal government's role in the nation's economy. He also agreed to extend the Social Security system to an additional 10 million people, extended unemployment compensation, increased the minimum wage, and continued to provide some government aid to farmers. In some cases, Eisenhower took an activist role. For example, he advocated passage of the Federal Highway Act and authorized construction of the Great Lakes–St. Lawrence Seaway.

23. Rock 'n' roll—a form of music adapted by white musicians from African American rhythm and blues—became wildly popular with American teenagers in the 1950s for a number of reasons. First and foremost, it was loud music with a heavy beat that made it ideal for dancing, and it had lyrics about themes that appealed to young people. Early stars such as Buddy Holly, Chuck Berry, Bill Haley and the Comets, and especially Elvis Presley electrified young audiences. Social, economic, and cultural factors were also important. In the postwar period, U.S. teenagers had disposable income to spend on entertainment designed specifically for them, such as rock 'n' roll records. New mass media meant that teens around the country could hear the same music. Rock 'n' roll became an important part of a youth culture that gave many teenagers their identity. Given all of this, it is hardly surprising many adults opposed rock 'n' roll. Elvis Presley's hip-swinging dance moves were considered so shocking that popular television host Ed Sullivan initially refused to invite him to appear on his variety show. Some adults considered rock 'n' roll music so dangerous that they tried to ban it.

24. The termination policy was a program launched by the federal government after World War II to bring Native Americans into mainstream U.S. society. Native Americans had become the poorest ethnic group in the United States in the mid-1900s, and the new program was intended to help them escape poverty. Under the termination policy, the federal government withdrew official recognition of the Native American groups, made them subject to the same laws as white citizens, and encouraged them to move from reservations to the cities. As the excerpt suggests, the policy was a disaster for most Native Americans, who found themselves living in terrible conditions in urban centers. The experience of Native Americans was similar to that of groups such as African Americans, Hispanics, and the people of rural Appalachia who were trapped below the poverty line during a period when most Americans were experiencing unprecedented prosperity. The suffering of Native Americans and other groups was virtually invisible to the public, in large part because middle-class Americans assumed that everyone shared in their new affluence.

CHAPTER 14 TEST, FORM B

Short Answer

1. In presenting his legislative agenda to Congress, Truman stated that all Americans have "a right to expect from . . . government a fair deal." By proposing a wide range of programs and reforms that would help all segments of society, Truman attempted to make the federal government provide assistance fairly to all Americans.

2. The groups that were affected by the failure to pass all of the Fair Deal programs were farmers, students, and Americans without adequate access to health care. Farmers did not receive government subsidies, schools did not receive federal aid, and Americans did not receive national health insurance.

3. In the excerpt, Harrington is describing the "tens of millions" of Americans left behind by the prosperity of the postwar years. They included single mothers, senior citizens, minorities and minority immigrants, rural Americans, and inner city residents.

4. Harrington describes tens of millions of Americans, invisible to most people in the middle and upper classes, who were suffering below the poverty line. Americans who lived in the "affluent society," on the other hand, enjoyed a prosperous decade of increased income and education, new homes, and new consumer goods.

5. There was wide disagreement about the causes and reasons for the rise in juvenile delinquency. As the illustration shows, a wide range of experts expressed a great number of opinions about the causes of juvenile delinquency.

6. The graphic suggests that many adults stereotyped young people as juvenile delinquents and even criminals. Faced with rising rates of delinquency, it was easier to point fingers at young people—much like the arrows pointing from all directions at "juvenile delinquents" in the graphic—than to take the time and effort to understand young people's experiences and problems.

Essay

7. Although many Americans feared that the end of World War II would bring a wave of unemployment and recession, the postwar economy in fact grew. A number of factors helped to promote this growth. Federal policy eased the transition from a wartime to a peacetime economy. The GI Bill boosted the economy by providing generous funds to veterans to help them establish businesses, buy homes, and attend college. President Truman's Fair Deal reforms increased the minimum wage and Social Security benefits. President Eisenhower supported the Federal Highway Act and the St. Lawrence Seaway, two large government projects that improved the U.S. infrastructure. Americans, eager to buy consumer goods after years of Depression and wartime sacrifice, drove the economy with consumer spending. At the same time, new business techniques and technologies increased production, ensuring that abundant goods and services were available to buy. The growth of suburbia, the Baby Boom, and the growth of the advertising industry added further fuel to economic growth by spurring still more consumer spending. The new prosperity dramatically changed American society. In the words of economist John Kenneth Galbraith, the United States became an "affluent society." While millions of African Americans, Hispanics, Native Americans, rural Americans in Appalachia, and others were left behind in poverty, most Americans experienced an era of unprecedented prosperity in which the average family income roughly tripled.

CHAPTER 15

LESSON QUIZ 15-1

Completion

1. gender
2. church
3. Democratic
4. reapportion
5. minimum wage

Multiple Choice

6. d **7.** a **8.** d **9.** a **10.** b

LESSON QUIZ 15-2

True/False

1. False
2. False
3. True
4. False

Multiple Choice

5. d **6.** a **7.** b **8.** c **9.** d

LESSON QUIZ 15-3

Completion

1. poverty
2. Education
3. Housing and Urban Development
4. Head Start

Multiple Choice

5. b **6.** b **7.** c **8.** a **9.** c

CHAPTER 15 TEST, FORM A

Matching

1. f **2.** j **3.** i **4.** a **5.** g
6. d **7.** e **8.** c **9.** b **10.** h

Multiple Choice

11. b **12.** a **13.** a **14.** a **15.** a
16. c **17.** d **18.** c **19.** a **20.** a

Essay

21. Before Kennedy became president, many countries in Latin America were controlled by a wealthy few, while most citizens lived in extreme poverty. These conditions spurred the growth of left-wing movements aimed at overthrowing these governments. Because the United States was concerned about these left-wing groups spreading communism, it tried to help the ruling governments stay in power (even though a majority of the citizens suffered). Many Latin Americans resented the intrusion, just as they resented American corporations that operated in their countries. They viewed the companies' presence as a kind of imperialism.

22. Although concerned about having a Soviet-backed Communist state less than 90 miles from the United States, President Kennedy expressed that there was an even greater peril to the nations of the Western Hemisphere. According to the domino theory, the major component of American foreign policy of the time, the steady advancement of communism threatened not just the freedom of people in Latin America, but the freedom of the entire Western Hemisphere. The goal of the United States was to assist any free nation under outside attack from Communist influence.

23. The Berlin Wall, built by the East Germans with Soviet backing, closed the borders between Communist-controlled East Berlin and free West Berlin. The Berlin Wall cut communication between the two parts of the city, and it came to symbolize Communist repression, the failures of the Communist system, and the division between the East and West during the Cold War.

24. Since it was the *first* televised presidential debate, viewers watching the two men on television noticed very different appearances. Kennedy appeared relaxed and outgoing. Many people thought Nixon looked stiff in manner and too formal. Nixon had been ill prior to the debate and looked sickly and haggard, boosting the photogenic appeal of the younger Kennedy. Although Nixon and Kennedy gave voters two very different styles, their views on the two most important issues of the campaign—the economy and the Cold War—were similar. Both promised to fight communism and boost the economy. Many point to Kennedy's media advantage as the decisive factor in the 1960 presidential election.

CHAPTER 15 TEST, FORM B

Short Answer

1. He was responding to many Americans, particularly Protestants, who were concerned about Kennedy because of his Catholic religion. Kennedy had to reassure the American public that he would make decisions independent of the Catholic Church.

2. Kennedy appeared to win the debate because he looked healthy, strong, and confident. Nixon, however, looked tired and frazzled. Nixon did not "perform" as well and close-ups revealed perspiration and darting eyes that made him seem weak and nervous.

3. In the early 1960s, Kennedy worried that the Soviet Union's successes in space, such as the launch of *Sputnik* in 1957, might convince the world that communism was better than capitalism.

4. The writer was saying that the social, economic, and educational problems in the United States in the 1960s could not be solved quickly. It would take time and great effort to fix these problems.

5. Nuclear war seemed imminent during the Cuban missile crisis until Khrushchev and Kennedy reached a deal. After a flurry of secret negotiations, the Soviet Union offered to withdraw its missiles from Cuba in exchange for a promise from the United States not to invade Cuba and to remove its missiles from Turkey.

6. The due process decisions strengthened the protections given to those accused of a crime. The decisions forced police and the courts to carefully follow all procedures throughout a suspect's arrest, interrogation, and trial.

Essay

7. The Great Society improved thousands, if not millions, of lives. Still, debate continues about its success. Many of the programs grew so quickly they became unmanageable and difficult to evaluate. Groups eligible for aid began to expect significant and immediate benefits, but were often left frustrated. Other Americans opposed the massive growth of federal programs and criticized the Great Society for intruding too much into their lives. Lack of funding also hurt the programs, as the Vietnam War required an ever-increasing share of the federal budget. Some Great Society initiatives continue, such as Medicare and Medicaid. An important legacy of the Great Society was the debate it produced—how the federal government can help its disadvantaged citizens, how much government help a society can have without weakening the private sector, and how much help people can receive without losing motivation to help themselves.

CHAPTER 16

LESSON QUIZ 16-1

Completion

1. NAACP
2. Manifesto
3. King
4. Freedom Riders
5. register to vote

Multiple Choice

6. a **7.** c **8.** a **9.** b

LESSON QUIZ 16-2

True/False

1. False
2. False
3. True
4. True
5. True

Multiple Choice

6. a **7.** d **8.** c **9.** d

LESSON QUIZ 16-3

Completion

1. Nation
2. racism
3. Malcolm X
4. African
5. poverty

Multiple Choice

6. c **7.** a **8.** b **9.** b

CHAPTER 16 TEST, FORM A

Matching

1. g **2.** i **3.** f **4.** e **5.** a
6. b **7.** d **8.** h **9.** c **10.** j

Multiple Choice

11. a **12.** c **13.** b **14.** c **15.** d
16. b **17.** d **18.** b **19.** d **20.** a

Short Answer

21. Upon moving north during the Great Migration, African Americans gained the right to vote. Politicians in the North recognized the power of winning the African American vote and began

listening to their concerns. This gave African Americans more political power than they ever had. Roosevelt's New Deal programs also helped a great number of African Americans during the 1930s. As a result, many African Americans began supporting the Democratic Party. This allowed Democratic leaders in the North to wield greater influence than Southern Democrats, who were often pushing for segregation.

22. When Kennedy made this speech, the Civil Rights Act of 1964 had not been passed. Many public places were segregated, as were schools. African Americans in the South were prevented from voting, and it wasn't until 1965 that the Voting Rights Act was passed allowing African Americans in the South to vote safely. Kennedy meant that as long as segregation and voter discrimination existed, African Americans in the United States were not truly free.

23. Dr. King wrote that African Americans had been waiting for more than three centuries for their constitutional and God-given rights and that waiting was no longer an option in a nation where lynching, police brutality, and Jim Crow laws denied basic human rights to 20 million citizens. In his letter, King justifies the breaking of certain laws by explaining that although protesters were breaking the law, they were following a higher moral law based on divine justice. Injustice had to be exposed to the air of national opinion before it could be cured.

24. To support the goal of social change, Dr. King advocated using the tactics of non-violent passive resistance and non-cooperation to combat institutional and individual racism. Dr. King believed that hatred and prejudice are taught to people when they are children and, therefore, many adults have never had the chance to feel anything but hate for African Americans. They must be taught not to hate, and the best way to teach that is by living the examples of tolerance and understanding.

25. Thurgood Marshall means that the Constitution has been a great foundation for the ideals of the United States. Its greatest attribute, however, is how the document has changed and been adapted to reflect the social changes in the United States over time. The Constitution is a living, breathing document that has evolved from its original incarnation to ensure the protection of the life, liberty, and property of all people. In addition, it protects everyone against deprivations without due process and guarantees equal protection of the laws. These protections are especially relevant for formerly enslaved Africans.

CHAPTER 16 TEST, FORM B

Short Answer

1. Stokely Carmichael was trying to motivate African Americans to take more control over their own lives. He gave his audience examples of how the goal could be accomplished.

2. The term "psychological equality" meant African Americans did not consider themselves equal to white people. Carmichael's position was that by doing things for themselves, African Americans would achieve a feeling of equality they did not previously have.

3. King praises the strength of democracy. He points out that the freedom to protest and demonstrate peacefully does not exist in Communist or totalitarian countries.

4. Wallace made this statement while standing in front of the University of Alabama's admissions office to block the enrollment of two African American students. He was trying to prevent forced integration by the federal government.

5. *Sweatt* v. *Painter* enabled more African Americans to attend law schools of their choosing and work toward a legal career. *Norris* v. *Alabama* ensured that African Americans would be allowed to serve on juries. With these two civil rights decisions, greater opportunities for direct participation in American courtrooms were available to African Americans.

6. *Plessy* v. *Ferguson* established the doctrine of "separate but equal." This doctrine stood until *Brown* v. *Board of Education*, in which the Supreme Court said that "separate but equal" is inherently unequal, and that segregation in schools is unconstitutional.

Essay

7. To most African Americans—including Stokely Carmichael—"black power" meant African Americans should control the social, political, and economic directions of their struggle. African Americans should take pride in their heritage and emphasize their distinctiveness rather than assimilate into the white culture. The Black Muslims viewed themselves as their own nation, running their own businesses and schools and distributing their own newspaper. Although they did not advocate violence, they did advocate self-defense, and encouraged their members to respect each other and strengthen their families. The Black Panthers wanted to end racial oppression and control the key institutions in their communities.

CHAPTER 17

LESSON QUIZ 17-1

Completion

1. domino theory
2. Tonkin
3. China
4. Dien Bien Phu
5. Ho Chi Minh Trail

Multiple Choice

6. a **7.** d **8.** c **9.** d

LESSON QUIZ 17-2

True/False

1. True
2. False
3. True
4. True
5. True

Multiple Choice

6. c **7.** d **8.** a **9.** d

LESSON QUIZ 17-3

Completion

1. Watergate
2. Kissinger
3. Cambodia
4. linkage

Multiple Choice

5. d **6.** d **7.** d **8.** d

CHAPTER 17 TEST, FORM A

Matching

1. j **2.** f **3.** b **4.** e **5.** i
6. h **7.** a **8.** d **9.** c **10.** g

Multiple Choice

11. d **12.** c **13.** c **14.** b **15.** a
16. a **17.** a **18.** b **19.** c **20.** b

Short Answer

21. The Tet Offensive was a massive surprise attack by the Vietcong and North Vietnamese on virtually all American airbases and most cities in the south. Militarily, Tet turned out to be a disaster for the Communist forces. Politically, however, they had scored a major victory. The American people were shocked that an enemy, supposedly on the verge of defeat, could launch such a large-scale attack. When General Westmoreland requested a huge number of additional troops, it seemed another admission that the United States could not win the war. After Tet, the mainstream media, which had tried to remain balanced in their war coverage, began openly criticizing the effort. Public opinion no longer seemed with the president. His approval ratings plummeted. The administration's credibility gap now seemed too wide to repair. Most likely, Tet contributed to Johnson's decision not to run for a second term.

22. Every male age 18 or over was assigned a draft card, which meant he was eligible to be drafted into the U.S. military and could be assigned to serve in the Vietnam War. The burning of draft cards was an act of rebellion and a statement of refusal to serve in the military forces.

CHAPTER 17 TEST, FORM B

Short Answer

1. Ball's speech stated that the United States needed to stay in Vietnam to halt the spread of communism not only in South Vietnam, but also in other parts of the world.

2. Ball believes Soviet-backed Communists invaded the country and thus violated internationally recognized boundaries beyond which Communist influence was not allowed to reach.

3. Johnson knew the country was sharply divided over the Vietnam War. When this division carried over into the Democratic primaries, Johnson thought it would be better for the nation if he left politics.

4. Kennan is against American involvement in Vietnam, which is in line with the antiwar views of many Americans at the time. Kennan explains that the world is seeing what appears to be American troops inflicting harm on helpless people, which causes them to react negatively to American involvement in the war. This is supported by the views of many Americans that the war in Vietnam was costing lives unnecessarily and no progress was being made. Kennan points out that this "spectacle" is giving the world a negative view of the United States, while at home many Americans also began distrusting their own government because of what they were seeing about the war on television.

5. President Eisenhower's quote describes the foreign policy of the United States after World War II that was based on the domino theory. The belief was that since China was already a Communist country, if Vietnam fell to communism, so would other nations in Southeast Asia.

6. The circle graphs show that although African Americans made up a small percentage of the entire United States population in 1967—about 10 percent—they were dying at almost twice that rate in Vietnam. This was because African Americans made up a disproportionately large number of American soldiers in Vietnam.

7. The War Powers Act was passed in 1973 during the Vietnam War and attempted to resolve the problems caused by the Gulf of Tonkin Resolution. At the time, many in Congress questioned the extent of presidential power in committing troops to war without first obtaining congressional approval as required by the Constitution.

Essay

8. After nearly eight years of U.S. involvement in the Vietnam War (the longest in American history at the time), the United States withdrew its troops. Only two years later, North Vietnam invaded and took over South Vietnam. After spending more than $170 billion, sacrificing approximately 58,000 American lives, and suffering an additional 300,000 U.S. casualties, it seemed to many Americans that U.S. involvement in the conflict had been in vain. Countless South Vietnamese civilians and about 1 million Vietnamese soldiers on both sides died during the war. Vietnam War veterans who returned home from the jungles of Southeast Asia found that most Americans simply wanted to forget the war. Instead of the parades and celebrations that had greeted veterans of earlier conflicts, their sacrifices often went unrecognized. This made it even more difficult for these soldiers to readjust to civilian life and escape from the psychological impact of the war. Many American families of soldiers who were classified as either missing in action (MIA) or prisoners of war had a difficult time finding out what had happened to their relatives and friends. The end of the war left many Americans cynical about their government leadership, and less confident, and led to a spirit of isolationism. Congress passed the War Powers Act to reestablish limits on executive powers.

CHAPTER 18

LESSON QUIZ 18-1

Completion

1. New
2. Port Huron
3. hippies
4. utopian
5. communes

Multiple Choice

6. a **7.** a **8.** c **9.** d

LESSON QUIZ 18-2

True/False

1. True
2. True
3. False
4. False

Multiple Choice

5. b **6.** d **7.** b **8.** c

LESSON QUIZ 18-3

Matching

1. e **2.** c **3.** a **4.** b **5.** d

Multiple Choice

6. b **7.** d **8.** c **9.** c **10.** a

CHAPTER 18 TEST, FORM A

Matching

1. f **2.** e **3.** h **4.** j **5.** b
6. i **7.** c **8.** d **9.** g **10.** a

Multiple Choice

11. d **12.** d **13.** a **14.** c **15.** d
16. a **17.** b **18.** d **19.** d **20.** c

Essay

21. In the 1960s counterculture ideals were often expressed through music and fashion. The musicians associated with the counterculture gave voice to the hopes and fears of their generation. Bob Dylan's lyrics were especially important for the movement. In this excerpt from "The Times They Are A-Changin'," Dylan issues a challenge to the previous generation, reflecting many young people's rejection of the values their parents embraced. The counterculture generation also adapted fashions that set them apart from the stereotypical white-collar "man in the gray flannel suit" of their parents' generation. Beaded garments, ragged blue jeans, and long hair were potent symbols of counterculture values. Although the utopian ideals of the counterculture were never realized, the music and fashion had lasting impact on American culture. Jeans and longer hair on men and women became generally accepted. Bob Dylan and artists such as Joan Baez, Pete Seeger, Jimi Hendrix, Janis Joplin, and The Who are still heard today. Their music continues to influence the work of today's popular artists.

22. People in favor of passing the ERA believed that because women were human beings and Americans, they should be treated equally and have the same life opportunities as men. They also believed that prejudice against women is "reflected in our laws," as Steinem points out. ERA supporters argued there was no reason to allow that prejudice to continue being enshrined in the law. Opponents of the ERA feared it would take away some of women's traditional rights, such as the right to alimony in divorce cases or the right to attend single-gender colleges. Phyllis Schlafly and other ERA opponents also argued that the act would open the doors to women being drafted into the military, a possibility that they flatly rejected. Many people feared the amendment would grant the federal courts too much power to interfere with state laws.

23. Americans of Mexican heritage have lived in the United States since before the founding of the republic. For much of the twentieth century, most lived in segregated communities called *barrios*. After World War II, Mexican Americans were joined by large numbers of new immigrants from Puerto Rico and Cuba. Many of these newcomers settled in urban centers such as New York City and Miami. They faced residential segregation, poverty, limited access to education and employment, and were often treated as outsiders by the English-speaking majority regardless of their immigration status. With the example of the achievements of the African American community, Latino groups began to organize a series of campaigns during the 1950s and 1960s to improve their economic situation and end discrimination. Organizations such as LULAC brought lawsuits to end school segregation and end the abuses of the deportation authorities. The American GI Forum was founded to defend the rights of Mexican American veterans. The United Farm Workers Union founded by César Chávez and Dolores Huerta fought to obtain union recognition, higher wages, benefits, and better working conditions for farmworkers.

CHAPTER 18 TEST, FORM B

Short Answer

1. Savio was specifically describing the University of California at Berkeley and the effect of confusing and seemingly arbitrary rules enforced by administrators. However, the "machine" analogy also may have expressed many students' feelings about mainstream society, the U.S. government, or the Vietnam War.

2. Members of the free speech movement staged sit-ins and delivered speeches. After hundreds of student protesters were arrested, a campus-wide strike stopped classes and won the support of many faculty members.

3. The Equal Pay Act and Title VII of the Civil Rights Act of 1964 protected women's rights in the workplace. Eight years later, Title IX of the Educational Amendments expanded women's rights in education.

4. Neither the Equal Pay Act nor Title VII of the Civil Rights Act of 1964 was able to overcome ingrained attitudes about women's roles and truly end gender discrimination. However, the laws provided a strong legal basis for changes the women's movement later demanded. Title IX was more effective in ending discriminating against women in federally funded schools.

5. The United Farm Workers fought for better wages and working conditions for low-wage agricultural workers, many of them Latinos. Unionizing farmworkers was also a goal. *La Raza Unida*'s goals included mobilizing Mexican Americans to vote and increasing their access to important services.

6. The United Farm Workers was a labor union that was focused primarily on improving conditions for workers. *La Raza Unida*, on the other hand, was a political party that focused on mobilizing voters to elect candidates that supported civil rights for Latinos.

Essay

7. The major social movements that began in the 1960s—the youth movement, the women's liberation movement, and the Latino civil rights movement—all drew inspiration from the African American civil rights movement and adopted some tactics from the civil rights movement. However, these social movements differed in their goals and strategies. The youth movement comprised various groups, such as Students for a Democratic Society (SDS), the free speech movement, and the counterculture, each with its own focus. For example, the SDS focused on political issues such as protesting against the Vietnam War, while the counterculture aimed to establish a vaguely defined utopia. The women's movement, revitalized by phenomena including the President's Commission on the Status of Women and the publication of Betty Friedan's *The Feminine Mystique*, pushed for legislation aimed at ending gender discrimination and expanding women's rights. Strongly influenced by the civil rights movement, the Latino movement fought against discrimination in the courts and through organized protests. Groups such as *La Raza Unida* focused on mobilizing Latino voters and expanding access to needed services. These movements had a profound impact on American society and political culture. Despite the failure of the Equal Rights Amendment, the women's movement was largely successful in outlawing discrimination against women and changing the social roles of women in the United States. Likewise, the Latino movement ended many discriminatory practices and helped Latinos gain a political voice. The youth movement had a significant impact on American culture, undermining the conformity that characterized the 1950s and creating new openings for individual expression.

CHAPTER 19

LESSON QUIZ 19-1

Completion

1. Revenue-sharing
2. Vietnamization
3. détente
4. Strategic Arms Limitation

Multiple Choice

5. b **6.** a **7.** c **8.** c **9.** d

LESSON QUIZ 19-2

Matching

1. d **2.** a **3.** b **4.** e **5.** c

Multiple Choice

6. a **7.** d **8.** b **9.** c

LESSON QUIZ 19-3

Matching

1. d **2.** c **3.** e **4.** b **5.** a

Multiple Choice

6. c **7.** c **8.** a **9.** b **10.** d

LESSON QUIZ 19-4

Completion

1. reverse
2. Native Americans
3. independent
4. Rehabilitation

Multiple Choice

5. b **6.** a **7.** a **8.** c

LESSON QUIZ 19-5

True/False

1. True
2. False
3. True
4. True

Multiple Choice

5. a **6.** b **7.** b **8.** c

CHAPTER 19 TEST, FORM A

Matching

1. e **2.** g **3.** h **4.** b **5.** i
6. f **7.** j **8.** d **9.** a **10.** c

Multiple Choice

11. c **12.** a **13.** b **14.** c **15.** d
16. b **17.** c **18.** d **19.** d **20.** a

Essay

21. Détente was a new approach to international relations developed by Nixon and his national security adviser, Henry Kissinger. Its goal was to relax tensions between the United States and its two major Communist rivals, the Soviet Union and China. While Nixon and Kissinger still hoped to contain communism, they believed that the reality of a multipolar world required the United States to build a better relationship with its main rivals in the interest of world peace. Détente led to major foreign policy successes, beginning with Nixon's visit to China in 1972. Also in 1972, Nixon held a summit with Soviet leaders that produced the first Strategic Arms Limitation Treaty, or SALT I. Although détente was diminished by conflicts in countries on the periphery of the Cold War, such as Chile and Angola, it succeeded in easing tensions and established the strongest relationship between the United States and the Soviet Union of the Cold War period.

22. The Watergate scandal did have a number of positive effects. The crisis led Congress to pass new laws, including the Federal Campaign Act Amendments, the Ethics in Government Act, and the FBI Domestic Security Investigation Guidelines Act. The overall effect of these laws was to limit the power of the executive branch. Congress also established a means for appointing independent counsels to investigate and prosecute wrongdoing by high government officials. The scandal also served as a demonstration that no American, not even the president, is above the law, as Woodward points out in the excerpt. On the other hand, the scandal left Americans with a deep distrust of their public officials. The damage done to the relationship between Americans and their government cannot be described as "a good thing."

23. During the 1950s and 1960s, many Americans enjoyed tremendous prosperity in the postwar economic boom. The growth of the economy was based in large part on easy access to raw materials around the world and a strong manufacturing industry at home. By the mid-1960s, the economy began to change. President Johnson increased federal deficit spending to fund the war in Vietnam and the Great Society programs. However, he did not raise taxes. This caused inflation. In the 1970s, the price of oil began to rise, leaving Americans with less money for other goods. This caused a recession. In addition, American manufacturing began to lag behind that of other nations. The United States began to import more goods than it was able to export. American factories closed, causing unemployment figures to rise. The economy experienced "stagflation"—a combination of inflation and a stagnant economy with high unemployment. Throughout the decade, various attempts were made to control inflation and end the recession by controlling spending, raising interest rates, and reducing the demand on foreign oil. These efforts met with little success.

24. Baston was describing the problem of de facto segregation in American schools. Although the Supreme Court's decision in *Brown* v. *Board of Education* outlawed segregation, in many areas—especially in the North—schools remained segregated because children attended schools near where they lived. As Baston explains in the excerpt, schools attended by white children had better access to resources and were superior to schools attended by African American children. Court-ordered busing was intended to be a solution to this problem. Busing helped in the short term because it forced African American children into white schools and vice versa, creating more integrated schools. However, it provoked strong reactions in white communities, including riots. Over time, busing led to "white flight," in which white families moved to predominantly white suburban school districts or sent their children to private schools to avoid integration and busing. As a result, in the long run, busing did not completely solve the issue of racially imbalanced schools.

25. Environmental issues became national concerns in the 1960s and early 1970s as Americans became increasingly aware of the damage being done to the environment. The 1962 publication of Rachel Carson's book *Silent Spring* played an important role in increasing environmental awareness. *Silent Spring* focused on the increasing use of pesticides, particularly DDT, and the damage caused to birds, fish, and other creatures that might ingest them. The book triggered an enormous response in part because evidence of environmental damage and disaster was becoming impossible to ignore. Many U.S. rivers were considered unsafe; air pollution and smog clouded major cities; a 1969 oil spill in California killed fish and ruined beaches; and pollution in Lake Erie caused nearly all its fish to disappear. As more and more Americans became concerned, a grassroots environmental movement began to emerge. The movement is generally considered to have started with the first national celebration of Earth Day in April 1970. After Earth Day, environmental organizations grew in number, size, and influence.

CHAPTER 19 TEST, FORM B

Short Answer

1. Nixon hoped to reduce the size of the federal government by dismantling federal programs and giving more power and control to state and local governments. In practice, these goals were to be achieved through revenue-sharing bills that gave federal funds to state and local agencies.

2. Revenue sharing was a major part of the New Federalism. It was intended to give state and local agencies more power, but over time, it gave the federal government the power to impose conditions on the states. Unless the states met those conditions, the federal government would cut off funds on which the states had come to depend.

3. The break-in itself was not a major scandal, and Nixon was reelected in a landslide less than five months later. In early 1973, however, James McCord and Gordon Liddy were convicted of conspiracy, burglary, and wiretapping, and McCord implicated John Dean. By July, the revelation of the Watergate tapes and Nixon's refusal to turn them over marked the emergence of the scandal.

4. In July 1974, the House Judiciary Committee began voting on articles of impeachment. In addition, the Supreme Court ruled that Nixon must turn over tapes of conversations in the White House. The tapes revealed that Nixon had ordered the CIA to stop the FBI's investigation six days after the Watergate burglary. Rather than face impeachment by the House and conviction by the Senate, Nixon resigned from the presidency.

5. The Camp David Accords were a peace treaty between Israel and Egypt, two countries that had been bitter enemies for decades. The treaty was a historic first step towards achieving peace in the Middle East. For President Carter, the accords represented a high point of triumph that would soon be undermined by the crisis in Iran.

6. The hostage crisis was a disastrous failure that greatly damaged Carter's presidency. The hostages were held for over a year, as shown on the time line. President Carter authorized a rescue mission, but the mission failed. Ultimately, Carter was unable to secure the hostages' freedom and lost the 1980 election. The hostages were released only as Carter left office.

7. Section 504 outlawed discrimination against people with disabilities by any program, service, or activity that received funding from the federal government. By implication, this provision required that people with disabilities must have equal access to public facilities, including public buildings and transportation.

8. The provisions of the Rehabilitation Act could not take effect until the Department of Health, Education, and Welfare (HEW) had issued regulations for enforcement. In 1977 the American Coalition of Citizens with Disabilities organized sit-ins at regional HEW offices to put pressure on the agency. Protesters in San Francisco maintained their sit-in for over three weeks, until HEW's director signed the regulations. In 1990 Congress enacted the Americans with Disabilities Act, which expanded the civil rights protected by the Rehabilitation Act.

Essay

9. During the period from 1968 to 1980, the United States faced new challenges while continuing to struggle with ongoing problems. The Cold War between the United States and the Soviet Union continued to dominate international affairs, but the rising importance of China, Japan, and Western Europe required new strategies. President Nixon responded with the policy of détente, shifting U.S. foreign policy to ease Cold War tensions. President Ford largely continued this policy. Turmoil in the Middle East presented President Carter with new opportunities and new troubles. In helping to negotiate the Camp David Accords, Carter brought the region a step closer to peace, yet his administration faltered disastrously when faced with the hostage crisis in Iran. The United States also faced enormous economic problems in this period. Inflation, dependence on foreign oil, and the decline of manufacturing locked the economy into "stagflation," a combination of rising prices, stagnant growth, and high unemployment. Presidents Nixon, Ford, and Carter took a variety of approaches to solving the nation's economic problems—cutting spending and raising taxes, raising interest rates, increasing spending and cutting taxes, encouraging energy conservation—but none of these approaches were effective. Although civil rights had expanded for many groups in the 1960s, African Americans, Native Americans, and people with disabilities still faced discrimination and lacked access to education, good jobs, and other resources. Civil rights leaders and new organizations of Native Americans and people with disabilities pressed for government action, engaged in activism and protest, and also took to the courts. Finally, damage to the environment emerged as a serious problem during this period. A grassroots environmental movement emerged and gained momentum as Americans became aware of the degradation of the environment. The movement led to significant government action, including establishing the Environmental Protection Agency and enacting the Clean Air and Clean Water Acts.

CHAPTER 20

LESSON QUIZ 20-1

Matching

1. c **2.** d **3.** a **4.** e **5.** b

Multiple Choice

6. b **7.** c **8.** a **9.** c

LESSON QUIZ 20-2

True/False

1. True
2. False
3. True
4. False
5. True

Multiple Choice

6. d **7.** b **8.** b **9.** a

LESSON QUIZ 20-3

Completion

1. wealthiest
2. WTBS
3. AIDS
4. senior

Multiple Choice

5. a **6.** b **7.** b **8.** d

LESSON QUIZ 20-4

Matching

1. b **2.** d **3.** c **4.** a **5.** e

Multiple Choice

6. c **7.** a **8.** b **9.** b

CHAPTER 20 TEST, FORM A

Matching

1. g **2.** e **3.** d **4.** h **5.** c
6. i **7.** a **8.** j **9.** f **10.** b

Multiple Choice

11. d **12.** a **13.** c **14.** a **15.** b
16. c **17.** a **18.** d **19.** c **20.** b

Essay

21. The new conservative coalition held a common belief that American society had somehow lost its way. The Watergate scandal had undermined many Americans' faith in their government. Rising unemployment, rapid inflation, higher taxes, and the energy crisis had eroded confidence in the economy. The violence and looting that followed the New York City blackout was an example of crime that suggested society itself was falling apart. The retreat from Vietnam, the hostage crisis in Iran, and the Soviet invasion of Afghanistan made the nation look weak and helpless internationally. Many Americans wanted stability. Conservative responses to these problems appealed to these Americans. For example, Midge Decter argued that "progressive liberal policy" of the 1960s and 1970s had created social problems such as crime and violence. Conservatives built their coalition by promising a nation in distress a return to what many remembered as a better time.

22. Ronald Reagan made the economy his first priority. He pursued "trickle-down" economics. This was a combination of strategies that kept interest rates high and taxes low. Reagan believed cutting taxes would help corporations invest extra capital, create new jobs, and increase the supply of goods for consumers who would have more money to spend. However, cutting taxes meant the government would be getting less revenue to fund programs. So, to keep the government deficit down, Reagan made funding cuts to government programs such as welfare benefits that included the food stamp and school lunch programs. He also cut Medicare payments, unemployment compensation, student loans, and housing subsidies. Later Reagan realized he would never be able to cut programs enough to balance the budget. He began to accept the increasing deficit and continued to increase spending on the military and other projects.

23. Many of the changes in the entertainment industry were pioneered by entrepreneurs creating new business models. Businessman Ted Turner turned a failing television station in Atlanta, Georgia, into WTBS, the first "superstation" that sold low-cost sports and entertainment programs via satellite to cable companies throughout the nation. Turner's innovation helped spread cable television across the country. Until the late 1970s, television viewers were limited to three national networks, local stations, and the public television network, but now dozens of networks appeared on cable. Many specialized in one type of broadcasting, such as sports, movies, or music. MTV, for example, made music videos popular, boosting the careers of some musical artists. Rap music also became popular during this time. New technology led to other changes. The Sony Walkman made music portable and videocassette recorders (VCRs) allowed people to tape television shows or watch taped films whenever they wanted to. New technology also generated home video games, which became a new entertainment industry.

24. The U.S. economy went into a recession in 1990, in part because the end of the Cold War cost thousands of soldiers and defense industry workers their jobs. At the same time, companies in other industries began downsizing to increase efficiency. The recession was made worse by the huge budget deficit that forced the government to borrow money to pay for its programs and by high levels of personal debt in the United States. Furthermore, as the economy slowed, savings-and-loan institutions that had been deregulated by President Reagan began to collapse under the weight of bad investments. President Bush tried to address the economic problems by cutting capital gains taxes, but Congress rejected the idea. To reduce the deficit, Bush agreed with Congress to raise income taxes while cutting spending. These steps were unpopular, however, and they did not end the recession, which Americans began to blame on President Bush.

CHAPTER 20 TEST, FORM B

Short Answer

1. The populations of the Sunbelt states grew dramatically between 1950 and 1980. The populations of Arizona, Florida, California, and Colorado all more than doubled, and Nevada's population increased by 400%. In contrast, not one Northeastern state saw its population grow by 50% or more during this period.

2. The conservative message that the federal government was becoming too strong appealed to Sunbelt voters. As more Americans moved to the Sunbelt, they began to oppose high taxes and federal regulations that might interfere with the region's growth. When the population of the Sunbelt surpassed that of the Northeast, it became possible for a conservative candidate to win the presidency.

3. Reagan's belief that people do not want to be saved by someone else reflected a philosophy of self-reliance and independence. He believed Americans could find solutions and strength to solve problems within themselves and that government could not help and should not interfere.

4. The wealthiest 5 percent of Americans benefited more than anyone else from the economic growth of the 1980s. From 1967 to 1986, the top 5 percent earned between 15 percent and 17 percent of the nation's total income, but as the economy began to grow, their share of U.S. income began to increase.

5. Gorbachev instituted perestroika in response to an economic crisis in the Soviet Union. By the late 1980s, the Soviet economy was suffering from years of inefficient central planning and huge expenditures on the arms race. By allowing some private enterprise and profit making, Gorbachev hoped to rescue and reform the Soviet economy.

6. With Gorbachev's support, glasnost spread to Eastern Europe. More freedom led to revolutions, and the Communist rulers of Bulgaria, Czechoslovakia, Hungary, Poland, and Romania were replaced with democratic governments. By November 1989, the Berlin Wall fell and East and West Germany were reunited. The weakened Soviet government collapsed after a coup against Gorbachev failed.

Essay

7. The resurgence of conservatism changed the United States on every level. Conservatives formed a coalition of Sunbelt voters, suburban voters, and religious conservatives that became a powerful force in American politics. The election of conservative Ronald Reagan in 1980 marked a dramatic shift in domestic and foreign policy. President Reagan's economic program focused on a huge reduction of taxes, cuts to social programs, and deregulation of several industries. He also launched a massive military buildup, in part to force the Soviet Union into a financially ruinous arms race. As taxes were lowered and defense spending was increased, the U.S. economy experienced strong growth. The retail, news, and entertainment industries were revolutionized by new business strategies and new technology. Many Americans became focused on accumulating wealth, while many others were left behind. Conservatism had enormous long-term impacts on the United States and the world. The military buildup hastened the collapse of the Soviet Union, ending the Cold War. Increased defense spending and cutting taxes without making significant cuts in other government spending, however, created a large budget deficit in the United States. When the Cold War ended and defense spending slowed, the resulting recession was made worse by deficit spending and the national debt. Today, conservatism remains a powerful force in American politics. The "new world order" that began to emerge after the Cold War continues to develop. Also, taxes, government regulation and spending, and budget deficits remain at the center of political debate.

CHAPTER 21

LESSON QUIZ 21-1

True/False

1. True
2. False
3. True
4. True
5. False

Multiple Choice

6. a **7.** c **8.** a **9.** a

LESSON QUIZ 21-2

Matching

1. e **2.** b **3.** d **4.** a **5.** c

Multiple Choice

6. c **7.** b **8.** c **9.** c

LESSON QUIZ 21-3

Completion

1. blog
2. telecommunications
3. computer

4. Internet
5. ozone

Multiple Choice

6. c **7.** a **8.** c **9.** c

CHAPTER 21 TEST, FORM A

Matching

1. g **2.** c **3.** e **4.** d **5.** j
6. a **7.** i **8.** b **9.** h **10.** f

Multiple Choice

11. a **12.** b **13.** d **14.** b **15.** c
16. c **17.** b **18.** c **19.** d **20.** a

Short Answer

21. In one scandal, Clinton was accused of arranging illegal loans for an Arkansas real estate development company. Later, a new scandal emerged involving a personal relationship between the president and a White House intern. Some evidence suggested that the president had committed perjury about the relationship. The independent counsel, Kenneth Starr, submitted a report that argued that Clinton had obstructed justice, abused his power as president, and committed perjury. Clinton's supporters charged that Starr's report was politically motivated. The House passed two articles of impeachment, one of perjury and one for obstruction of justice, moving the case to trial in the Senate. There, the vote was fairly even, but short of the two-thirds needed to remove the president from office. However, Clinton's reputation suffered.

22. Many experts believe carbon dioxide emissions from factories and power plants cause global warming, but others disagree. The issue is very controversial because the cost of controlling emissions would affect the global economy. Industries would have to pay the cost of further reductions in emissions, and those costs would be passed on to consumers. Developing nations trying to industrialize would be hurt the most, but economic growth in wealthier nations would be hurt too.

23. During Clinton's first term, he was faced with a large budget deficit. During the Reagan and Bush administrations, the deficit grew drastically and the government borrowed large sums of money. Interest rates were high and economic growth was minimal. Clinton needed to reduce the deficit. To do so, he submitted a plan to Congress. As a part of the plan, Clinton proposed raising taxes instead of cutting social programs. The plan passed, and taxes were raised for middle- and upper-income Americans. Taxes remained higher during Clinton's second term. However, the economy was strong and people earned more, leading to a greater amount of taxes paid. In addition, the president and Congress continued to reduce the budget whenever possible. In 1997 Clinton submitted a balanced budget to Congress. Beginning in 1998, the government began running a surplus and collected more money than it spent.

24. Before the Immigration Act of 1965 was passed, immigration policies favored those people coming from northern and western Europe. The policy seemed to be biased and racially motivated. The Immigration Act of 1965 eliminated the quota system allowing non-Europeans an equal chance of immigrating to the United States. Now immigrants come from Asia, Latin America, and other places. In this sense, current policies have achieved the goal of eliminating discrimination.

CHAPTER 21 TEST, FORM B

Short Answer

1. One perspective is that human action and neglect of the environment are responsible for global warming. The second perspective is that global warming and temperature shifts have occurred repeatedly, so they cannot be blamed on humans.

2. Unions feared the loss of jobs, diminishment of workers' rights, and the lack of environmental protections, and were concerned with China's poor human rights record.

3. Bridging the digital divide and increasing broadband access to more citizens has affected how people communicate with one another and improved how services are delivered in the areas of business, health care, education, and home security.

4. In the late 1960s, electronic mail was only available to scientists, government agencies, and defense contractors. The Internet made e-mail available to the rest of society. Although the Internet and e-mail were once confined to limited networks, its uses have broadened and grown to encompass families, businesses, and organizations around the world.

5. Although rising exports have created new high-skilled jobs, since NAFTA was enacted, American industries seeking lower labor costs have relocated to Mexico.

Essay

6. The problem of illegal immigration prompted changes in the immigration laws. During the Reagan years, Congress passed the Immigration Reform and Control Act of 1986. This law established penalties for employers who hired unauthorized immigrants and strengthened border controls to prevent illegal entry. It also set up an amnesty program for any undocumented alien who could prove that he or she entered the country before January 1, 1982 and lived in the United States since. These changes seemed to lead to increasing numbers of unauthorized immigrants. By 1990, about 3.5 million unauthorized immigrants lived in the United States. In the mid-1990s, Congress debated new ways to stop illegal immigration. In 1996 it passed the Illegal Immigration Reform and Immigrant Responsibility Act. This required families sponsoring immigrants to have incomes above the poverty line. The law also funded efforts to stop illegal immigration. It put in place tougher penalties for smuggling immigrants and creating false papers.

CHAPTER 22

LESSON QUIZ 22-1

True/False

1. False
2. True
3. True
4. False

Multiple Choice

5. b **6.** d **7.** b **8.** d

LESSON QUIZ 22-2

Completion

1. mass destruction
2. Afghanistan
3. elections
4. Taliban
5. weapons inspectors

Multiple Choice

6. d **7.** a **8.** d **9.** d

LESSON QUIZ 22-3

Completion

1. National Security
2. John Roberts
3. illegal enemy combatants
4. unemployment
5. prescription drugs

Multiple Choice

6. b **7.** a **8.** d **9.** d

LESSON QUIZ 22-4

True/False

1. False
2. True
3. False
4. False
5. False

Multiple Choice

6. d **7.** a **8.** d **9.** c

CHAPTER 22 TEST, FORM A

Matching

1. j **2.** a **3.** c **4.** e **5.** f
6. b **7.** i **8.** g **9.** d **10.** h

Multiple Choice

11. c **12.** c **13.** a **14.** b **15.** a
16. d **17.** b **18.** a **19.** a **20.** b

Essay

21. Immediately after 9/11, a national emergency was declared and the military was mobilized. Congress authorized the use of force to fight whoever had attacked the United States. The United States then began a war on terrorism and targeted al-Qaeda, other global terror groups, and nations or regimes such as the Taliban that sponsored terrorist groups. The antiterror policy also took advantage of financial tactics by cutting off the funding sources of these groups. Finally, Bush began building an international coalition of nations to fight alongside the United States.

22. The 2000 presidential election was one of the closest in American history. The election came down to Florida, which carried 25 electoral votes that both candidates needed to win. The vote was so close that state law required a recount of the ballots using machines. Thousands of votes were thrown out because the machines could not read them. Gore asked for a hand recount of the ballots in several counties, but the machine recount showed Bush ahead. Then a battle for hand counting began. Questions arose over how to count partially attached chads, and each county did so differently. The state required that results be certified by a certain date, so Gore went to court for more time. The Florida Supreme Court agreed to set a new deadline. Bush had the U.S. Supreme Court intervene. Before their lawyers got to that court, Florida finished the machine count and declared Bush the winner by 537 votes. However, the Florida Supreme Court allowed the hand recounts to continue. The U.S. Supreme Court stopped the hand counting and ruled it was unconstitutional, as different vote counters used different standards. The court then ruled there was not enough time to continue counting and finish by the federal deadline. Florida then declared Bush the winner.

23. The voting in the 2000 election was so close in the pivotal state of Florida that officials authorized a hand recount of the votes. Problems arose, however, because of chads, which voters had to punch out of their ballot to make their votes. One problem was that vote counters had to decide how to count a ballot when the chad was still partially attached. On some ballots, the chad was still in place, and the voter had left only a dimple on the surface of the ballot. When looking at the ballots, vote counters had to determine what the voter intended, and different counties used different standards to judge the ballots. Ultimately, the Supreme Court decided in *Bush* v. *Gore* that the hand recounts of questionable ballots violated the equal protection clause, resulting in the election of President Bush.

24. Osama bin Laden fought against the Soviet Union in Afghanistan in the 1980s. During that time, he became convinced superpowers could be defeated. In this speech bin Laden questions the use of the term "terrorism" in reference to attacks against Western interests. He interprets these attacks as revenge killings in response to decades of Western oppression against Muslims all over the world. He was especially outraged after Iraq's invasion of Kuwait when Saudi Arabia, home to the two holiest sites in Islam, Mecca and Medina, allowed American troops into Saudi Arabia. Bin Laden then dedicated himself and his terrorist organization to driving Americans and other non-Muslims out of the Middle East.

CHAPTER 22 TEST, FORM B

Short Answer

1. Rumsfeld warned Americans that the war on terrorism would be fought in many ways, on nontraditional fronts, and may take a long time.

2. Rumsfeld wanted the American people to understand that only part of the war would be fought on a battlefield. Terrorist groups and their guerrilla war tactics would have to be combatted by increasing homeland security and denying terrorists access to resources.

3. Americans came together in many ways, such as donating food and supplies. Others volunteered their services to help the nation recover. Graham was commenting on this unity that the nation experienced given its recent division over the election of 2000 and other differences that arose in the 1990s.

4. The journalist was expressing sympathy for and unity with the American people on the tremendous loss of life on the day of the attack. International sympathy poured in to the United States.

5. President Bush was identifying Afghanistan as a country that harbored and supported terrorists such as Osama bin Laden. The U.S. military invaded Afghanistan on October 7, 2001.

6. The law grants nationwide search warrants for any jurisdiction and tracking of all forms of communication, which critics say violates Fourth Amendment protections.

7. Over half of American workers experienced some form of work-related problem, such as taking a pay cut, having their hours scaled back, or being unemployed at some point during the recession.

Essay

8. As oil became important to the American economy in the 1920s, the United States invested heavily in the oil industry in the Middle East. This industry brought great wealth to the ruling families in some Middle Eastern kingdoms, but it left most of the people poor. Some became angry at the United States for supporting these kingdoms and ruling families. The growth of the oil industry also increased the Middle East's contact with Western society. As Western ideas spread through the region, many devout Muslims feared their traditional values and beliefs were being weakened. Throughout the Middle East, new movements arose calling for a return to traditional Islamic religious laws. These movements sought to overthrow the pro-Western governments in the Middle East and hoped to establish a pure Islamic society. The Islamic fundamentalist militants of these movements began using terrorism to achieve their goals.